at IQ

11-13 years

Getting Better at IQ Tests

11-13 Years

The Mensa UK Puzzle Editors

Ken Russell & Philip Carter

foulsham
LONDON • NEW YORK • TORONTO • SYDNEY

foulsham
Bennetts Close, Cippenham SL1 5AP

ISBN 0-572-01972-6

Phototypeset in Great Britain by Typesetting Solutions, Slough, Berks.
Printed in Great Britain by Cox & Wyman Ltd., Reading, Berks.

Acknowledgements

We are indebted to our wives, both named Barbara, for their encouragement in our various projects, and to Lynn Moore for typing the manuscript.

Contents

Introduction

About the Authors

Ken Russell is a London surveyor and is Puzzle Editor of the *British Mensa Magazine*, a magazine which is sent to its 40 000 British members monthly.

Philip Carter is a JP and an Estimator from Yorkshire. He is Puzzle Editor of *Enigmasig*, the monthly newsletter of the Mensa Puzzle Special Interest group.

About Mensa

Mensa is a Social Club for which membership is accepted from all persons with an IQ (Intelligence Quotient) of 148 or above. This represents the top 2% of the population. Therefore one person in 50 is capable of passing the entrance test, which consists of a series of intelligence tests.

Mensa is the Latin word for 'table'. We are a round-table society where all persons are of equal standing. There are three aims: social contact amongst intelligent people; research in psychology; and the identification and fostering of intelligence.

Mensa is an International Society and has 110 000 members of all occupations: clerks, doctors, lawyers, policemen, industrial workers, teachers, nurses, etc.

Enquiries to: **MENSA FREEPOST**
Wolverhampton WV2 1BR,
England.

MENSA INTERNATIONAL
15 The Ivories,
6-8 Northampton Street,
London N1 2HV,
England.

What is IQ?

IQ is the abbreviation for Intelligence Quotient. The dictionary definition of quotient is 'the number of times one quantity is contained in another'. The definition of intelligence is 'intellectual skill', 'mental brightness', 'quick of mind'.

When measuring the IQ of a child, the child would attempt an intelligence test which had been given to thousands of children, and the results correlated so that the average score had been assessed for each age group. Thus, a child who at eight years of age obtained a result expected of a ten-year-old, would score an IQ of 125 by the following simple calculation:

$$\frac{\text{Mental age}}{\text{Chronological age}} \times 100 = IQ$$

$$\therefore \frac{10}{8} \times 100 = 125 \ IQ$$

This does not apply to adults, whose assessment would be based on results correlated to known percentages of the population.

A child with a high IQ would have a great advantage at school with his or her studies, as understanding of lessons would be easily absorbed, but, in itself, a high IQ is not a key to success in later life. More important would be the qualities of competitiveness, personality, ambition, determination and temperament. In most walks of life, however, problem-solving is encountered and a person with a high IQ is well adapted to be successful in this field.

The average IQ is, obviously, 100. The population can be split roughly into three groups: 50% would be between 90 and 110, 25% would be above 110 and 25% would be below 90.

Until recently, Intelligence Tests have been mainly related to knowledge of words, but with the advent of the increasing larger proportion of immigrants to Britain, whose knowledge of English would not be expected to be of a high standard, there is a swing towards Culture free tests. These are tests that use logic rather than word knowledge, so that diagrams are used instead of words. This makes no difference to the outcome, as spacial understanding and logical reasoning are good guides to one's degree of intelligence. These tests also have been standardised.

The twelve tests which have been specially compiled for this book have not been standardised, so an IQ assessment has not been given. They are intended for practice for readers intending to take IQ tests in the future, and a guide is given as a check of success in undertaking each of these twelve separate tests. There is also a further accumulated score for performance in all twelve tests.

It is now considered that one's IQ factor has a hereditary basis, but that it is possible to improve slightly by practice with IQ tests, but only marginally. Generally speaking, the IQ factor remains constant throughout one's life, trailing off slightly with age.

How to use this book

The book consists of twelve separate tests, each of 30 questions. The tests are of approximately the same degree of difficulty. It is suggested that you tackle each test separately and note your score, after checking your answers against those given at the end of each test. A scoring chart for each test is also shown, one mark being awarded for each correct answer.

Each further test taken should show a slight improvement in your score, as practice will improve performance. The total can then be taken for the twelve tests and checked against the total scoring chart, shown below and also at the end of the book.

Each test has a time limit of 90 minutes which must not be exceeded.

Notes: The answers to some of the questions have been explained. You may find these explanations useful if you are 'stuck' on certain types of question.

In questions where you are required to find, or complete, a missing word, the number of dots or asterisks shown is equal to the number of missing letters in the word that you are looking for.

Total scoring chart for the twelve tests

	11 years	12 years	13 years
Average	156–191	180–215	204–239
Good	192–227	216–251	240–275
Very Good	228–263	252–287	276–311
Excellent	264–299	288–323	312–347
Exceptional	300–360	324–360	348–360

Test 1

1   Which of these is the odd one out?

      parrot, swallow, salmon, pelican, magpie

2   Place two of these three-letter 'bits' together to make a tree.

      ban, low, kin, haz, pop, wil

3   Solve the anagram (one word).   CLUE: Far away.

      METEOR

4   Which word inside the brackets is opposite in meaning to the word in capital letters?

      FOE (hostage, enemy, friend, opponent, stranger)

5   What number is 20 less than five times itself?

6 Which of the squares, A to H, will fit in at the square with a question mark?

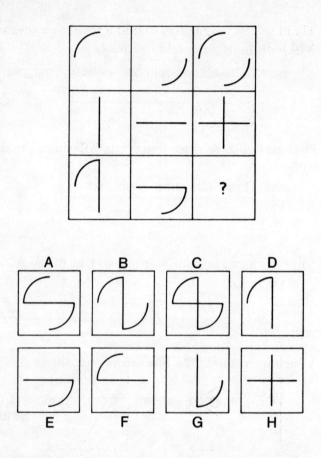

7 Place two of these three-letter 'bits' together to find a word meaning grasp.

fra, tch, mes, ses, clu

8 Which number comes next in this sequence?

1, 3, 2, 4, 3, 5, ?,

9 Remove a girl and leave a boy.

   CAONNLEIN

10 Fill in the missing letters to find a word that means find out.

   . I . CO . E .

11

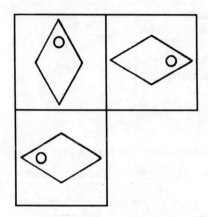

Which is the missing square, above, from the choice below?

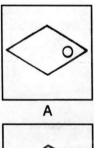

A

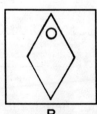

B

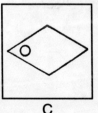

C

D

15

12 Underline the two words which are closest in meaning:

fear, meek, horror, unseen, crafty

13 What is a hamlet? Is it:
- (a) a vacant house
- (b) a vegetable
- (c) a story
- (d) a small village
- (e) a small pig?

14 Underline the name given to a group of stamps.

cluster, collection, clutch, caste

15 If NAVY is to BLUE, then LEMON is to which of these?

EBONY, ORANGE, YELLOW, GINGER, GREY

16 Which of these is the odd one out?

look, watch, see, listen, observe

17 Which of the circles marked A, B, C, D, E, fits
logically into the blank top circle in the diagram,
below?

There is a logical sequence to how the diagram is
built up, starting at the bottom row.

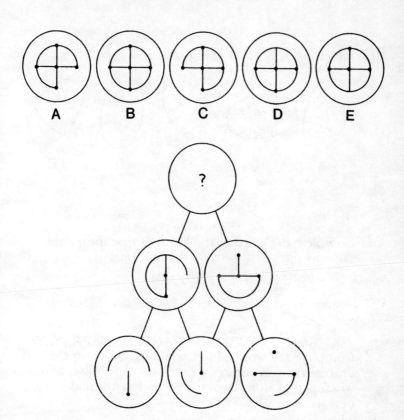

18 Unscramble these anagrams and say which one of
them is not something you could wear.

LETB
EDAH
KSCO
HEOS

19 Complete the two words below, which sound alike, but are spelled differently and mean:
unimportant / colliery worker.

. I . O .   /   . I . E .

20 Which of A, B, C, D or E is the odd one out?

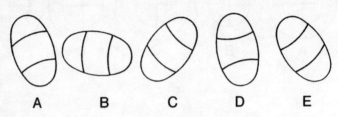

A   B   C   D   E

21 Complete the word in the brackets that means the same as the words outside the brackets.

INSECT   (F * *)   SOAR

22 Complete the word which, when added on to the end of the first word makes a new word or phrase, and when placed in front of the second word, makes a new word or phrase.

POP   (S * * *)   FISH

23 Which word is part of this group?

sprouts, cabbage, parsley, lettuce

Choose from:

oak, rowan, spinach, cedar

24 Find the missing number in the sequence.

7, 14, ?, 28, 35,

25

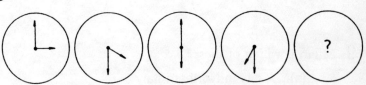

Which of A, B, C, D or E, should logically follow in the sequence above?

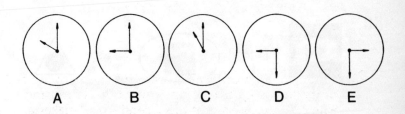

26 DUCHESS is to DUKE as COUNTESS is to which of these?

ROYALTY, BARONET, DOWAGER, EARL, AMBASSADOR

27 Which word inside the brackets means the same as the word in capital letters?

HELP   (cry,   assist,   try,   trust)

28 The sentence below has its words in the wrong order. Put the words in the correct order and then say whether the sentence is true or false.

SECRET VOTING IS BALLOT METHOD A OF A

29 Milan is which of these?

(a)   A city in Northern Italy
(b)   A famous painter
(c)   An English poet

30

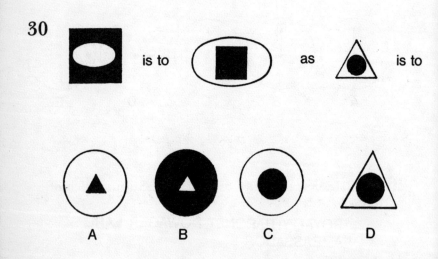

A   B   C   D

1 salmon.   (This is a fish. The others are birds.)

2 willow   3 REMOTE

4 friend   5 5.

6 C.   Column 3 is made by adding Column 1 to
        Column 2. Row 3 is made by adding Row 1 to
        Row 2.
        As an example:

7 clutch

8 4.   (Add 2, then take away 1, alternately.)

9 Remove ANNE to leave COLIN   (CAONNLEIN)

10 DISCOVER

11 D.   (So that the figure appears, pointing right, left,
up and down in the four squares.)

12 fear, horror   **13** (d)   a small village

14 collection   **15** YELLOW

16 listen

17 B.   (In the bottom row of the diagram, the left-hand
and the centre circles combine (are added
together) to form the circle which is above them.

The right-hand and the centre circles in the
bottom row combine to form the circle above
them.

These two new circles in the middle row then
combine to form the top circle which, to fit, is
filled by circle B.)

18 EDAH.   (This is an anagram of HEAD. The things
you could wear are BELT, SOCK and
SHOE.)

19 MINOR / MINER

20 D.   (All the others are the same figure rotated.)

21 FLY   **22** STAR.   (Pop star, Starfish)

23 Spinach.   (This is also a vegetable. The others are
                        trees.)

24 21.   (Add 7 each time to get the next number.)

25 B.   (The circles represent clock faces. In the sequence:

The first clock says 3 o'clock.
The second says half past 4.
The third says 6 o'clock.
The fourth says half past 7.

Each step increases by 1½ hours. Therefore:

The fifth clock will say 9 o'clock (which is clock B).)

26 EARL   **27** assist

28 A SECRET METHOD OF VOTING IS A BALLOT
or
A BALLOT IS A SECRET METHOD OF VOTING
or
A METHOD OF VOTING IS A SECRET BALLOT
or
A SECRET BALLOT IS A METHOD OF VOTING

(All of these statements are true.)

29 (a)   A city in Northern Italy.

30 B. (The black square reduces in size and goes inside the oval shape, which increases in size.

So the white triangle reduces in size and goes inside the black circle which increases in size. This is the case with B.)

Scoring Chart for Test 1

	11 years	12 years	13 years
Average	13–15	15–17	17–19
Good	16–18	18–20	20–22
Very Good	19–21	21–23	23–25
Excellent	22–24	24–26	26–28
Exceptional	25–30	27–30	29–30

Test 2

1 Underline the two words which are closest in meaning.

enormous, feeble, large, low, vivid

2 Solve the anagram (two words):

THEY SEE

3 What is a jester? Is it:

(a) a disease
(b) a milk dish
(c) a clown
(d) a coin
(e) a tester?

4 Underline the name given to a group of rugby players.

field, form, fifteen, fleet

5 Which number comes next in this sequence?

100, 94, 88, 82, ? ,

6

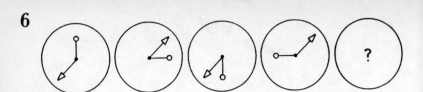

Which of A, B, C, D or E should logically follow on the sequence above?

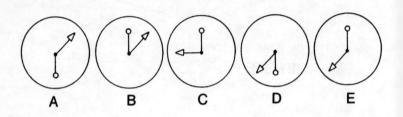

7 POP is to BURST as SNAP is to which of these?

DETONATE, BREAK, SPOIL, EXPLODE, SCRATCH

8 Which word inside the brackets means the same as the word in capital letters?

BLUNDER (deceive, spoil, error, confuse, boast)

9 The sentence below has its words in the wrong order. Put the words in the correct order and then say whether the sentence is true or false.

OXYGEN WATER WITH PRODUCE COMBINED HYDROGEN CAN

10 Garnet is which of these?

    (a)   A sea-bird
    (b)   A type of mineral
    (c)   A method of cooking

11

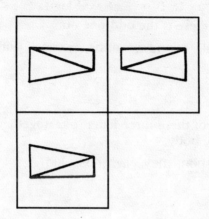

Which is the missing square, above, from the choice below?

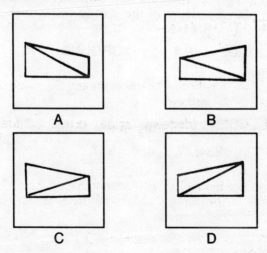

12 If CAT is to KITTEN, then COW is to which of these?

BISON, CALF, BEEF, OXON, BULL

13 Which of these is the odd one out?

jackal, minnow, rabbit, weasel, kitten

14 Place two of these three-letter 'bits' together to make a part of the body.

spi, bon, ney, liv, nos, kid

15 Complete the word which, when added on to the end of the first word makes a new word or phrase, and when placed in front of the second word, makes a new word or phrase.

STAGE   (P * * *)   GROUND

16 Find the missing number in this sequence:

123, 234, ? , 456, 567,

17 Which of the squares, A to H, will fit in at the square with a question mark?

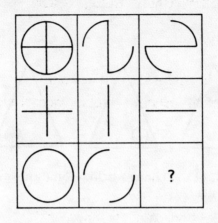

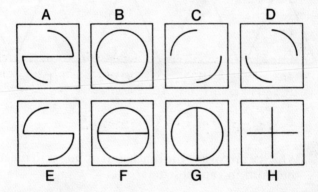

18 Place two of these three-letter 'bits' together to make a word meaning refrigerate.

nzy, eze, fro, fre, lic

19 Complete the two words below, which sound alike, but are spelled differently and mean: statue / lazy.

. D . L / . D . E

20 Which of these is the odd one out?

female, woman, lady, girl, person

21

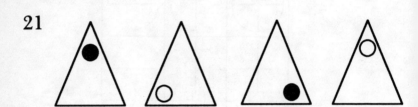

Which of the choices below comes next in the above sequence?

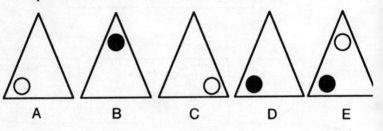

A   B   C   D   E

22 Which word inside the brackets is opposite in meaning to the word in capital letters?

DOE (pastry, palm, buck, animal, cake)

23 Complete the word in the brackets that means the same as the words outside the brackets.

FASTENER (B * * T) RUN OFF

30

24 Which word is part of this group?

   pink, violet, purple, orange

Choose from:

   quartz, ivory, oxide, mica

25

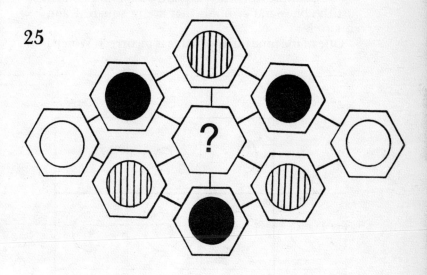

Which of the figures, A, B or C, should go inside the hexagon with the question mark?

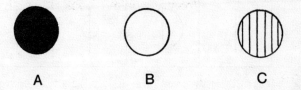

A   B   C

26 This grid has three squares along the top, marked A, B and C and three squares down the left side, marked 1, 2 and 3.

Each of the nine inner squares should contain just the lines and symbols in the square of the letter above, and also just the lines and symbols in the square of the same number to the left.

For example, the inner square 1B should contain just the lines and symbols that are in square 1 and square B.

One of the nine inner squares is incorrect. Which is it?

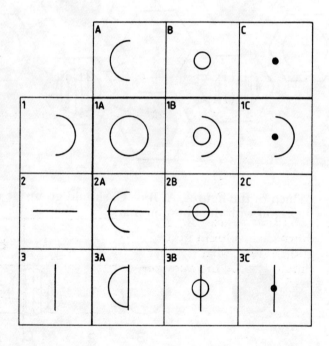

27 Fill in the missing letters to find a word that means entire.

. OM . L . . E

28 Unscramble these anagrams and say which one of them is not something to drink.

EACK
KMLI
IWEN
LCAO

29 Which one word means all of the following?

(a) Light in colour
(b) A travelling entertainment with sideshows
(c) According to the rules
(d) Fine and sunny

30 Look across each row and down each column in the grid, and say what number should replace the question mark.

2	4	6
1	2	3
3	6	?

Answers Test 2

1 enormous, large

2 THE EYES

3 (c) a clown

4 fifteen

5 76. (Take away 6 each time.)

6 E. (moves 90° clockwise for each step.

 moves 180° clockwise for each step.)

7 BREAK

8 error

9 OXYGEN COMBINED WITH HYDROGEN CAN PRODUCE WATER
or
HYDROGEN COMBINED WITH OXYGEN CAN PRODUCE WATER

(Either way, the sentence is true.)

10 (b) A type of mineral.

11 B.   (The figure flips over, across or down. It becomes a mirror image of its partner, across or down.)

12 CALF

13 minnow.   (This is a fish. The others are animals that live on land.)

14 kidney   **15** PLAY.   (Stage play, Playground)

16 345.   (Add 111 each time.)

17 D.   Column 3 is obtained by taking Column 2 away from Column 1. Row 3 is obtained by taking Row 2 away from Row 1.

As an example:

$$+ \; - \; | \; = \; -$$

18 freeze   **19** IDOL / IDLE

20 person.   (This is the only one that is not necessarily feminine.)

21 D.   (The dot visits each angle of the triangle in turn, travelling anticlockwise, and is black, then white, in turn.)

22 buck   **23** BOLT

35

24 ivory.   (This is a colour.)

25 B.   (So that each row of three connected hexagons contains a white–black–striped circle.)

26 2C.   **27** COMPLETE

28 EACK.   (This is an anagram of CAKE. The things to drink are MILK, WINE and COLA.)

29 fair

30 9.   (In the rows across and the columns down, the first two numbers are added to arrive at the end number.)

Scoring Chart for Test 2

	11 years	12 years	13 years
Average	13–15	15–17	17–19
Good	16–18	18–20	20–22
Very Good	19–21	21–23	23–25
Excellent	22–24	24–26	26–28
Exceptional	25–30	27–30	29–30

Test 3

1 What is an orbit? Is it:

    (a)   a path of a planet
    (b)   a discus
    (c)   a nightmare
    (d)   a pathway
    (e)   a promenade?

2 If DOOR is to STEP, then WINDOW is to which of these?

    MULLION, SILL, GLASS, PUTTY, FASTENER

3 Underline the two words which are closest in meaning.

    soothe, brief, dense, solid, observe

4 Which word is part of this group?

    skiff, lugger, barge, cutter

Choose from:

    lorry, capstan, canoe, hawser

5 Remove a tree and leave a flower.

    DAPIINSEY

6 Which of the squares, A to H, will fit in at the square with a question mark?

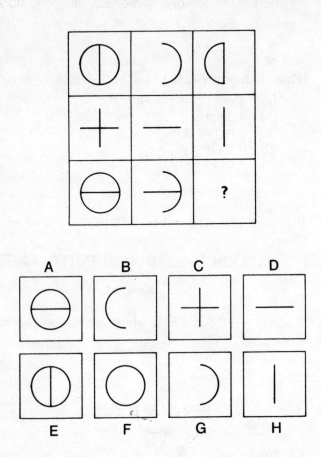

7   **SCHIEM**

Arrange the jumbled letters above, to find the correct word to fit in the quotation below.

We have heard the _____ **at midnight.**

(Shakespeare, *Henry IV, Part 2*).

8 Which word inside the brackets is opposite in meaning to the word in capital letters?

GREEDY (empty, generous, tender, hungry, weak)

9 Which of the circles marked A, B, C, D, E, fits logically into the blank top circle in the diagram below? There is a logical sequence to how the diagram is built up, starting at the bottom row.

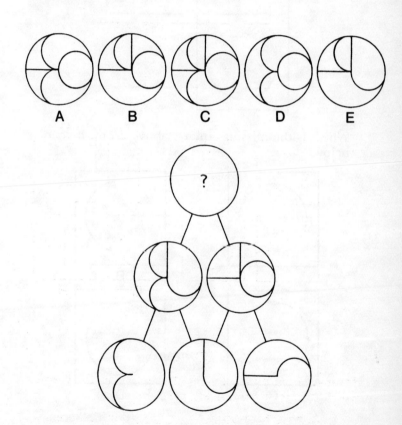

10 Which of these is the odd one out?

banana, cabbage, cherry, orange, grape

11

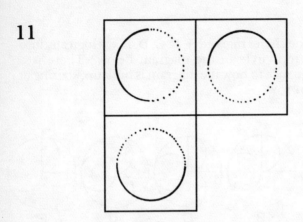

Which is the missing square, above, from the choice below?

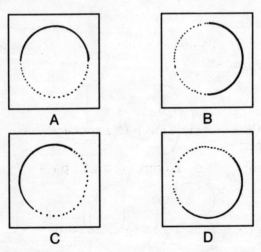

12 How many triangles appear in the figure below?

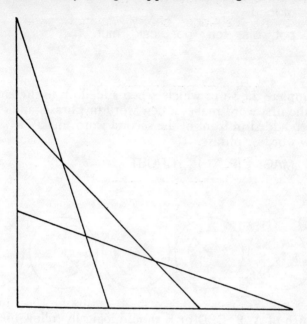

13 Solve the anagram (one word). CLUE: Full stop.

ON TIP

14 Underline the name given to a container for strawberries.

pack, pod, plump, punnet, pace

15 Fill in the missing letters to find a word that means clever.

I . T . LL . . E . .

16 Place two of these three-letter 'bits' together to make a type of food.

pot, bis, ton, por, cak, mut

17 Complete the word which, when added on to the end of the first word makes a new word or phrase, and when added in front of the second word, makes a new word or phrase.

MAG   (P * *)   CRUST

18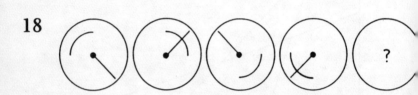

Which of A, B, C, D or E should logically follow on the sequence above?

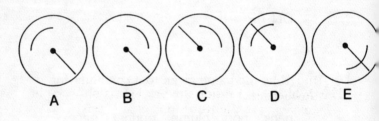

19 Complete the two words below, which sound alike, but are spelled differently and mean: two / a fruit.

. A . R / . E . R

42

20 Unscramble these anagrams and say which one of them is not a sport.

> FOGL
> DOJU
> LOOP
> EASC

21 Which number comes next in this sequence?

> 14, 10, 6, 2, ?,

22 Find the missing number in the sequence:

> 8, 27, ?, 125, 216,

23 Complete the word in the brackets that means the same as the words outside the brackets.

> LEFT SIDE (P * * *) INTOXICATING LIQUOR

24 Which word inside the brackets is opposite in meaning to the word in capital letters?

> HOST (guest, landlord, owner, ghost, party)

25 Which of these is the odd one out?

> plaice, sardine, mackerel, racoon, turbot

26

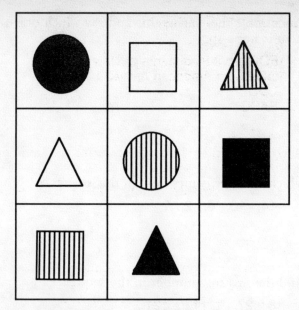

Look across each row and down each column and try to find the correct right-hand bottom tile from the choice below.

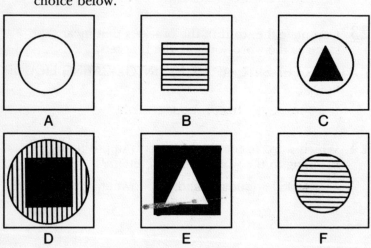

A   B   C

D   E   F

27 Maoris are which of these?

    (a)   An African tribe
    (b)   Native inhabitants of New Zealand
    (c)   South American natives

28 Which word inside the brackets means the same as the word in capital letters?

    LIVID   (dishonest, angry, agile, tiny, worried)

29 Insert a three-letter word that completes the first word and starts the second word.

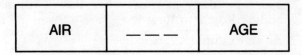

AIR	_ _ _	AGE

30 LISTEN is to HEAR as OBSERVE is to which of these?

    see, eye, heed, sound, light

Answers Test 3

1 (a) (a path of a planet). 2 SILL

3 dense, solid   4 canoe (This is also a boat.)

5 Remove PINE to leave DAISY (DA~~PINE~~SY).

6 B.   To find Column 3, add Column 2 to Column 1, but
where lines and shapes are the same in Columns 1
and 2, they will disappear in Column 3.

The same thing happens when Row 3 is made by
adding Row 2 to Row 1.

As an example:

$$+ \quad + \quad — \quad = \quad |$$

The horizontal line disappears.

7 CHIMES   8 generous

9 C.   (In the bottom row of the diagram, the left-hand and
the centre circles combine (are added together) to
form the circle which is above them.

The right-hand and the centre circles in the bottom
row combine to form the circle above them.

These two new circles in the middle row then
combine to form the top circle which, to fit, is filled
by circle C.)

10 cabbage.   (It is a vegetable. The others are fruits.)

11 B.   (So that the dotted half of the circle appears top, bottom, left and right.)

12 There are 10 triangles. These are made up:

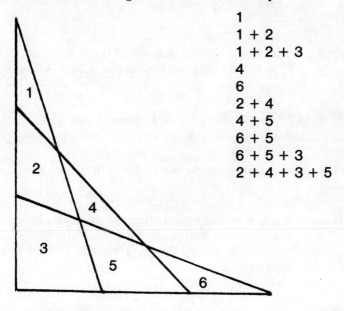

1
1 + 2
1 + 2 + 3
4
6
2 + 4
4 + 5
6 + 5
6 + 5 + 3
2 + 4 + 3 + 5

13 POINT   **14** punnet

15 INTELLIGENT

16 mutton   **17** PIE.   (Magpie, Pie-crust)

18 A.   (The quarter circle moves 90° clockwise at each step.

The straight line moves 90° anticlockwise at each step.)

19 PAIR / PEAR

20 EASC.   (This is an anagram of CASE. The sports are GOLF, JUDO and POLO.)

21 −2.   (Take away 4 each time.)

22 64.   (The sequence is made up of the cubes of 2, 3, 4, 5, 6. The cube of 4, which is 4 × 4 × 4 = 64.)

23 PORT   **24** guest

25 racoon.   (This is a mammal. The others are fish.)

26 A.   (Each row and each column contains a circle, a square and a triangle. Also, each row and column contains a black, white and shaded figure.)

27 (b)   Native inhabitants of New Zealand.

28 angry

29 MAN   (to give AIRMAN and MANAGE.)
or
MEN   (to give AIRMEN and MENAGE.)

30 see

Scoring Chart for Test 3

	11 years	12 years	13 years
Average	13–15	15–17	17–19
Good	16–18	18–20	20–22
Very Good	19–21	21–23	23–25
Excellent	22–24	24–26	26–28
Exceptional	25–30	27–30	29–30

1   If GERMANY is to MARK, then FRANCE is to which
of these?

ESCUDO, PIASTRE, FRANC, NICKEL,
FLORIN

2   Complete the word inside the brackets that means the
same as the words outside the brackets.

TIMBER UPRIGHT   (P * * *)   MAIL

3   Which of these is the odd one out?

pumpkin, greengage, bluebell, pineapple, pear

4   What is shingle? Is it:

(a)   tingling
(b)   loose gravel
(c)   part of a horse
(d)   shining
(e)   a patio?

5   Solve the anagram (one word):

IT RAN

6 Which of the squares, A to H, will fit in at the square with the question mark?

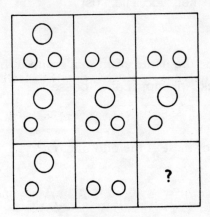

A   B   C   D

E   F   G   H

7 Look across each row and down each column and say what number should replace the question mark.

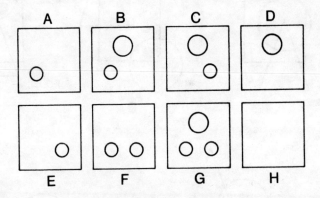

9	7	2
3	2	1
6	5	?

8 Place two of these three-letter 'bits' together to make a word meaning find.

ate, ket, loc, tle, ust

9 Underline the name given to a group of hounds.

pack, plump, park, posse

10 Which of these is the odd one out?

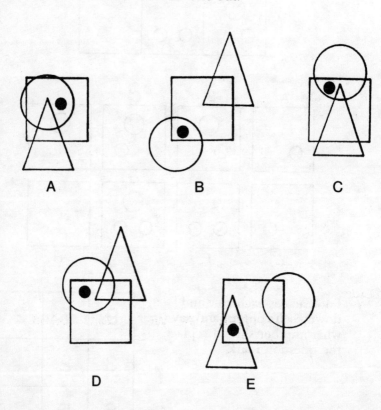

A   B   C

D   E

11 Which word in brackets means the same as the word
    in capital letters?

   PRISE (reward, lever, original, pull, profit)

12 Place two of these three-letter 'bits' together to make a
    little person.

   ogr, get, tin, mid, dwa, kin

13 Underline the two words which are closest in
    meaning:

   limited, gallant, brave, stupid, sharp

14 A mixture of all the colours in a rainbow in equal
    quantities produces which of these?

   (a) white
   (b) black
   (c) purple

15 SUNNY is to CLOUDY, as DRY is to which of these?

   DULL, OVERCAST, WET, COLD, DARK

16 Select the missing piece from A, B, C or D, so that the whole square will contain an even, symmetrical pattern.

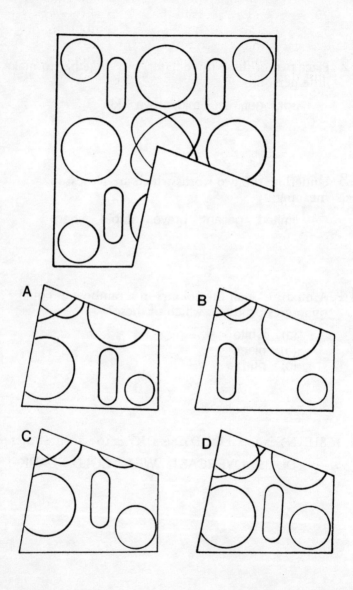

17 This grid has three squares along the top, marked A, B and C and three squares down the left side, marked 1, 2 and 3.

   Each of the nine inner squares should contain just the lines and symbols in the square of the same letter above, and also just the lines and symbols in the square of the same number to the left.

   For example, the inner square 1B should contain just the lines and symbols that are in square 1 and square B.

   One of the nine inner squares is incorrect. Which is it?

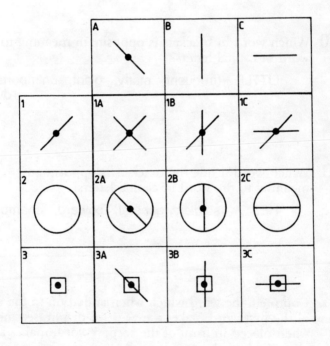

18 Insert a three-letter word that completes the first word and starts the second word.

CAR	_ _ _	TEN

19 Divide £6 among Pat, Sue and Alan and give Pat £1 more than Sue, and Sue £1 more than Alan. How much does Alan get?

20 Which word in brackets is opposite in meaning to the word in capital letters?

LITTLE (frequent, many, giant, unimportant, dwarf)

21 Which word inside the brackets is opposite in meaning to the word in capital letters?

HERO (soldier, general, coward, champion, battle)

22 Complete the word which when added on to the end of the first word makes a new word or phrase, and when placed in front of the second word, makes a new word or phrase.

STICKLE (B * * *) BONE

23 Which word is part of this group?

olive, melon, plum, blueberry

Choose from:

radish, onion, carrot, mandarin

24 Find the missing number in the sequence:

3, 5, ?, 13, 21, 34, 55,

25 Which of these is the odd one out?

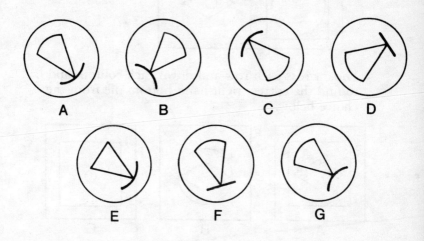

A   B   C   D

E   F   G

26 Fill in the missing letters to find a word that means incomplete.

. A . TI . L

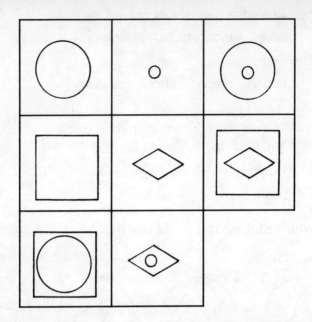

Look across each row and down each column and try to find the correct right-hand bottom tile from the choice below.

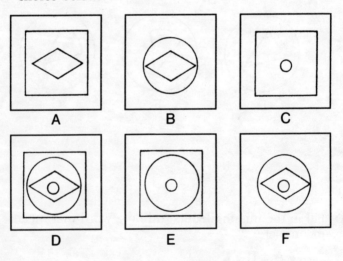

A B C

D E F

28 Which of these is the odd one out?

Asia, Europe, China, Africa, Australasia

29 Unscramble these anagrams and say which one of them is not something that may be eaten.

SIHF
ITMS
ETAM
KPRO

30 What number comes next in this sequence?

0, 10, 19, 27, 34, ?,

Answers Test 4

1 FRANC   **2** POST

3 bluebell. (This is a flower. The others are fruits.)

4 (b) loose gravel   **5** TRAIN

6 A.   Column 3 is obtained by adding Column 2 to
         Column 1 but only the circles that are common to
         both Columns are carried forward.

         Row 3 is obtained from adding Row 2 to Row 1
         but again, only the circles common to both Rows
         are carried forward.

         As an example:

7 1.   (In both the rows and the columns, the second
         number is subtracted from the first number to
         give the number in the third square.)

8 locate   **9** pack

10 E.   (This is the only one where the dot is not inside
         the circle.)

11 lever   **12** midget

13 gallant, brave

14 (a) white

15 WET

16 C.

17 2B.

18 ROT.   (To give CARROT and ROTTEN.)

19 £1.   (Pat gets £3 and Sue gets £2.)

20 giant

21 coward

22 BACK.   (Stickleback, Backbone)

23 mandarin.   (This is a fruit. The others are vegetables.)

24 8.   (The two previous numbers are added at each stage.)

25 E.   (A is the same as C, but rotated.
 B is the same as G, but rotated.
 D is the same as F, but rotated.)

26 PARTIAL

27 D.   (Looking both across and down, the last (third)
 square is made up by combining (adding
 together) the contents of the first two squares.)

28 China. (This is a country. The rest are continents.)

29 ITMS. (This is an anagram of MIST. The things that may be eaten are FISH, MEAT and PORK.)

30 40. (Add 10, then 9, then 8, then 7, then 6.)

Scoring Chart for Test 4

	11 years	12 years	13 years
Average	13–15	15–17	17–19
Good	16–18	18–20	20–22
Very Good	19–21	21–23	23–25
Excellent	22–24	24–26	26–28
Exceptional	25–30	27–30	29–30

Test 5

1   What is a tenon? Is it:

     (a)   a tenant
     (b)   a magistrate
     (c)   a part of a joint
     (d)   a sport
     (e)   a part of the body?

2   Complete the word inside the brackets that means the same as the words outside the brackets.

    CONTAINER   (J * *)   SHAKE

3   Underline the two words which are closest in meaning:

    petty,   help,   accuse,   blame,   blend

4   If TRANSLATOR is to LANGUAGES, then VICAR is to which of these?

    RELIGION,   MEDICINE,   SCULPTURE,   WRITER, MUSICIAN

5   Solve the anagram (one word).   CLUE: It is an animal.

    CORONA

63

6

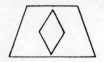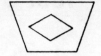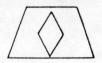

Which of the choices below comes next in the above sequence?

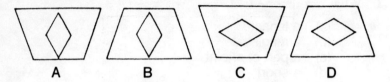

A   B   C   D

7 Place two of these three-letter 'bits' together to find a word meaning dress.

rue, the, sta, clo, sis

8 The Sphinx is a mythological monster with which of these?

(a) A human head and a horse's body
(b) A horse's head and a human body
(c) A human head and a lion's body

9 The sentence below has its words in the wrong order. Put the words in the correct order and then say whether the sentence is true or false.

MARE IS SHEEP A FEMALE CALLED A

10 Which word in brackets means the same as the word in capitals?

FIELD (earth, grass, meadow, sport, place)

11 Which of the squares, A to H, will fit in at the square with the question mark?

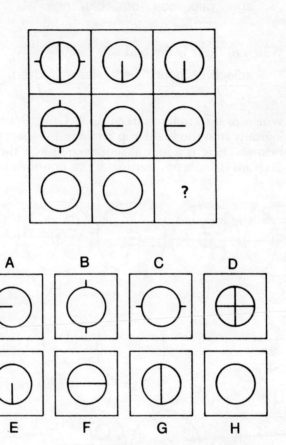

12 Underline the name given to a group of foxes.

stalk, sedge, skulk, sord, string

13 Which of these is the odd one out?

trumpet, harp, saxophone, clarinet, horn

14 Place two of these three-letter 'bits' together to make a colour.

agu, pup, sca, ora, blu, nge

15 Which of these is the odd one out?

adjective, noun, verb, letter, adverb

16 Which of the circles marked A, B, C, D, E, fits logically into the blank top circle in the diagram below? There is a logical sequence to how the diagram is built up, starting at the bottom row.

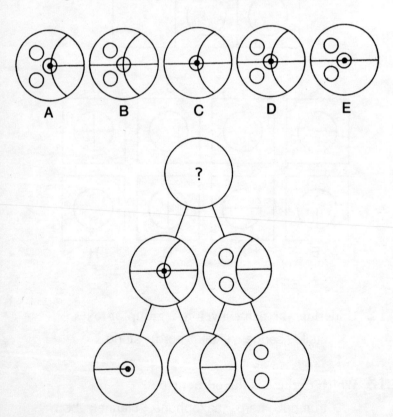

17 Insert the name of a bird (5 letters) to complete this word.

P . . . . G

18 Fill in the missing letters to find a word that means level.

. OR . . ON . A .

19

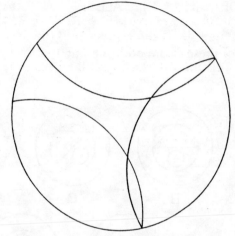

Can you draw this figure without taking your pencil off the paper and without crossing over a line which you have previously drawn?

20 Which word inside the brackets is opposite in meaning to the word in capital letters?

POVERTY (starvation, scarcity, rags, benefit, wealth)

21 Which word is a part of this group?

table, chair, bookcase, dresser

Choose from:

pantry, settee, galley, lobby

22 Find the missing number in this sequence:

4, 9, ? , 25, 36,

23 Complete the word which, when added on to the first word makes a new word or phrase, and when placed in front of the second word, makes a new word or phrase.

TOE   (H * * *)   ALL

24 Which of these is the odd one out?

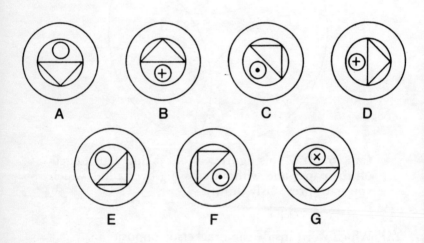

A   B   C   D

E   F   G

25 SPAIN is to COUNTRY, as SPANISH is to which of these?

LANGUAGE, LAND, ABROAD, SEA, EUROPE

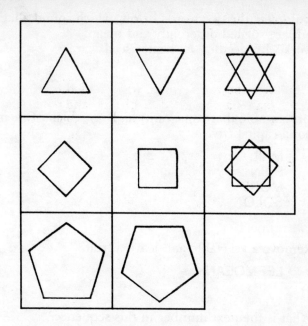

Look across each row and down each column and try to find the correct right-hand bottom tile from the choice below.

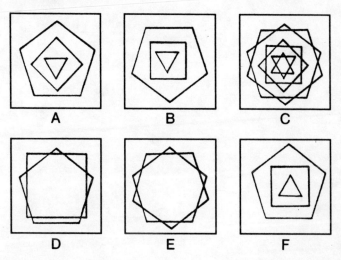

27 Complete the two words below, which sound alike, but are spelled differently and mean:
work with needle / scatter seeds.

. E . / . O .

28 Unscramble these anagrams and say which of them is not a capital city.

MAIL
RAIN
MORE
SOLO

29 Remove a vegetable and leave a fruit.

LEPMOEAN

30 What is the next number in this sequence?

100, 91, 82, 73, ? ,

1 (c) (a part of a joint)   2 JAR

3 accuse, blame   4 RELIGION

5 RACOON

6 C. (The trapezium turns over at each stage. The diamond is horizontal, then vertical, in turn at each stage.)

7 clothe   8 (c) (A human head and a lion's body.)

9 A FEMALE SHEEP IS CALLED A MARE

(The sentence is false. A female sheep is called a ewe.)

10 meadow

11 H. Column 3 is obtained by adding Column 2 to Column 1, but only the circles and lines that are common to both Columns are carried forward. The same thing happens with the Rows. Thus:

12 skulk

13 harp.   (This is a stringed instrument. The rest are
wind instruments.)

14 orange

15 letter.   (The others are grammatical 'parts of speech'.)

16 D.   (In the bottom row of the diagram, the left-hand
and the centre bottom circles combine (are
added together) to form the circle which is above
them.

The right-hand and the centre circles in the
bottom row combine to form the circle above
them.

These two new circles in the middle row then
combine to form the top circle which, to fit, is
filled by circle D.)

17 ROBIN.   (Making the word PROBING.)

18 HORIZONTAL

19

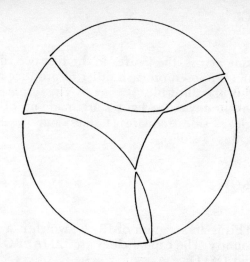

(Of course, different starting/finishing points are possible.)

20 wealth

21 settee.   (This is furniture. The rest are rooms.)

22 16.   (The sequence is made up of the squares of 2, 3, 4, 5, 6. The square of 4 is 16.)

23 HOLD.   (Toe-hold, Holdall)

24 G.   (C is the same as F, but rotated.
B is the same as D, but rotated.
A is the same as E, but rotated.)

25 LANGUAGE

26 E.   (Looking across, the figures in the first two tiles
are superimposed on each other to produce the
figure in the third tile.
  Looking down, the figures are made up of
triangles (3 sides), squares (4 sides) and
pentagons (5 sides).)

27 SEW / SOW

28 RAIN.   (This is an anagram of IRAN, which is a
country. The capital cities are LIMA, ROME
and OSLO.)

29 Remove PEA and leave LEMON (LE̶P̶MO̶E̶A̶N).

30 64.   (Take away 9 each time.)

Scoring Chart for Test 5

	11 years	12 years	13 years
Average	13–15	15–17	17–19
Good	16–18	18–20	20–22
Very Good	19–21	21–23	23–25
Excellent	22–24	24–26	26–28
Exceptional	25–30	27–30	29–30

Test 6

1 What is a foxglove? Is it:

    (a) an animal
    (b) an article of clothing
    (c) a dance
    (d) a plant
    (e) a dog?

2 Which is the odd one out?

    France, Berlin, Austria, Poland, Belgium

3 Underline the name given to a group of horses.

    scrum, set, stable, skein, sord

4 If NOVEL is to CHAPTER, then POEM is to which of these?

    WORD, LETTER, VERSE, COLON, COMMA

5 Solve the anagram (one word).   CLUE: Animal.

    LESIONS

6 Which of the squares A to H, will fit in at the square with the question mark?

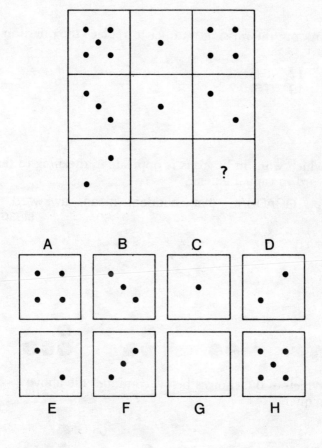

7 CUE is to QUEUE, as MARSHAL is to which of these?

SHERIFF, MARTYR, MARTIAL, SWAMPY, SNOOKER

8 Complete the two words below, which sound alike, but are spelled differently and mean: falling water / rule.

.A.N / .E.G.

9 Work out the missing number to replace the question mark.

17 (51) 3
19 (76) ?

10 Which word in brackets is opposite in meaning to the word in capital letters?

GRADUAL (flat, sudden, mean, awkward, steady)

11

Which of the choices below continues the above sequence?

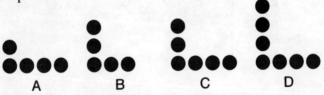

A   B   C   D

12 This grid has three squares along the top, marked A, B and C and three squares down the left side, marked 1, 2 and 3. Each of the nine inner squares should contain just the lines and symbols in the square of the letter above, and also just the lines and symbols in the square of the same number to the left.

For example, the inner square 1B should contain just the lines and symbols that are in square 1 and square B.

One of the nine inner squares is incorrect. Which is it?

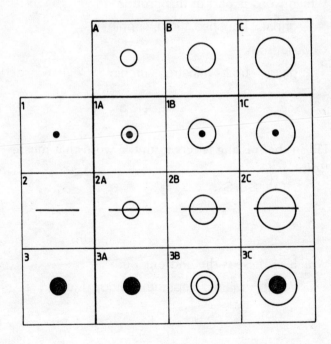

13 Place two of these three-letter 'bits' together to make an aid to drawing.

bir, cra, bru, cil, yon, pai

14 Complete the word inside the brackets that means the same as the words outside the brackets.

BIRD (R * * K) CHESS PIECE

15 Which word is part of this group?

ghost, banshee, imp, sprite

Choose from:

gipsy, troll, minstrel, urchin

16 Fill in the missing letters to find a word that means own.

. O . S . S .

17 Which of these is the odd one out?

Venus, Mars, Neptune, Pluto, Moon

18 Unscramble these anagrams and say which one of them is not a country.

> ABCU
> RUPE
> ILNO
> JIIF

19 What number comes next in this sequence?

> 1, 2, 4, 7, 11, 16, 22, ? ,

20 Which of these is the odd one out?

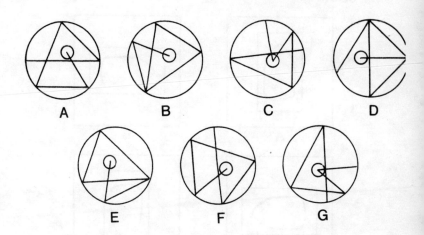

A   B   C   D

E   F   G

21 Underline the two words which are closest in meaning.

> uncover, defile, reveal, notorious, desire

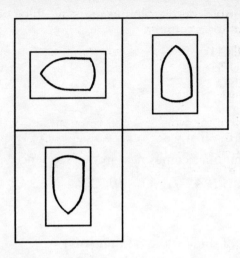

Which is the missing square, above, from the choice below?

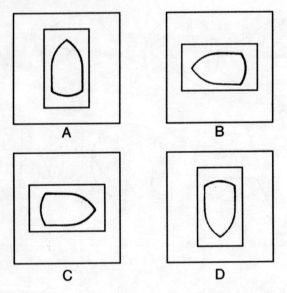

A

B

C

D

23 Which word inside the brackets is an opposite of the word in capital letters?

DRAKE (sailor, chicken, duck, magpie,
                                        pigeon)

24 Complete the word which, when added on to the end of the first word makes a new word or phrase, and when placed in front of the second word, makes a new word or phrase.

LOCK (J * *) BONE

25 Find the missing number in the sequence.

13, 17, ? , 23, 29,

26 Which of the nine triangles below is the odd one out?

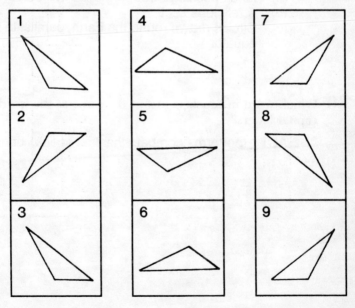

27 Complete the two words below, which sound alike, but are spelled differently and mean:
delay / heaviness.

　　. A . T　/　. E . G . T

28 Look across each row and down each column in the grid, and say what should replace the question mark.

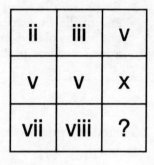

29 Lines of latitude are which of these?

　　(a)　Lines passing through the Earth's poles
　　(b)　A religious sect
　　(c)　Circles drawn round the Earth, parallel to the equator

30 Which word in brackets means the same as the word in capital letters?

　　ACT　(perform, combat, theatre, speak, dance)

Answers Test 6

1 (d) a plant

2 Berlin. (This is a city. The others are countries.)

3 stable   **4** VERSE

5 LIONESS

6 D. (Column 3 is obtained by adding Columns 1 and 2, but the dots that appear in both of these are not carried through to Column 3. The same thing happens with the Rows.)

7 MARTIAL. (They are words that sound the same.)

8 RAIN / REIGN   **9** 4. (17 × 3 = 51
                                        19 × 4 = 76)

10 sudden

11 B. (A further dot is added at each stage. This dot is added to the right of the bottom row, then on top of the vertical column, in turn.)

12 3B.   **13** crayon

14 ROOK

15 troll.   (The others are humans.)

16 POSSESS

17 Moon.   (This is a satellite. The others are planets.)

18 ILNO.   (This is an anagram of LION. The countries are CUBA, PERU and FIJI.)

19 29.   (Add 1, then 2, then 3, then 4, then 5, then 6, then 7.)

20 D.   (A is the same as F, but rotated.
B is the same as E, but rotated.
C is the same as G, but rotated.)

21 uncover, reveal

22 C.   (So that the figure points left, right, up and down, in the diagram.)

23 duck

24 JAW.   (Lockjaw, Jawbone)

25 19.   (They are consecutive prime numbers.)

26 6.   (It is the only triangle which is not a mirror-image of the triangle above or below it.)

27 WAIT / WEIGHT

28 xv (This is 15 in Roman numerals. Each end square is produced by adding together the numbers in the first two squares, across and down.)

29 (c) Circles drawn round the Earth, parallel to the equator.

30 perform

Scoring Chart for Test 6

	11 years	12 years	13 years
Average	13–15	15–17	17–19
Good	16–18	18–20	20–22
Very Good	19–21	21–23	23–25
Excellent	22–24	24–26	26–28
Exceptional	25–30	27–30	29–30

Test 7

1 Place two of these three-letter 'bits' together to make an area of water.

str, lak, oon, riv, lag, pon

2 Underline the name given to a group of geese.

spinney, spring, skein, swarm, span

3 Complete the word which, when added on to the end of the first word makes a new word or phrase, and when placed in front of the second word, makes a new word or phrase.

LUMBER   (J * * *)   DAW

4 What is a massacre? Is it:

    (a)   a slaughter
    (b)   a field
    (c)   a large lump
    (d)   eye shadow
    (e)   the name of a painter?

5 Remove something to drink and leave something to eat.

BCROFEAFEDE

6

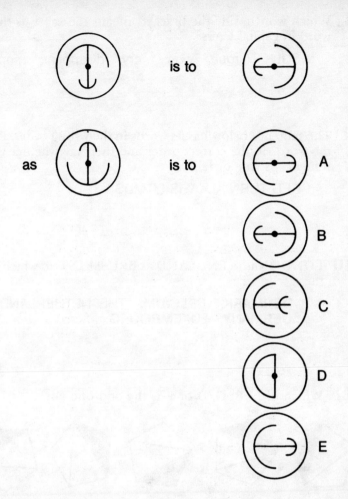

7 Insert a three-letter word that completes the first word and starts the second word.

CAN	_ _ _	ICE

89

8 Which word inside the brackets means the same as the word in capital leters?

SULK (argue, worry, cry, disappear, mope)

9 The sentence below has its words in the wrong order. Put the words in the correct order and then say whether the sentence is true or false.

RED TURN ALKALIS LITMUS

10 LONDON is to ENGLAND as BRUSSELS is to which of these:

DENMARK, BELGIUM, THE NETHERLANDS, GERMANY, LUXEMBOURG

11 Which of A, B, C, D or E is the odd one out?

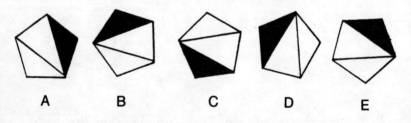

A   B   C   D   E

12 Solve the anagram (one word). CLUE: An English county.

SORTED

13 Underline the two words which are closest in meaning:

hat, saint, halo, ring, shining

14 If BOW is to ARROW, then SLING is to which of these?

SPEAR, STONE, BULLET, KNIFE, SWORD

15 Which word is part of this group?

pout, frown, smirk, simper

Choose from:

covert, fidget, flirt, scowl

16

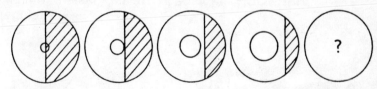

Which of A, B, C, D or E should logically follow on the sequence above?

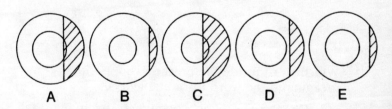

17

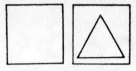

Which of the choices below comes next in the above sequence?

A   B   C   D   E

18 Which word inside the brackets means the same as the word in capital letters?

HARBOUR (approach, relate, fasten, omit, refuge)

19 Complete the word inside the brackets that means the same as the words outside the brackets.

TRAP RABBIT ILLEGALY (P****) COOK EGGS

20 Which word inside the brackets is opposite in meaning to the word in capital letters?

GIGANTIC (huge, pompous, enormous, fat, tiny)

21 Which of these is the odd one out?

ant, ladybird, whelk, centipede, midge

22 Which of the circles marked A, B, C, D, E, fits logically into the blank top circle in the diagram below. There is a logical sequence to how the diagram is built up, starting at the bottom row.

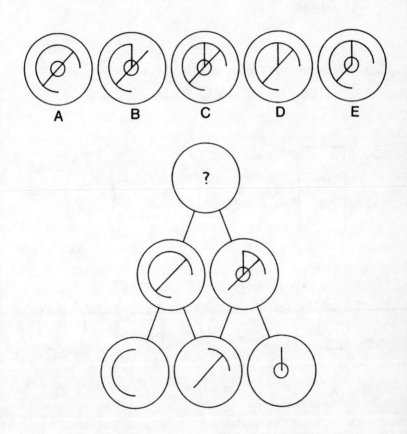

23 Which of these is the odd one out?

repaper, level, redder, motor, rotator

24 Unscramble these anagrams and say which one of them is not shown on a weather map:

LEAS
INAR
WOSN
LHIA

25 What number comes next in this sequence?

100, 99, 97, 94, 90, 85, ? ,

26

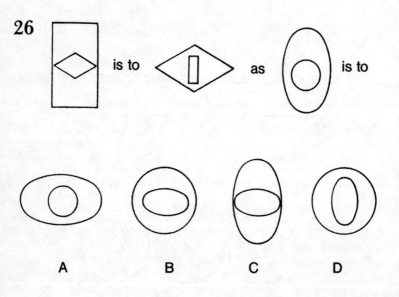

A   B   C   D

94

27 When a ray of light travels from one substance into another, the ray 'bends'. This 'bending' is known as which of these?

    (a) reflection
    (b) refraction
    (c) reformation

28 Complete the two words below, which sound alike, but are spelled differently and mean:
plank / wearied.

    . O . R . / . O . E .

29 Which one word can be placed in front of all five of the words below to make five other words?

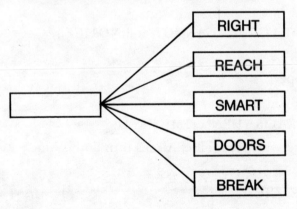

RIGHT

REACH

SMART

DOORS

BREAK

30 Fill in the missing letters to find a word that means a lamp.

    . A . TE . .

Answers Test 7

1 lagoon   2 skein

3 JACK   (Lumberjack, Jackdaw)

4 (a) a slaughter

5 Remove COFFEE to leave BREAD (B̶C̶R̶Ø̶F̶E̶A̶F̶E̶D̶Ø̶).

6 A.   (The semicircles swing 90° to the right.)

7 NOT   (To give CANNOT and NOTICE.)

8 mope

9 ALKALIS TURN LITMUS RED
   (The sentence is false. Alkalis turn litmus blue.)

10 BELGIUM

11 B.   (The other four are all the same figure, but are
      rotated.)

12 DORSET   13 halo, ring

14 STONE

15 scowl.   (This is something you do with your face only.)

16 E.   (Going from left to right, the small circle gets larger each time and the area which is shaded gets smaller each time.)

17 A.   (Starting at Stage 1 with a single square, a symbol is added each time until three symbols appear together (Stage 3).

Then a symbol is taken away each time until just one symbol remains (Stage 5).

Then a symbol is added each time until three symbols once more appear (Answer A).)

18 refuge   **19** POACH

20 tiny

21 whelk.   (This is a marine shellfish. The others are land creatures.)

22 C.   (In the bottom row of the diagram, the left-hand and the centre bottom circles combine (are added together) to form the circle which is above them.

The right-hand and the centre circles in the bottom row combine to form the circle above them.

These two new circles in the middle row then combine to form the top circle, which, to fit, is filled by circle C.)

23 motor. (The others are palindromes, which means that they read the same backwards as forwards.)

24 LEAS. (This is an anagram of SEAL. The things shown on a weather map are RAIN, SNOW and HAIL.)

25 79. (Take away 1, then 2, then 3, then 4, then 5, then 6.)

26 D. (The rectangle stays upright but gets smaller. It goes inside the diamond, which gets bigger. So, the ellipse (oval shape) stays upright but gets smaller and goes inside the circle, which gets bigger. This only happens in choice D.)

27 (b) refraction

28 BOARD / BORED

29 OUT

30 LANTERN

Scoring Chart for Test 7

	11 years	12 years	13 years
Average	13–15	15–17	17–19
Good	16–18	18–20	20–22
Very Good	19–21	21–23	23–25
Excellent	22–24	24–26	26–28
Exceptional	25–30	27–30	29–30

Test 8

1   Which word inside the brackets is opposite in meaning to the word in capital letters?

      RETREAT   (follow, proceed, blend, advance, discover)

2   What is a squire? Is it:

      (a)   a bog
      (b)   a canal
      (c)   a country gentleman
      (d)   a mop
      (e)   an oblong?

3   Solve the anagram (one word).
    CLUE: It is a dance from Cuba.

      BURMA

4   Which of these is the odd one out?

      reel, tango, espresso, waltz, cancan

5   Which number comes next in this sequence?

      1, 18, 35, 52, 69, 86, ? ,

6

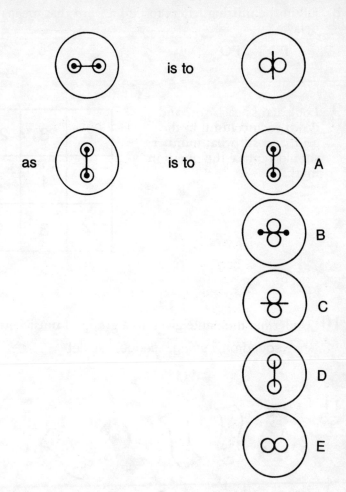

7 Which word in the brackets is opposite in meaning to the word in capital letters?

OPENING (blockage, split, secretly, broad, clear)

8 Fill in the missing letters to find a word that means delay.

PO . . PO . .

9 Look across each row and down each column in the grid, and say what number should replace the question mark.

7	3	21
2	1	2
14	3	?

10 Underline the name given to a group of musicians.

squadron, string, sedge, sextet

11

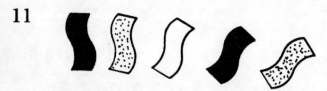

Which of the choices below comes next in the above sequence?

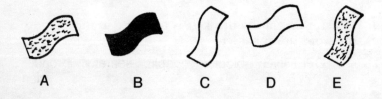

A   B   C   D   E

12 Place two of these three-letter 'bits' together to make a learning place.

tow, ool, pri, aca, lib, sch

13 If NECK is to SCARF, then HEAD is to which of these?

STOLE, TOGA, FEZ, KHAKI, SUEDE

14 Complete the word which, when added on to the first word makes a new word or phrase, and when placed in front of the second word, makes a new word or phrase.

MEMBER   (S * * *)   MATE

15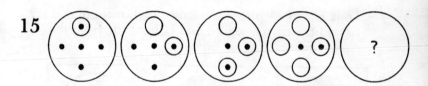

Which of A, B, C, D or E, should logically follow on the sequence above?

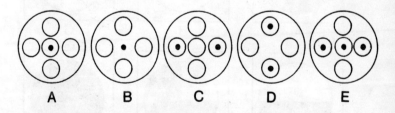

A   B   C   D   E

16 Which of these is the odd one out?

flood, hurricane, cyclone, gale, tornado

17

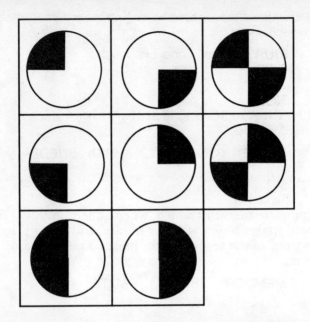

Look across each row and down each column and try to find the correct right-hand bottom tile from the choice below.

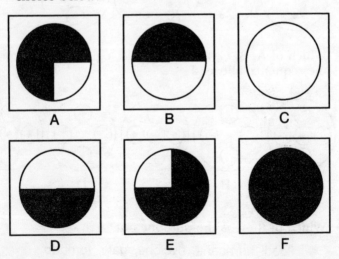

104

18 Unscramble these anagrams and say which one of them is not a musical instrument.

> MDUR
> EOOB
> RAPH
> UNON

19 Insert a three-letter word that completes the first word and starts the second word.

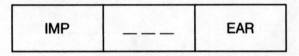

| IMP | _ _ _ | EAR |

20 JEAN is to JANE, as RONALD is to which of these?

> **REAGAN, ARNOLD, DONALD, GEORGE, FRANK**

21 A decibel is a unit for measuring which of these?

> (a)   sound
> (b)   length
> (c)   atmospheric pressure

22 Complete the two words below, which sound alike, but are spelled differently and mean:
expensive / kind of animal

> . E . R / . E . R

23 This grid has three squares along the top, marked A, B and C and three squares down the left side, marked 1, 2 and 3.

   Each of the nine inner squares should contain just the lines and symbols in the square of the same letter above, and also just the lines and symbols in the square of the same number to the left.

   For example, the inner square 1B should contain just the lines and symbols that are in square 1 and square B.

   One of the nine inner squares is incorrect. Which is it?

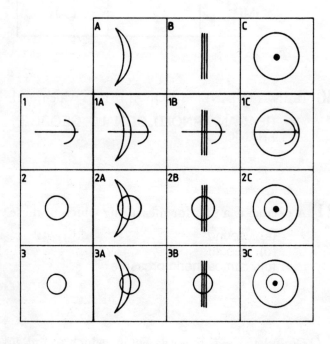

24 Study the pyramid below and, in particular, the lines which appear in each hexagon. Moving up the pyramid from the bottom row, these lines appear in each hexagon according to a set rule, depending on the lines which appear in the two hexagons directly below it.

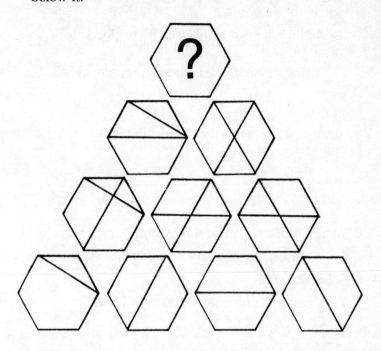

Which of A, B, C or D, below, should replace the hexagon with the question mark at the top of the pyramid?

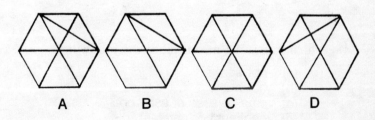

25 Which word in the brackets means the same as the word in capital letters?

ORATION (story, thesis, words, elude, speech)

26 Underline the two words which are closest in meaning.

emit, insect, discharge, prepare, enter

27 Complete the word that means the same as the words outside the brackets.

RED (R * * *) JEWEL

28 Which word is part of this group?

crayon, chalk, pencil, paints

Choose from:

carton, charcoal, drawing, fresco

29 Which word inside the brackets means the same as the word in capital letters?

PHIAL (bottle, folder, magazine, cup, paper)

30 Which one word means all of the following?

(a) not tight
(b) not busy
(c) small pieces of ashy coal
(d) negligent or careless

Answers Test 8

1 advance

2 (c) a country gentleman

3 RUMBA

4 espresso. (It is a drink, or where such a drink is served. The others are dances.)

5 103. (Add 17 each time.)

6 C. (In the top row, the two small circles come together. The horizontal line becomes a vertical line and loses the two 'knobs'.

In the second row, therefore, the two circles must come together. The vertical line must become a horizontal line and lose the two 'knobs'. This is so only for Answer C.)

7 blockage

8 POSTPONE

9 42. (In the rows across and the columns down, the first two numbers are multiplied together to produce the end number.)

10 sextet

11 D. (The figure is tumbling over gradually and is black, then dotted, then white, in turn.)

12 school   **13** FEZ

14 SHIP.   (Membership, Shipmate)

15 A.   (The first circle has one small circle; the second
has two; the third has three; the fourth has four;
so the fifth circle must have five small circles.

The first circle has five dots; the second has four;
the third has three; the fourth has two; so the
fifth circle must have one dot.

The option with five small circles and one dot, is A.)

16 flood.   (The others are winds and storms.)

17 F.   (Looking both across and down, the first two
squares merge (join together) to form the third
square.)

18 UNON   (This is an anagram of NOUN. The musical
instruments are DRUM, OBOE and HARP.)

19 END   (To give IMPEND and ENDEAR.)

20 ARNOLD.   (This is an anagram of RONALD, as
JEAN is an anagram of JANE.)

21 (a)   sound   **22** DEAR / DEER

23 1C.

24 A. (Each hexagon contains the lines which appear in the two hexagons directly below it **except,** where the same line appears in the two hexagons, this disappears in the hexagon above.)

25 speech

26 emit, discharge

27 RUBY

28 charcoal. (This, also, is used by an artist.)

29 bottle

30 slack

Scoring Chart for Test 8

	11 years	12 years	13 years
Average	13–15	15–17	17–19
Good	16–18	18–20	20–22
Very Good	19–21	21–23	23–25
Excellent	22–24	24–26	26–28
Exceptional	25–30	27–30	29–30

Test 9

1 Which of these is the odd one out?

   silk, wool, cotton, nylon, jumper

2 Place two of these three-letter 'bits' together to make a position on the cricket field.

   bat, mid, lon, off, sto, bow

3 Solve the anagram (one word). CLUE: Women.

   IDEALS

4 What is a stallion? Is it:

   (a) a farmer
   (b) a horse
   (c) a frog
   (d) a dolt
   (e) a tuft of grass?

5 Underline the name given to a group of whales.

   span, skulk, school, smuck

6

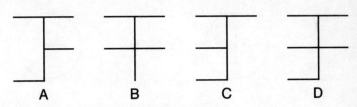

Which of the choices below comes next in the above sequence?

A   B   C   D

7 Complete the two words below, which sound alike, but are spelled differently, and mean: moan / developed.

. R . A . / . R . W .

8 A ligament is which of these?

    (a)   Fibrous tissue that 'ties' one bone to another
    (b)   Part of an electric light bulb
    (c)   A device used for treating wounds

9 SEE is to SAW as KNOW is to which of these?

    KNEW, KNOWN, KNOWED, KNOWL, NEW

10 The sentence below has its words in the wrong order. Put the words in the correct order and then say whether the sentence is true or false.

LIQUID IS INTO EVAPORATION VAPOUR OF CONVERSION

11

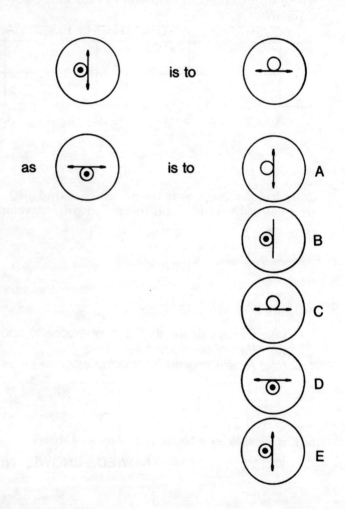

12 Which word inside the brackets is opposite in meaning to the word in capital letters?

> TAUT (loose, teach, learn, think, wish)

13 If LATE is to UNPUNCTUAL, then HOLIDAY is to which of these?

> OVERTIME, CHRONOGRAPH, PUNCTUAL, VACATION, ROUTINE

14 Imagine that the line drawn diagonally which splits each of the squares A, B, C, D and E, in two, is a mirror.

In four of these squares the correct mirror-image has been shown, but one of the squares does not have the correct mirror-image in its other half.

Can you say which of the squares is incorrect?

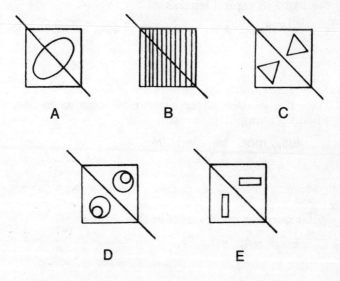

15

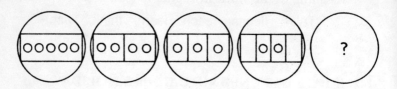

Which of A, B, C, D or E should logically follow on the sequence above?

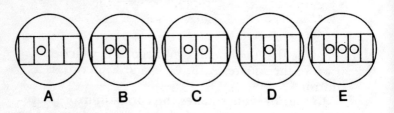

16 Which of the words in the brackets means the same as the word in capital letters?

LUCK (observe, attract, hope, chance, joy)

17 Place two of these three-letter 'bits' together to find a word meaning brightness.

lus, mor, tre, ted, tar

18 What number comes next in this sequence?

−7, −4, −1, ? ,

19 Unscramble these anagrams and say which one of them is not an animal.

     TOBO
     GAST
     ROBA
     TOGA

20 Which of the circles marked A, B, C, D, E, fits logically into the blank top circle in the diagram below? There is a logical sequence to how the diagram is built up, starting at the bottom row.

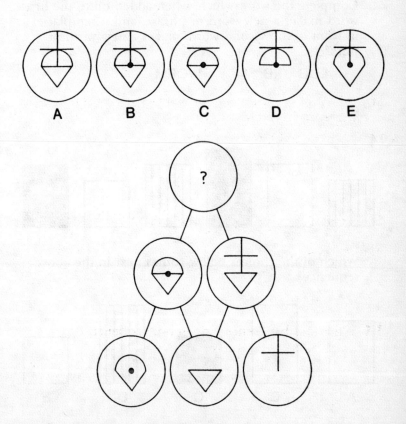

21 Underline the two words which are closest in meaning.

scamper, scurry, descend, stroll, climb

22 Complete the word that means the same as the two words outside the brackets.

NEW   (N * * * L)   BOOK

23 Complete the word which, when added on to the first word makes a new word or phrase, and when placed in front of the second word, makes a new word or phrase.

LOG   (B * * *)   WORM

24

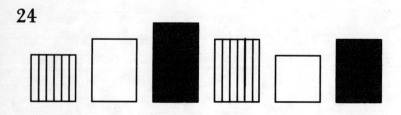

Which of the choices below comes next in the above sequence?

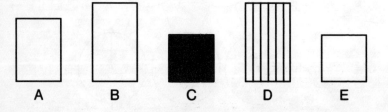

A   B   C   D   E

25 Which word is part of this group?

conundrum, rebus, acrostic, anagram

Choose from:

puzzle, picture, pantomime, playhouse

26 Which of these is the odd one out?

swan, heron, squid, jackdaw, penguin

27 Look across each row and down each column in the grid, and say what number should replace the question mark.

12	6	2
3	3	1
4	2	?

28 Fill in the missing letters to find a word meaning rise.

. S . . ND

29 Unscramble this anagram to find a well-known profession (one word) with which you are all familiar.

THE RACE

30 Which word inside the brackets means the same as the word in capital letters?

ORAL (written, spoken, listen, loud, trim)

119

Answers Test 9

1 jumper

2 mid-off

3 LADIES

4 (b) a horse

5 school

6 B.   (A line is added each time, first to the right, then
to the left, moving down the vertical line.)

7 GROAN / GROWN

8 (a) Fibrous tissue that 'ties' one bone to another.

9 KNEW

10 EVAPORATION IS CONVERSION OF LIQUID
INTO VAPOUR
or
CONVERSION OF LIQUID INTO VAPOUR IS
EVAPORATION

(Both are true.)

11 A.   In the top line, the arrow and circle swing round
90° clockwise and the centre dot vanishes.

Therefore, in the second line the arrow and
circle must swing round 90° clockwise and the
dot must vanish. This is so only for choice A.

12 loose   **13** VACATION

14 B.

15 D.   (The first circle has 1 rectangle and 5 small circles.
        The second   has 2 rectangles and 4 small circles.
        The third   has 3 rectangles and 3 small circles.
        The fourth   has 4 rectangles and 2 small circles.

        So, the fifth must have 5 rectangles and 1 small
        circle, which is so only for Choice D.)

16 chance   **17** lustre

18 2.   (Add 3 each time.)

19 TOBO   (This is an anagram of BOOT. The animals
        are STAG, BOAR and GOAT.)

20 B.   (In the bottom row of the diagram, the left-hand
        and the centre circles combine (are added
        together) to form the circle which is above them.

        The right-hand and the centre circles in the
        bottom row combine to form the circle above
        them.

        The two new circles in the middle row then
        combine to form the top circle which, to fit, is
        filled by circle B.)

21 scamper, scurry   **22** NOVEL

23 BOOK.   (Log-book, Bookworm)

24 D. The figures gradually increase to a peak, then decrease to a low, then increase again. A graph would look like this:

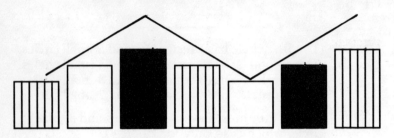

As well as this, the figures are shaded, then white, then black, in turn.

25 puzzle.   (This, also, is a poser.)

26 squid.   (This is a fish. The others are birds.)

27 2.   (In the rows across and the columns down, the first number is divided by the second number to arrive at the end number.)

28 ASCEND   **29** TEACHER

30 spoken

Scoring Chart for Test 9

	11 years	12 years	13 years
Average	13–15	15–17	17–19
Good	16–18	18–20	20–22
Very Good	19–21	21–23	23–25
Excellent	22–24	24–26	26–28
Exceptional	25–30	27–30	29–30

Test 10

1 Place two of these three-letter 'bits' together to make a number.

   sev, eig, nin, for, ety, fiv

2 Solve the anagram (one word). CLUE: Musical instrument.

   GROAN

3 What is a lapel? Is it:

   (a) a book
   (b) a staple
   (c) part of a coat
   (d) part of the lips
   (e) a tongue?

4 Which of these is the odd one out?

   soccer, croquet, ravioli, fencing, karate

5 Remove an ocean and leave a sea.

   ABRCLTIACCK

6

Which of the choices below comes next in the above sequence?

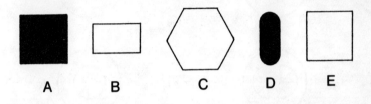

A   B   C   D   E

7 'Everything _____ and nothing stays.' (*Plato*)

Arrange the jumbled letters below to find the correct word to fit in the quotation.

OFWLS

8 Which word in the brackets is opposite in meaning to the word in capital letters?

FALSE (fake, story, increase, good, true)

9 Fill in the missing letters to find a word that means a young horse.

. OA .

10 Which of these is the odd one out?

     friend, mate, family, chum, pal

11

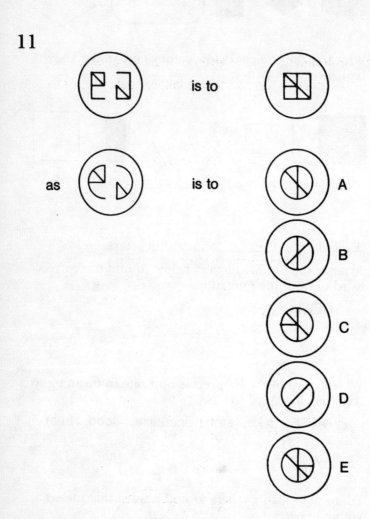

12 Which word in the brackets means the same as the word in capital letters?

     COY (reserved, silly, patient, grim, cold)

13 If ARM is to ULNA, then LEG is to which of these?

TIBIA, SCAPULA, RADIUS, THORAX, LUMBAR

14 Underline the name given to a group of stars.

charm, crop, constellation, catch, clump

15 Which word inside the brackets is opposite in meaning to the word in capital letters?

TARNISH (polish, flower, border, recipe, pride)

16 Which of these is the odd one out?

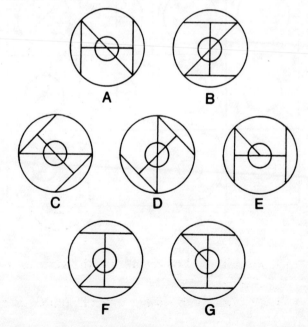

17 This grid has three squares along the top, marked A, B and C and three squares down the left side, marked 1, 2 and 3.

Each of the nine inner squares should contain just the lines and symbols in the square of the same letter above, and also just the lines and symbols in the square of the same number to the left.

For example, the inner square 1B should contain just the lines and symbols that are in square 1 and square B.

One of the nine inner squares is incorrect. Which is it?

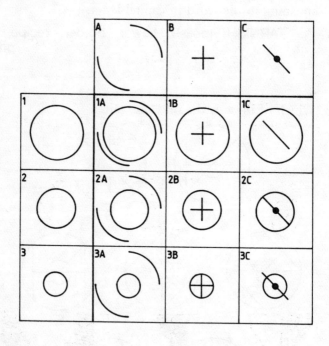

18 Unscramble these anagrams and say which one of them is not a colour.

> LEUB
> KNPI
> TASL
> EGRY

19 What number comes next in this sequence?

> 100, 50, 25, 12.5, 6.25, ? ,

20 Insert a three-letter word that completes the first word and starts the second word.

LEE	_ _ _	LAY

21

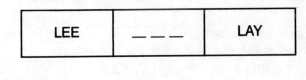

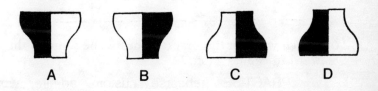

A   B   C   D

129

22 Which word is part of this group?

gorge, abyss, gully, chasm

Choose from:

peak, ravine, summit, mountain

23 Complete the word which, when added to the first word makes a new word or phrase, and when placed in front of the second word, makes a new word or phrase.

TEAR   (G * *)   JET

24 Complete the word in the brackets that means the same as the words outside the brackets.

GRIM   (S * * * N)   REAR

25 Underline the two words which are nearest in meaning.

mislead, praise, deceive, perceive, remonstrate

26 Which word in the brackets means the same as the word in capital letters?

PRACTISE   (rehearse, custom, admire, work, run)

27 CRICKET is to BAT as TENNIS is to which of these?

BALL, NET, RACKET, UMPIRE, COURT

28 Reykjavik is which of these?

    (a) A mountain in Alaska
    (b) A language spoken by Eskimos
    (c) The capital of Iceland

29 Complete the two words below, which sound alike, but are spelled differently and mean:
street / propelled by oars.

    . O . D / . O . E .

30

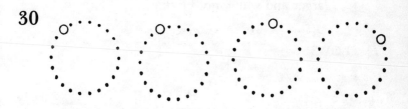

Which of the choices below comes next in the above sequence?

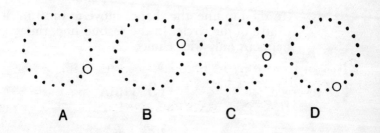

Answers Test 10

1 ninety

2 ORGAN

3 (c) part of a coat

4 ravioli. (This is a type of pasta. The others are sports.)

5 Remove ARCTIC to leave BLACK (A̶B̶R̶C̶L̶I̶A̶A̶C̶CK).

6 E. (The first three figures are being repeated, but larger and white, not black.)

7 FLOWS

8 true

9 FOAL

10 family

11 C. (In the top line, the shapes move to meet in the centre of the circle. In the second line, this happens only with choice C.)

12 reserved

13 TIBIA

14 constellation

15 polish

16 G.   (A is the same as B, but rotated.
C is the same as D, but rotated.
E is the same as F, but rotated.)

17 1C.

18 TASL.   (This is an anagram of SALT, or LAST, or
SLAT. The colours are BLUE, PINK and
GREY.)

19 3.125.   (The previous number is halved each time.)

20 WAY   (To give LEEWAY and WAYLAY.)

21 B.   (The black figure flips over sideways and a white
figure of the same shape, appears where it was.)

22 ravine.   (This also is a 'valley'.)

23 GAS.   (Tear-gas, Gas-jet)

24 STERN   **25** mislead, deceive

26 rehearse   **27** RACKET

28 (c)   The capital of Iceland

29 ROAD / ROWED

30 A. (At each stage, the small circle moves clockwise one place, then two places, then three places, then four places (in choice A).)

Scoring Chart for Test 10

	11 years	12 years	13 years
Average	13–15	15–17	17–19
Good	16–18	18–20	20–22
Very Good	19–21	21–23	23–25
Excellent	22–24	24–26	26–28
Exceptional	25–30	27–30	29–30

Test 11

1 What is an ogre? Is it:

   (a) a wolf hound
   (b) a fairy
   (c) a water sprite
   (d) an old woman
   (e) a monster?

2 Which of these is the odd one out?

   ruby, pearl, opal, quoin, emerald

3 Complete the word in the brackets that means the same as the words outside the brackets.

   PIECE OF BREAD   (C * * * *)   SOLID EARTH

4 Place two of these three-letter 'bits' together to make a golf club.

   lik, iro, dri, ter, put, nib

5 Fill in the missing letters to find a word that means ever.

   . L . A . S

6

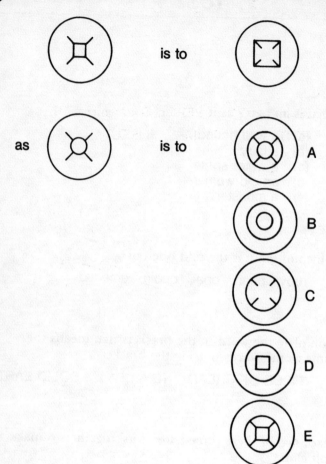

is to

as

is to

A

B

C

D

E

7 The SI unit of length is which of these?

    (a)   yard
    (b)   kilogram
    (c)   metre

8 Complete the two words below, which sound alike, but are spelled differently and mean: amount / portion.

. U . / . O . E

9 FINCH is to BIRD as PERCH is to which of these?

ROD, FISH, ANIMAL, INSECT, DOG

10 The sentence below has its words in the wrong order. Put the words in the correct order and then say whether the sentence is true or false.

OF JORDAN THE AMMAN CAPITAL IS

11 Solve the anagram (one word).   CLUE: Sport.

BOLT LOAF

12

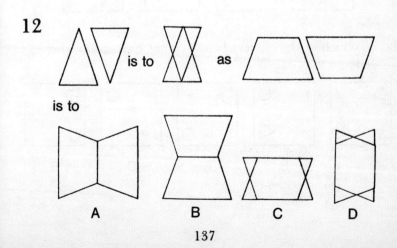

13 Underline the name given to a group of soldiers.

deceit, desert, division, dray, den

14 Which word is part of this group?

speck, dot, mote, particle

Choose from:

slab, jot, section, sector

15 Which word in the brackets means the same as the word in capital letters?

CHORE (task, choir, chewy, singer, meek)

16

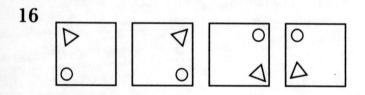

Which of the choices below comes next in the above sequence?

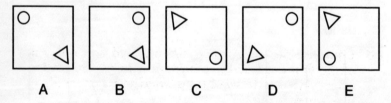

A   B   C   D   E

17 Which of the circles marked A, B, C, D, E, fits logically into the blank top circle in the diagram below. There is a logical sequence to how the diagram is built up, starting at the bottom row.

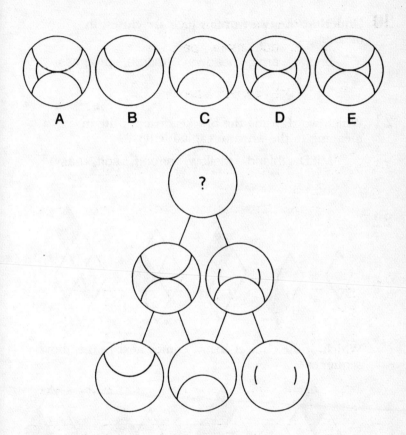

18 Complete the word which, when added on to the end of the first word makes a new word or phrase, and when placed in front of the second word, makes a new word or phrase.

JUMPING   (B * * *)   BAG

19 If BEER is to HOPS, then SUGAR is to which of these?

   CEREAL, MILLET, FODDER, BORAX, BEET

20 Underline the two words which are closest in meaning:

   bridge, arch, headway, march, progress

21 Which word inside the brackets is opposite in meaning to the word in capital letters?

   MILD (bland, mellow, strong, soft, easy)

22

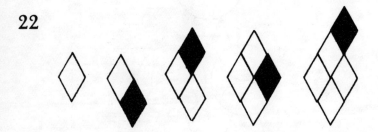

Which of the choices below comes next in the above sequence?

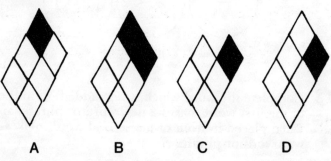

A   B   C   D

23 Look across each row and down each column in the grid, and say what number should replace the question mark.

2	4	6
3	5	7
4	6	?

24 Which one word can be placed in front of all five of the words below to make five other words?

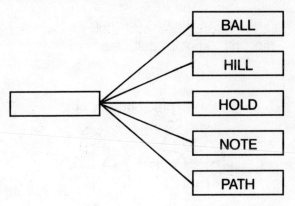

BALL

HILL

HOLD

NOTE

PATH

25 Which word in the brackets means the same as the word in capital letters?

GADGET (muzzle, device, lid, container, cover)

26 Place two of these three-letter 'bits' together to find a word meaning entrance.

ord, ess, dur, acc, ept

141

27 What number comes next in this sequence?

   −20, −13, −6, ? ,

28 Unscramble these anagrams and say which one is not a fruit.

   LUMP
   SORE
   ADET
   AREP

29 Which of these is the odd one out?

   rap, hit, knock, pull, tap

30 Which one of these is the odd one out?

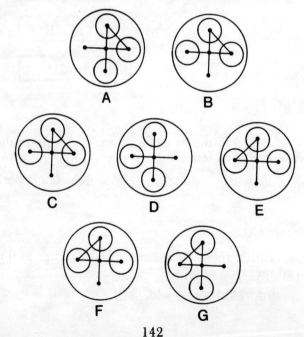

A

B

C

D

E

F

G

142

Answers Test 11

1   (e) a monster

2   quoin.   (This is not a jewel.)

3   CRUST   4   putter

5   ALWAYS

6   C.   (In the top line, the small square gets bigger.
     Therefore, in the second line, the small circle
     must get bigger in the same way. This is so for
     choice C.)

7   metre   8   SUM / SOME

9   FISH

10   THE CAPITAL OF JORDAN IS AMMAN
        or
        AMMAN IS THE CAPITAL OF JORDAN

        (Both sentences are true.)

11 FOOTBALL

12 C.   (The two figures are superimposed upon each
     other, that is, one figure is put on top of the
     other figure.)

13 division

14 jot.　(This also is a　　**15** task
　　　　small spot.)

16 E.　(The circle visits each corner of the square in
　　　turn, travelling anticlockwise. The triangle visits
　　　each corner of the square in turn, travelling
　　　clockwise.)

17 D.　(In the bottom row of the diagram, the left-hand
　　　and the centre circles combine (are added
　　　together) to form the circle which is above them.

　　　The right-hand and the centre circles in the
　　　bottom row combine to form the circle above
　　　them.

　　　These two new circles in the middle row then
　　　combine to form the top circle, which, to fit, is
　　　filled by circle D.)

18 BEAN.　(Jumping-bean, Bean-bag)

19 BEET　　　　　　　**20** headway, progress

21 strong

22 D.　(An extra diamond is added at each stage in a
　　　strict sequence: top, then bottom, then top, then
　　　bottom, and so on.

　　　This new diamond added at each stage, becomes
　　　black **only** at the stage when it is added. After
　　　that it becomes white, and the next new
　　　diamond becomes black – and so on.)

23 8.   In the rows across, add 2 each time. In the columns down, add 1 each time.)

24 FOOT

25 device   **26** access

27 1.   (7 is added each time.)

28 SORE.   (This is an anagram of ROSE. The fruits are PLUM, DATE and PEAR.)

29 pull.   (The others are all ways of striking something.)

30 D.   (Some of the shapes are rotated, but A, E and F are the same, and B, C, and G are the same.)

Scoring Chart for Test 11

	11 years	12 years	13 years
Average	13–15	15–17	17–19
Good	16–18	18–20	20–22
Very Good	19–21	21–23	23–25
Excellent	22–24	24–26	26–28
Exceptional	25–30	27–30	29–30

1 If ROWING is to OARS, then GOLF is to which of these?

   COURSE, CLUBS, LINKS, HANDICAP, FLAG

2 What is sherry? Is it:
   - (a) a cliff face
   - (b) a bird
   - (c) a wine
   - (d) a fish
   - (e) a gold mine?

3 Place two of these three-letter 'bits' together to make a home for an aeroplane.

   han, air, fly, gar, por, run

4 Which one of these is the odd one out?

   captain, major, machete, general, lieutenant

5 Solve the anagram (one word).   CLUE: A sport.

   SINK TAG

6

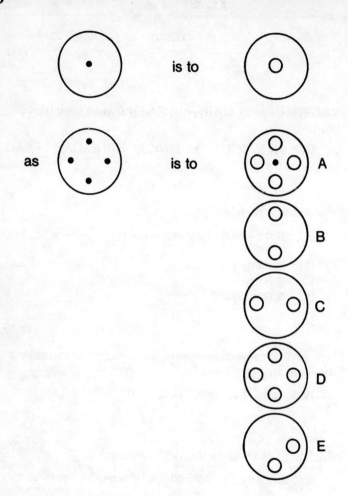

7 Work out the missing number which should replace
the question mark:

56 (34) 12
37 (22) 7
20 (?) 6

148

8 Which word in the brackets is opposite in meaning to the word in capital letters?

SMOOTH (dull, coarse, sleek, patterned, thick)

9 Fill in the missing letters to find a word that means owner.

. . SS . . SS . R

10 Which of these is the odd one out?

correct, approximate, exact, precise, accurate

11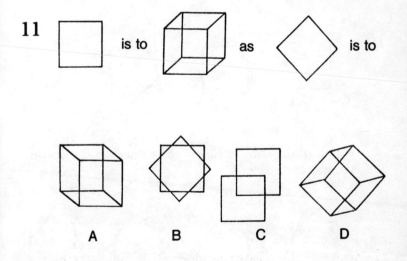

A   B   C   D

12 Which word in the brackets means the same as the word in capital letters?

BLADE (leaf, clasp, prime, clutch, firm)

13 Underline the name given to a group of pictures.

gang, guard, gallery, game, glean

14 Underline the two words which are closest in meaning:

severe, friendly, mankind, humans, thoroughfare

15 Which word is part of this group?

bloomer, howler, blunder, fault

Choose from:

skirt, mistake, misinform, false

16

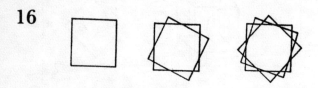

Which of the choices below comes next in the above sequence?

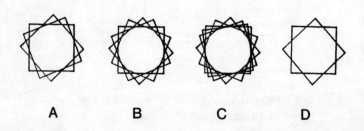

A   B   C   D

17 This grid has three squares along the top, marked A, B and C and three squares down the left side, marked 1, 2 and 3.

Each of the nine inner squares should contain just the lines and symbols in the square of the same letter above, and also just the lines and symbols in the square of the same number to the left.

For example, the inner square 1B should contain just the lines and symbols that are in square 1 and square B.

One of the nine inner squares is incorrect. Which is it?

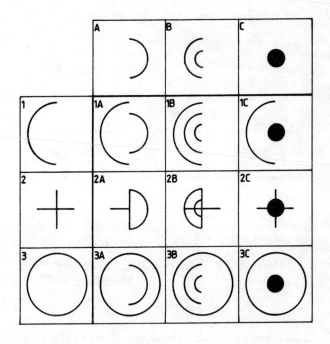

18 Unscramble these anagrams and say which one of them is not a girl's name.

> SAIL
> KLUE
> LAAM
> TAIR

19 Remove a city and leave a country.

> IPTARAILSY

20 What number comes next in this sequence?

> 1, 20, 39, 58, ? ,

21 Insert a three-letter word that completes the first word and starts the second word.

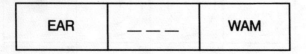

| EAR | _ _ _ | WAM |

22 Complete the word inside the brackets that means the same as the words outside the brackets.

> MATHEMATICAL FIGURE (T * * * * * * E)
> MUSICAL INSTRUMENT

23 Insert a word which when added on to the end of the first word makes a new word or phrase, and when placed in front of the second word, makes a new word or phrase.

> ROAD (S * * * * *) BELT

24 Which word inside the brackets is opposite in meaning to the word in capital letters?

SEVER (limit, break, mend, knock, knead)

25

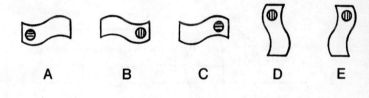

Which of the choices below comes next in the above sequence?

A   B   C   D   E

26 Which word in the brackets means the same as the word in capital letters?

MAYBE (never, perhaps, always, when, ever)

27 CELLAR is to BELOW as ATTIC is to which of these?

ROOF, ROOM, HIGH, ABOVE, STORAGE

28 The prefix deci- means which of these?

   (a) a tenth
   (b) a hundredth
   (c) a thousandth

29 Complete the two words below, which sound alike, but are spelled differently and mean:
ring / cry of excitement.

   . O . P / . H . O .

30 Which of these is the odd one out?

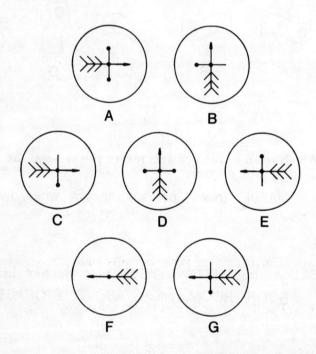

Answers Test 12

1 CLUBS

2 (c) a wine

3 hangar

4 machete. (This is a tool. The others are officers' ranks.)

5 SKATING

6 D. (In the top line, the dot becomes a small circle. Therefore, in the second line, the 4 dots become 4 small circles in the same way. This is so for choice D.)

7 13. $$\begin{array}{r} (56 + 12) \div 2 = 34 \\ (37 + 7) \div 2 = 22 \\ (20 + 6) \div 2 = 13 \end{array}$$

8 coarse

9 POSSESSOR

10 approximate. (This means 'nearly right'.)

11 D. (The flat figure grows into a cube.)

12 leaf

13 gallery

14 mankind, humans

15 mistake. (This also is an 'error'.)

16 B. (At each stage, a new square is added at a quarter-turn up from the bottom. So the next shape will have four squares altogether, which gives choice B.)

17 2A.

18 KLUE. (This is an anagram of LUKE. The girls' names are LISA, ALMA and RITA.)

19 Remove PARIS and leave ITALY (I̶P̶T̶A̶R̶A̶I̶L̶S̶Y̶).

20 77. (19 is added each time.)

21 WIG (To give EARWIG and WIGWAM.)

22 TRIANGLE

23 SAFETY (Road safety, Safety belt)

24 mend

25 C. (The figure is moving through 90° anticlockwise at each stage.)

26 perhaps

27 ABOVE

28 (a) a tenth

29 HOOP / WHOOP

30 F. (A is the same as D, but rotated.
B is the same as G, but rotated.
C is the same as E, but rotated.)

Scoring Chart for Test 12

	11 years	12 years	13 years
Average	13–15	15–17	17–19
Good	16–18	18–20	20–22
Very Good	19–21	21–23	23–25
Excellent	22–24	24–26	26–28
Exceptional	25–30	27–30	29–30

Total scoring chart for the twelve tests

	11 years	12 years	13 years
Average	156–191	180–215	204–239
Good	192–227	216–251	240–275
Very Good	228–263	252–287	276–311
Excellent	264–299	288–323	312–347
Exceptional	300–360	324–360	348–360

PAUL CURTIS

THE LANTERN BALCONY

Vanguard Press

A CIP catalogue record for this title is
available from the British Library.

ISBN 978 1 80016 187 0

Vanguard Press is an imprint of
Pegasus Elliot MacKenzie Publishers Ltd.
www.pegasuspublishers.com
First Published in 2021

Vanguard Press
Sheraton House Castle Park
Cambridge England

Printed & Bound in Great Britain

Dedication

To Chris.

The phone on my desk rang. There was nothing unusual about the ring-tone, nothing to forewarn of romance or adventure; it was the police requesting a psychiatrist to attend an incident. The only unusual circumstance was that I was directed to an outdoor location; the police normally take anyone perceived as a risk into custody, so I was surprised to be directed to a road junction.

Flashing blue lights guided me to my destination. A tall well-built young man with tousled blond hair paced up and down a triangular shaped traffic island, which at its widest was maybe twenty-five yards, but in the mind of the young man it was evidently an impenetrable barrier causing him to turn at the boundaries. A bemused looking policeman stood behind him. Motorists slowed to stare. A paramedic sat on a bollard smoking a cigarette, not a good advert for the NHS. I understood now why I had been called out; the young man posed no obvious threat and was breaking no law.

As for diagnosis my first consideration was schizophrenia because of the repetitive pacing but, as I approached, I saw that the young man carried what appeared to be a cardboard cut-out of a spotted dog under his arm. This caught me by surprise and I had to suppress a smile, but it settled the question: almost certainly autism. He didn't look threatening but had a remote look as if his mind was turned in, a possible indication of unpredictability. Also, he was powerfully built and his pacing was purposeful and compulsive. I was uncertain as to how he would react to any intervention, but in any event, he would need to be admitted for assessment.

I introduced myself to the policeman to see what he had to tell me. "Been here all morning, Doc — all night for all I know." He sounded aggrieved.

"Any idea who he is?"

"Not known to us, I mean not one of our regulars."

"No one reported missing?"

"Nope." The constable looked at me doubtfully, evidently wondering how I was going to deal with this.

I would see how the young man reacted; if necessary, I had the option of detaining him under section four of The Mental Health Act for seventy-two hours, although I would prefer more police officers in attendance, I was out of practice at restraining patients.

I fell into step with the young man as if it was the most natural thing in the world to march up and down a traffic island like a sentry on duty. I nodded towards the dog.

"Is he yours?"

It broke the spell. The young man paused, slid the cardboard dog shyly forwards towards me, stroked it lovingly, giggled and said:

"Naughty Max." He looked at me sideways for a brief instant before looking away. His glance was lowered from my eyes, another indicator of autism.

"Trevor hungry."

Which is how I met Trevor.

Back on the ward, I had a rather one-sided discussion with Trevor in my office. My initial impression of ASD (autistic spectrum disorder) from the limited staccato speech and lack of eye contact, was reinforced by the reference to himself in the third person: a curious trait of autism, the non-recognition of the concept of self. Possibly high functioning I thought; although this was not a scientific observation, there was something in his demeanour suggestive of intelligence. In spite of his limited speech, there was no such deficit in reception, he listened with attention rather than 'tuning out' as is often found in autism.

There was no need to detain him under section, in fact, he nodded with apparent enthusiasm when I suggested a voluntary stay. "To get him on his feet again," is how I put it, but in fact to assess what degree of independence he was capable of. I handed him over for admittance with a promise to, "Have a proper chat with him later."

The next day I was at my desk, struggling with reports, the part of the job I dislike most, and various other members of staff most enjoy burdening me with, particularly Sister Harris — in reality a modern matron but somehow her former title has persisted, supposedly my subordinate but, no doubt due to her strict Scottish Presbyterian upbringing, a self-appointed castigator of errant consultants. I was 'aided' in my task by helpful remarks from Morris.

Morris is my shadow, causing raised eyebrows from my colleagues; the truth is I don't have the heart to banish him from my office. He had been an inpatient before my time and returned in a pitiful condition after living rough. He was bedraggled, confused and depressed. His diagnosis came with him, rather as the label around Paddington Bear's neck, and it was nonsense, bipolar disorder — formerly known by its more descriptive name, manic depression — for which he had been medicated with mood-stabilisers and antipsychotics. I assumed from this that the beaten looking piece of human flotsam before me must have a history of self-harming or violence to justify this medication regime. But there was nothing, no aggression, no suicidal tendencies, only an embarrassing habit of exposing himself to the police, rightly taken seriously because this behaviour is often a precursor to dangerous sex offending, but in the case of Morris it was just to secure a nice warm cell for the night. Reading between the lines of the pompous garbage of his report, it was this pitiful behaviour that had earnt Morris a gratuitous prescription of lithium sulphate that if continued at such high dosage could result in kidney damage. The name at the bottom of the report was our own clinical director, Professor Neil Caldwell MA MB FRCPsych. No surprise for me there.

I took him off the lot and the real amazing Morris emerged like a dirty scruffy butterfly from the wreckage of his chrysalis.

Morris was twenty-three years old, medium height, wiry in build with lacklustre mousy hair. He was wearing a rally jacket, once blue, now muddy brown, and heavily impregnated with the scent of his outdoor adventures, which unfortunately he would not be parted from. His voice was nasal, his speech imitative of whatever he had just heard on the ward or television. He incorporated words that took his fancy and tended to repeat them endlessly. In character he was a hybrid of 'William' and 'Gollum'.

His diagnosis was uncomplicated, he was severely mentally retarded with an IQ under forty. When tested, he struggled blankly for page after page until at last, near the end, he finally found a question he could tackle. Question 24C, I remember it well, was a series of sketches, first a cat, then a dog, then two cats, then two dogs, then three cats, then a blank space. Morris' eyes gleamed with triumph; he picked up his pen confidently and began to draw, shielding his work with his unoccupied hand, presumably to prevent me from cribbing. After some minutes of tongue-hanging-out-of-mouth concentration, he pushed his completed work over to me with a look of proud complacency. I studied it thoughtfully. I know there are still thousands of undiscovered species of fauna roaming the world, but whatever it was, there was only one of it. Morris looked at me pityingly, shaking his head at my slowness. "That's a frog that is." Undoubtedly the right answer from Picasso but...

Somewhere in the dark recesses of Morris' brain filled with an absence of grey matter, an emotional connection was made. I think it stemmed from that very Question 24C where I had revealed my imbecility by not knowing a frog when I saw one. He deduced from this, not just a kindred spirit, but one that needed help. So, Morris became my self-appointed helper, always ready with advice. He opened doors for me. It was an ability he was proud of and suspected that I did not possess, explaining nasally, "Pull the 'andle down, don't do it up — don't work — gotta' do it down, like to the ground, not the other way."

Somehow, I didn't have the heart to shoo him away; you could see in his eyes the expectation of rejection, and when it failed to materialise, he became more confident and optimistic. With an inner sigh, I realised that I had missed the moment. I could not reject him now, although I had to banish him from meetings and consultations.

So it was that Mo was in attendance when I was working on Trevor's assessment. I sighed almost unconsciously, an invitation for him to sidle uncomfortably close to me to offer help. Morris has no conception of body space. He pointed to the top of the form and announced patronisingly, "Name," he stabbed with his finger imperiously. "That's where yer write it, that is, just there, yeah, need a pen for that, got no chance without a pen." He let me down gently. "Piece of piss when yer used to it, but if yer ain't..." He sucked in through his decayed teeth and shook his head darkly. At which point the door opened on Trevor, a moment of considerable significance although I was not aware of it just then.

Trevor met Morris.

Trevor clutched Max protectively and looked away to face the wall, which was, I came to learn, his default orientation when meeting strangers. Morris' greeting was decidedly chummy.

"Orl right mate?" It's what he would have said to the Queen, Morris is unspoilt by class distinction.

Trevor turned in order to view Mo warily from the extreme periphery of his vision. It seemed to me fancifully that fate teetered on the brink of doom, just as in the early universe, an accretion of dust and rocks reached critical mass under extreme pressure, burst into nuclear flames and a star was born: the first seconds of a lifelong friendship. Trevor slowly drew Max from under his arm and offered him tentatively to Morris.

"Max."

Amazingly, Mo did the appropriate thing and patted Max on the head, although even he was aware of the peculiarity of this and snuffled nasally, Mo's equivalent of laughter.

"Nice doggy."

Trevor beamed and Mo pointed to Max.

"Alsatian that is, tell by the spots, pedigree I reckon, got more spots they 'ave. Mongols got splodges."

Trevor giggled.

"Morris is an authority on animals," I explained.

Morris swelled. "Tell yer what, yer new ain't yer? I'd betta show yer 'ow to open the doors — bit tricky they are."

Morris led and Trevor and I followed. This I had to see, appeasing my guilty conscience with the justification of this being part of the assessment process. Morris headed through a maze of corridors, I knew exactly where he was going. There is an assortment of doors in the hospital, some normal, some with keypads but one in particular had a special door. Mulberry Ward houses the more disturbed dementia patients, most of whom are frail, elderly and confused; they're not held under section so legally have to be free to come and go, but this caused us a dilemma because they're not safe unsupervised. Previously we had locked the door at night but an inspection ordered it unlocked. A poor old boy had let himself out in the night, wandered out of the grounds and ended up under a truck. All of us were appalled, however you intellectualised that his life was beyond redemption and a quick end arguably more merciful than what awaited him, the actuality was awful. I felt too for the truck driver. I remember a rabbit hopping in front of my car one night, I felt a sickening bump as the little life was extinguished, it still upsets me to this day. How much worse it must have been for the truck driver.

After this an enterprising caretaker fitted a second handle at knee height. To open the door, you had to depress both handles simultaneously and this was beyond the faculty of the patients. There was something terribly poignant about seeing a frail old man or woman clutching pathetically at the upper handle, mouthing despair through the glass.

Morris spent the next six weeks determinedly working on this conundrum; this was also pathetic to watch, requiring a doubling of his thirty-eight points of IQ to achieve but, defeating all the statistics, he finally accomplished the miracle. Not that he had any business being anywhere near Mulberry Ward, but Morris is terribly nosey. I was pleased for him. The Morris of old wore an expression as if cowering from the threat of a beating, which abated to the mere impression that he was about to petulantly kick a tin can in the way of 'William' being ticked off for some schoolboy insubordination: a distinct improvement.

He now demonstrated his amazing ability to Trevor, manipulating both handles with a flourish. "See, like that. Yer won't get it straight away — takes weeks, an' that's if yer lucky."

We found ourselves face to face with an indignant long-term patient known as 'The Colonel', an old soldier, ninety-eight years old, amazingly fit and apart from absolutely no memory whatsoever and the inability to look after himself, was apparently normal — except at night, when his dreams came to life. We are in general only observers of the unscripted drama that runs through our heads when asleep, but in some dementia patients these dreams are experienced as reality. In the case of The Colonel, nightmares resurrected by his war experiences, animating him to defend himself physically and violently against the hallucinations that threatened him, but he was only so affected at night which is why I insisted on his freedom during the day. When morning dawned along with his sanity, he boiled with indignation at finding himself locked up. He wagged his finger furiously.

"Wrongful imprisonment. I know my rights. Should be ashamed of yourselves." He appeared to notice me for the first time, staring at me with disgust and anger from a countenance that had decency and honesty written all over it. "Uniform's a bloody disgrace." He zeroed in on Trevor. "And that dog should be on a lead."

I shepherded Morris and a bemused Trevor back to my office.

Trevor settled in. I learnt his story from Social Services. He had been living with his mother who had died the night before he was found. The front door was left open, announcing Trevor's flight, departing as his mother's soul. Although Social Services had been involved in earlier years, they had lost touch with him. It seemed that the mother had become less amenable to their visits and without due cause to warrant intervention, the visits stopped. Unbeknown to the family GP and Social Services, the mother became ill. The neighbours gossiped about her weight loss and apparent weakness but with true British reserve did not like to interfere. It was only after her death that all were astounded to find the house so well kept, the kitchen clean and tidy, clothes washed and ironed, the floors scrubbed and carpets vacuumed. The mother was pitifully wasted from colon cancer and the certifying doctor was of the opinion that she had been helpless and bed-ridden for weeks. So who had looked after her? It could only have been Trevor.

A sad story but a confusing one, suggesting that up until his mother's death, Trevor had been capable of more than just self-sufficiency, and yet from my first impressions he had apparently regressed to requiring assisted living, the implication being that this was due to trauma. But this was not my normal experience of autism, in fact I had never heard the like of it. I was intrigued, and, coupled with the fact that he had not reacted well to the psychologist who would normally assess him, I decided to deal with his case myself.

ASD is a clinical diagnosis, in other words, by assessment rather than medical tests. I knew by now that Trevor was severely discomfited by any form of personal questioning so I had to bypass all the questions I would like to have asked, particularly about his history, and concentrate on the more impersonal testing of faculty. These questions he appeared to enjoy with smiling and enthusiastic, albeit monosyllabic, responses.

One of the peculiarities of autism is that, to a varying degree, there is a deficit in interpreting and relating to the behaviour of others, so I missed out a large part of the approved diagnostic interview in favour of a test designed to reveal this, known as the Heider and Simmel animation. This is a short video showing the movement of geometric shapes. The non-autistic, see a story in the movements: a child hiding behind its mother or two men fighting over a girl. Trevor had nothing. He smiled with a grimace that seemed apologetic. Trevor was autistic.

Further tests revealed that, like many with his condition, he had heightened sensory perception, he found loud noises painfully distressing and winced as if in pain at the ambulance sirens. He also had synaesthesia which took the form of seeing numbers in colour, and he was high functioning with an extraordinary mathematical faculty and eidetic memory: an autistic savant. This explained my first impressions of his intelligence. There is a common belief that autists lack the empathy and sympathy required for comprehension, often this isn't the case, it's their communication deficit that makes it seem that way.

While his conversational speech remained obstructed, he became more articulate in another surprising way, breaking into strange dysfunctional monologues that had a previously unheard fluency: shipping forecasts, stock market reports and accusatory Biblical sounding passages. I was puzzled at what prompted these, they were apparently random but I had a feeling that they were inspired by mood and somewhat lyrically interpreted the shipping forecasts as an expression of the internal weather system in his brain. Mo had a different take.

"Reckon 'e was a lighthouse keeper."

Autists are notorious for their strangeness: one will endlessly flick light switches on and off, another will spend hours spellbound by a washing machine at work, another will rush over to a complete stranger to cut the crusts off their sandwiches. At first, Trevor's only bizarre behaviour was having a cardboard dog as a companion but in time he revealed other abnormalities. From his first day, he had shown himself to be an avid reader. One of his first daily rituals was to read all the newspapers in the Common Room from cover to cover, spending a particularly long time on the *Financial Times*, which I suspect was due to reading all the data as well as the reports. And I noticed that when he was in my office his eyes strayed to my bookshelves. While in general not a hoarder, I have a lot of books and rarely throw them away, and so have a considerable library, not just on psychiatry but neuroscience, pharmacology and all my earlier medical books. When he caressed the spine of one with a finger and darted a glance at me, quickly diverted to the floor, I understood his question.

"Read any one you like, Trevor." I was aware that my colleagues would disapprove, Professor Caldwell in particular, for him such knowledge is the currency of our profession that should not be given away.

Trevor systematically read each book in turn according to its position on the bookshelf. Some weeks later, he approached my desk, stretched out a hand gingerly to a pencil, stroked it and giggled.

"Trevor."

I willingly supplied the pencil along with a writing pad. After this, he began to draw, from exactly ten in the morning until eleven, watching the clock for the exact second of the turn of the hour before starting and finishing. He did not volunteer his drawings to me but, emboldened by his increasing ease with me, I stopped apparently casually to look, and he offered his work willingly. I was astounded. He had drawn without the aid of compass, ruler or set-square what looked like intricate and complex engineering drawings.

One of my friends is an engineer. I took him one of the drawings out of curiosity. He glanced at it, laughed derisively, frowned and then began to stare. Such is the process of bewitchment.

"This is very odd," he started before tailing off. "I mean it's a spoof, that is to say it's not an engineering drawing, it's the work of an artist complete with vanishing point, but then again it *is* the work of an engineer. The profile angles are described, the PCD's." I had to ask. "Pitch Circle Diameter — a gear's operating diameter is not the outside measurement but a line of contact..." He lost me. I think I'll stick to medicine. Eventually he continued. "I've never seen anything like it. It's a gear-train, all the ratios are correct, the geometry of the helicals, everything, but at the same time it's complete nonsense." He went on to explain why and lost me again. I was reminded of a detective story I had read, set in World War Two, when, in order to entice some fifth columnists to break cover, the War Office concocted a top-secret prototype of an aircraft, such a good fake that it deceived the Nazi engineers until they started trying to build the thing.

"Besides," laughed my friend, apparently immensely amused, "the ratio is exactly one to one, so it's completely pointless: gearboxes are either reduction or speed multipliers."

Machinery of all sorts is a common theme to ASD, pylons in particular. I have a theory, which I usually keep to myself, that they represent the wiring in the brain which is aberrant in autism. Not only were

Trevor's drawings exceptionally advanced in concept and detail, but his ability to draw perfect arcs and straight lines freehand was also extraordinary, although requiring a different faculty. Against this was his poor communication. As is common with ASD, he demonstrated frustration at his difficulty expressing himself. It was painful to watch him struggle to reply to, "How's Trevor today?" The usual response being a working of the jaw as if his speech formation was at war with an inhibitory mechanism, much anguished frowning and fidgeting, and after turning to face the wall:

"Trevor OK." Speech problems in autism are varied partly due to the differences in brain development, and in many cases, there is a lack of desire to communicate. Not Trevor though, he wanted to talk but couldn't.

I discussed him with my colleagues, some of whom have a greater experience of the condition than me. They were polite but puzzled by my interest. Treatment is simple in that expectations are modest, which encourages a lazy practitioner to go through the motions, I saw this in the unspoken expressions. 'Why such a fuss? Arrange for a needs assessment — job done'. In one of the more unguarded expressions, I read a look that suggested that there was a place where I belonged other than my current situation; a place requiring two handles to be operated simultaneously in order to get out — and my colleague had little faith in my ability to do so.

I made the unusual decision to consult Professor Caldwell, which gives some idea of how uncertainty had eaten away at my confidence, to consult someone whose clinical abilities I had so little respect for. 'The Caldwell', as we had disrespectfully nicknamed him, looked at me with that calculating stare with which he treated staff and patients alike. His detractors — most of the staff — read this as the front behind which evil cogs turn, perhaps even this was the gear-train that had inspired Trevor. There was a thought.

I gave him a resume of the case, showed him Trevor's drawings, outlined my therapy plans, iterating the title of *Applied Behaviour Analysis* because The Caldwell likes correct terminology; cynics accuse him of being more interested in the attachment of labels than treatments and results.

He relaxed slightly and frowned, I suspect because there was little here for him to turn to his advantage, no emotional levers, nothing with blackmail potential. He leaned back in his chair touching his fingers together — a caricature of contemplative wisdom. From this I gathered that in spite of his total lack of humanity he was pleased at being consulted; most of us avoided this at all costs. He announced with more than his usual bumptiousness that he would arrange for an assessment.

This happened the next day, an hour-long session. On Trevor's return he delivered one of his Biblical sounding utterances, "And he smote them hip and thigh with a great slaughter and dwelt in the top of the rock of Etam, sore athirst and called upon the Lord: Thou hast given this great deliverance."

From which I judged it had been an ordeal for him.

I arrived at work the next day to find a patient mutilating a newspaper with a pair of scissors in my office. This was Brian, another ASD inpatient with an unusual morbid fixation. Tearing out the obituaries and news of disasters from the papers was standard form for Brian. What was not, was acquiring a pair of scissors which were not allowed in our part of the hospital, and I would have to find out where he had got them and read the riot act. Brian was held under section, having been responsible for the death of his infant sister. Being dangerous to others is a rarity in autism; his diagnosis suggested that his fixation with death coupled with a lack of inhibitory mechanism, accounted for this. The truth was that no one really knew, and that made releasing him particularly fraught. He had not displayed any tendency to violence since admission, not even the frustration rages that are quite common in ASD.

Brian registered my presence with pompous oiliness. Unlike Trevor he has no speech impairment.

"Doctor, I hope you won't mind, there have been some recent deaths and I need to be informed of these matters."

"I quite understand. If I could just borrow your scissors for a moment."

Brian handed them over placidly and I sighed with relief. We chatted for a moment about recent admissions to the mortuary and a couple of celebrity suicides, then I made my excuses and he courteously withdrew.

Moments later, I was called to The Caldwell's office to receive his diagnosis. I found him at his most patronising.

"I understand of course that you have identified the disordered speech as evidence of ASD, but you should consider the broader picture; while I appreciate that there are indicators typical of ASD only, one has to bear in mind the high rates of comorbidity. A rigorous meta-analysis has shown an overlap between early autistic symptoms and psychotic experiences during adolescence reported in studies. Twenty to fifty per cent of individuals with childhood-onset schizophrenia met criteria for premorbid ASD..."

I switched off for a bit. It's the only way to survive a Caldwell lecture. There are four consultant psychiatrists under Caldwell and we play a game, to count the number of times he can use 'diathesis' in a sentence. The record is seven. I lost myself in a reflection of my early career: it was this lack of insight amongst some of my peers that led me into psychiatry.

Suddenly I was aware that The Caldwell was looking at me. I tuned back in. After circling around for a while longer and littering his conclusions with caveats, his diagnosis was identical to mine which was both reassuring and depressing. I had hoped for an independent second opinion but I suspected I had received a reiteration that's only intelligence was in its semantics, after which the professor announced:

"I know that at present, medication is out of fashion for ASD but prescription of antipsychotics — Aripiprazole would be my choice — has statistically demonstrated some marginal improvement." He then treated me to a diatribe on longitudinal studies in support of this and finished with a typical demonstration of the man's utter callousness. "I wouldn't waste too much time on it if I were you, Dr Bartlett."

I left the room disappointed but not surprised. It even crossed my mind that this prescription would cause sadistic pleasure to that twisted mind by destroying the beautiful precision of Trevor's drawing with the tremors Aripiprazole produces as a side-effect.

I started Trevor on therapy, nominally behavioural therapy but, like most of my talking therapies, somewhat modified. The Caldwell would have disapproved; unstructured interviews or therapies are an abomination to him. I wanted to find out more about Trevor's history but this was complicated by his aversion to inquisition, which was unusually marked in my experience. To avoid this, I made statements, it was evident that he listened and every now and again, would respond with a few hurried staccato words; three

28

seemed to be his limit. But even so he appeared to divine my intent, he turned to the wall as if frustrated, and announced, "Faeroes south or south-easterly gale eight to storm ten losing its identity moderate or rough occasionally very rough later rain later good occasionally moderate."

I tried again, making my comments even more abstract. His response improved. I talked about childhood. He listened carefully when I spoke of how mothers loved their children, nodding with a stifled giggle as if in agreement, and inwardly I counted this as evidence of the empathy that I suspected. Then I spoke of fathers, also impersonally, how they too loved their children. At which point Morris chipped in. I allowed Morris' presence in spite of this being an appalling breach of ethics because Trevor seemed so much calmed by his company.

"Pfoof — orlright for some. My ol' man used to beat me wiv 'is belt buckle — 'urts more if yer use the buckle," he explained. "Got the blame for everyfink I did. If summat got broke or went missin' — it'll be that wretched Morris. If it rained — it'll be that wretched Morris. You should give 'im a good thrashin', Gerald."

It was a revelation to me that Morris could have a father called Gerald.

"Roll up his sleeves he did. Coo, didn't like that when he rolled up his sleeves." Morris' face became a mask of over-dramatised B-movie fear, which was supremely comical even though I was aware it shouldn't be.

Trevor's face dropped and in reply to nothing in particular, suddenly said crossly, "Fucker."

Morris sniggered; swearing was a great source of amusement to him, along with people breaking wind or falling over, particularly if they hurt themselves. Some of the patients swore almost continuously, this made Mo giggle, but nothing like as much as when it was one of the staff; that really cracked him up.

I was intrigued at this glimpse of anger from Trevor, I had not seen him so agitated. He stood up suddenly, clutching Max protectively, and left the room. This too was unusual.

I sighed. "If only he could talk."

Which set Morris off on a particularly appalling Doctor Dolittle impersonation. "If 'e could talk to the animals, walk an' grunt an' squeak an' squawk with the animals, why then 'e'd — can't 'member the next bit."

This was followed by what looked like an impression of a monkey dancing, remarkably surreal, maybe there is a career for Morris in modern dance. He then chuckled with the smug look he wears on the rare occasion where he knows something others don't, or more accurately, when he thinks he knows something others don't. He sidled up to me with a look of confidentiality, unpleasantly close, he had successfully avoided bath-time for the past week.

"He can talk orl right." He nodded his head significantly and tapped the side of his nose. "Highfalutin."

I looked at Morris questioningly, fatally revealing my curiosity, a cue for him to retreat into a mysterious silence. I kicked myself. All I had to do was look bored and I would have been treated to an endlessly repetitive explanation.

As it was, I found out some days later by accident. We have two common rooms for the patients. For some reason the smaller of the two is rarely used. I was passing this room and paused at the sound of a voice that was somehow familiar and yet not. The door was ajar so I could hear clearly. It was Trevor. I recognised the changed rhythm of one of his episodes of fluency, so different from his everyday clipped faltering speech, but I listened with a growing amazement: this was something different from shipping forecasts and prognostications. I understood now the choice of that single word by Morris: highfalutin.

"How, due to the carelessness of officials, traitors have been allowed to conceal themselves as doctors under the banner of socialist internationalism. Let the way be cleared of this foetid scum and filth."

Trevor was interrupted by the sound of Morris' snuffling laughter, for which he received a stern admonishment.

"Silence in Court. For the murder of our beloved comrades, A.A. Zhdanov and A.S. Shcherbakov, this court demands the supreme penalty for the cursed vermin: Vovsi, Kogan, Feldman. Grinshtein, D.G. Egorov, Etinger, and last but by no means least, the reptile N. D. Caldwell. This last one deserves the special attention of the court, dishonouring the holy banner of science with his excuse of axis one pervasive developmental disorders to administer inadvisable prescriptions. I refer, comrades to seven-four-four-two-three dichlorophenyl one piperazinyl butoxy thirty-four dihydrocarbostyril."

I was astonished to recognise the chemical formula of aripiprazole: the very treatment Caldwell had suggested for Trevor.

"He describes himself as a theorist pronouncing on impairment of non-verbal behaviours encompassing repetitive or stereotyped behaviours or interests. Let the mask of treason be torn from the face of this filthy degenerate. Let the grave of the hateful traitor grow over with weeds and thistles. Let the verdict of the court be heard like thunder."

At this point I caught sight of Sister Harris approaching and decided to avoid awkward explanations by moving off. Sister Harris has a somewhat cynical view of yours truly and to be frank scares the hell out of me. While she normally keeps up a veneer of genteel politeness, when stirred she lapses into her native Glaswegian which can beat any Tourette's patient.

So Trevor could talk. Boy, could he talk! I retained hardly any memory of school history but I had read a treatise on the causative pathology of Stalin's paranoia, and recognised the 'Doctors' Trials' from Trevor's presumably garbled transcript. But it was his other utterances that astounded me. He had not only understood and memorised the books borrowed from my office but, more spectacularly, had pronounced his own damning judgement on the nature of Professor Caldwell. It had taken us, the staff, a longer association to do this. Beatrice Kwame, our lead psychiatrist, was the first to express her misgivings.

"I find some of Professor Caldwell's treatments questionable," which had elicited a cynical response from Sister Harris.

"Do you really? Now, there's a thing."

At which another of my colleagues, Vivienne Roberts, had confided. "I do find him difficult to take to."

Sister Harris nodded indulgently and patted Vivienne on the arm. Yes, the women got there first. I have to admit, rather uncomfortably given my pride in reading character, that I was guilty of giving the professor the benefit of the doubt for longer than I should have. Worse than that, my instincts had been alerted, they had not betrayed me, but I had suppressed them with the prejudice that the clinical director by virtue of his position must be not only competent but benign. Also, I had been flattered by the professor's apparent affability towards me in the early days of our association. He had taken me out to dinner several times. Sister Harris brought me down to earth with the somewhat hurtful observation that his game was to take down one at the rear of the pack in order to get the goods on the others. She was right: Professor Caldwell was a calculating manipulative schemer. He manoeuvred his staff like pieces on a chessboard, plotting his moves to achieve his dark designs by proxy.

But contrarily, the professor's understanding of abnormal psychology had a peculiar quality of naivety about it. He had an encyclopaedic knowledge of research data and was particularly strong on pharmacology. I think our first doubts about him were aroused by his medicating most of the dementia patients with antipsychotics — our suspicion: that this was not for therapeutic benefit but chemical restraint.

And Trevor had sussed him out, but how? He had failed the Heider and Simmel test fairly spectacularly, he shouldn't be able to.

I made discreet enquiries over the next few days and was satisfied that none of the staff were responsible for unguarded conversations in front of him. This reinforced what had started as an irrational whim, that his knowledge of The Caldwell came purely from his own penetration of the professor's meticulously constructed artifice of a persona, beyond into the reaches of the dark soul within. This was a subject of particular interest to me. I have come across patients with insight so profound that it strays into the realms of telepathy. The mentally ill do not have exclusivity of such powers, but sensitivity and intelligence dance hand-in-hand with vulnerability and susceptibility. It is the stupid and bovine that often live such peaceful untroubled lives.

I was intrigued. I decided to expose Trevor to someone who he could not possibly know anything about, in effect a control. It must be a patient or member of staff he had not encountered before. Where better than one in "H" block (a nickname derived from the TV), the high-security wing occupied by patients held under section and not considered safe outside. I had a particular patient in mind: Graham.

Some weeks before, I discovered to my horror that Morris had not only cracked the code for getting into the dementia ward but done the same for the high security wing; not only got in but had been doing so for weeks without anyone knowing. This caused a major security scare and investigation into who was responsible. A certain red-faced consultant owned up when faced with the damning CCTV evidence. He had approached the door to find Morris lurking, all ready to leap into helpful action, shaking his head patronisingly.

"Top security mate, got to know the combo, 'ere, I'll show yer." And before the nonplussed gentleman could protest, Morris tapped apparently deftly at the keypad; it was almost as though he knew what he was doing.

Of course, the door didn't open and the irritated consultant shooed him away impatiently, muttering as he did, "Four eight seven three." To add insult to injury, being flustered, he must have entered a number incorrectly and the door wouldn't open.

Mo was delighted and took over with a flourish. "Tricky innit? Watch me: four eight seven three, 'open sesame'." Mo stepped aside for the fussed-up consultant and slipped in behind like Gollom following Frodo into Mordor.

What puzzled me was that this episode demonstrated faculty way beyond Mo's normal capacity. He can't even tie his own shoelaces and I've seen him try to use a toaster upside down, and yet he somehow managed to remember the numbers and press the correct buttons. My theory is that his incredible nosiness and fascination for forbidden places somehow marshalled his thirty-eight points of IQ to all fire simultaneously to provide this feat of excellence.

Morris is not judgemental in his associations. Rather as a Labrador will wag its tail and lick the hand of a burglar, so will Morris converse with all comers. A high body count was no bar to friendship with Morris, he had introduced himself to Graham with his usual hang-dog chumminess. If Graham had a mad dangerous stare, Mo did not appear to notice.

As is so often the way with the violently deranged, you feel pity for the person they once were when you know their history. Graham spoke English with a West

Indian accent that one of the staff recognised as Trinidadian. He had been horrifically abused. We all have different vulnerabilities and breaking strains. Some people survive trauma and abuse relatively intact, but they are few. The majority are broken along their own personal fault line which could be eating disorder, promiscuity, paedophilia, depression, addiction, self-harming, bipolar disorder, dissociation or, as in the case of Graham, schizophrenia, which caused him on three occasions to be driving in city centres and be ordered by the voice of his satnav to stop his car and brutally murder three random people. Most of us have had some bizarre commands like being told to drive down a bridle path or turn into someone's front garden but not, "After fifty yards, stop the man in the red shirt and club him to death for he is Beelzebub and the Lord has chosen you to destroy him."

Morris entertained Graham with stories of the road, his proud boast is that he had once been a van driver and his claim to fame was that one of his delivery drops had been to a firm in Godalming. This was apparently particularly tricky, what with bad signposting, traffic jams, roadworks etc., but somehow, heroically, Morris always got through. I am ashamed to say that several of the staff would encourage him to talk about these feats because they were sublimely comical. Driving a van was way beyond Mo's cognitive ability but no one was unkind enough to point this out, he obviously derived enormous pride and satisfaction from these fictitious exploits. I noticed with interest that his original boasts of a seven hundredweight van had escalated to a, "Two-tonne Tranny."

Just as Trevor, Graham seemed to find Mo's presence calming, so much so that on his regular visits, witnessed so damningly on CCTV, it could be seen that Graham would spot him and choose to sit next to him and, although Graham's conversation was an internalised monologue, it seemed that he shared this with some sort of dysfunctional camaraderie.

My idea was to let Trevor accompany Mo on one of these encounters but supervised. Graham was responding to antipsychotics and, as is often the way with schizophrenia, the acute phase subsides into something more slow-burning, but one of the unpredictables was that a new face could randomly become the subject of a psychotic episode, just as a dangerous dog will welcome some complete strangers as friends but turn viciously on the postman.

I witnessed the encounter from a short distance away. Graham was sitting on a bench seat, one of his regular spots, staring intensely at his feet. Mo took the place next to him and announced to Trevor, "Graham that is, good mate o' mine." And turning to Graham, "Orlrite mate?"

Graham switched his gaze from his own feet to Mo's filthy plimsolls and Mo nodded as if acknowledging a compliment and stretched out his legs proudly.

"Rubber soles, for speed that is, turn on a sixpence, Snoop Dogg's they was, got rid of 'em cos 'e got new ones I reckon."

Graham appeared to notice Trevor for the first time and leaned towards him conspiratorially, which was a relief to me because this was a good indicator of his intentions.

"Dey been in my room and raaffed de bath taps. Oh Lawd. Dem was clean and new; now dey's blighted. Dere's caca comin' outa 'em, it make me bad and dey won't change 'em back; dey laff at I."

Trevor listened intently, adopting what looked like an uncomfortable body posture with all his weight on one leg. I had not seen this before and wondered at the significance of it.

Mo was undiverted. "Top of 'em's real canvas, gotta be, innit, if they made it out o' rubber 'n all, it'd be well 'spensive."

Graham continued, "Dey're watchin' me t'rough a hole in de ceilin'. I hear 'em breathin'."

The pathos of this speech hit me strongly and I felt responsible: I had reduced Graham's dosage. You could see the fear in his eyes and hear it in his voice and was very likely responsible for the tremor in his hands which I had previously ascribed to his medication.

Mo was, as usual, oblivious. "Yeah, well these've got two 'oles." He splayed open his feet to display the inner eyelets proudly. "Let's 'em breave. Cheap uns ain't got 'em but these 'ave."

Graham's tremor increased to a shake. "I can' go back; dey's waitin' fo' me."

This appeared to discomfort Mo. He stared fixedly at his plimsolls. "Rubber them toecaps, pure rubber, feel that." He kicked Graham's shin. "Soft innit?"

Graham now shook and rocked. I needed to intervene but, even as I deliberated, Trevor showed another behaviour I hadn't seen before. He reached gently with one hand and stroked the top of a nearby cabinet. I interpreted this apparently incoherent gesture along with the unusual body posture as evidence of emotional sensitivity, strengthening my suspicion of his capacity for empathy.

Mo was taken differently. He stared at Graham with a smirk of obvious significance, and to rub it in, which he always has to, he tapped the side of his head, then as if only just aware of the awkwardness of the situation, moved stealthily away with furtive movements as if given the power of invisibility by his magic plimsolls.

I made my intervention with a charade of mild disapproval, but not mild enough. Morris slipped into persecution mode. "That's it, blame that wretched Morris, not like 'e's done nuffink, but blame 'im anyway cos it'll be his fault, always is." He kicked a nearby chair and broke off for a moment to announce proudly, "Cor, soft that is," before slipping back into oppression. "Mean s'not like no one else never does nuffink wrong, oh no, it'll be that Morris for sure, might as well blame 'im anyway, just in case."

I guided him firmly away. It's best to let him whinge, it puts him back in his comfort zone, allowing him to believe that his situation is due to a conspiracy of all the authority figures in his life, including God, to keep him down. This is a comfort, reinforcing the wisdom of his decision not to try and achieve anything — except of course to break through locked doors, which I liken to the imprisonment of his spirit — but this is another thought I usually keep to myself.

I shepherded my charges into the small common room, Mo still grumbling, apparently obscurely, probably because I hadn't been listening.

"Big geezer 'e was in a black hat — mean what would I want with 'is soddin' waterin' can?"

I returned to "H" Block in order to change Graham's medication. This took a while, but even while so occupied, my thoughts returned to Trevor. My plan, half-baked as it was, had been to hang around after this encounter in the hope that he would launch into an episode of 'Highfalutin'. All the conditions were in place: a new encounter, the presence of Morris, and something more nebulous, a look about him that suggested he was about to break out. And irritatingly, I would have missed it. Or maybe not. The common room, like most of the hospital, was covered by CCTV which I have access to; we are not supposed to use it for diagnostic purposes but there are times when the rules get broken. It can be invaluable to observe patients when they think themselves unobserved.

I duly collared the security officer, a large self-important man with dubious psychology called Albert. He found the appropriate footage and sure enough, my intuition was proved correct, and I witnessed another bizarre episode of 'Highfalutin'.

This time though, I couldn't understand a word of it. It was fluent enough, it was just not recognisable as any language I knew, but as I listened, I caught a few words and phrases, and once I'd deciphered one, a few more became understandable. "Mercy massa, don't strop dis...... Dey kaint gittum bells off — kiver wid dirt — gwine out gunnin — lee bro — folkses done told us — and hum 'til dem was funeralised."

The odd word I picked out made no sense of the whole, but enough to recognise that this was the archaic language of slavery, further suggested by the liberal use of a word that white people should not use, and which of course amused Morris immensely. You could see him dancing absurdly as well as hear his snuffling laughter. This was not for any offensive reason, just that he recognised the word as forbidden which was hilarious to him in the same way as swearing.

I thanked Albert and took my leave, I was impressed with his stony inscrutability. Not a muscle twitched, in fact, no glimmer of any emotion, a match for The Caldwell in dormant limbic activity.

I returned to my office to refresh my memory from Graham's case history. He had indeed been a slave, a modern-day slave, trafficked to work in horrific conditions in an illegal drugs factory, abused and beaten so severely that his back was permanently scarred. He was rescued in a bust by the police but because he had no residential status, was imprisoned again, this time in a holding centre. When he was finally rehabilitated, he apparently made a good recovery, passed his driving test and became a cab driver, but he had not escaped unharmed and slipped inexorably into psychosis.

Trevor could not possibly have known any of this. It was hard to avoid the logic that he had a faculty of divination. I was aware that I would have been ridiculed by my colleagues for this conclusion but I do not ascribe it to the paranormal. Our knowledge of the brain is incomplete, consciousness and memory only partially understood. It is feasible to suggest reasons that do not stray outside the boundaries of science, that everyone's life story is engraved upon them, in the creases of their face, the expression in their eyes, modulation of their voice, in the sculpture of the hundreds of muscles that determine posture and expression, forming a subliminal cipher that a rare few are attuned to interpret. There is also a possibility of the reception of electrical emissions from thought processes, and sensory mechanisms which we know exist in animals but are also not fully understood: the ability of a dog to smell fear, illness, even cancer. These systems are presumed to be dormant or undeveloped in humans, but maybe there are exceptions.

Whatever the reason, Trevor had this extraordinary gift and something very different from the normal presentation of autism. It seemed that, in spite of his inability to anthropomorphize revealed by the Heider and Simmel test, he had no such deficit in interpreting human behaviour. I determined to ignore the advice of Professor Caldwell and devote as much time as possible to him and, perversely, it was the machinations of The Caldwell that aided in this.

The next day, I happened to be complaining to Sister Harris about the amount of paperwork a research project on clinical depression was causing, which led to a more general complaint about the unusual number of such projects for a primary care setting. Sister Harris enlightened me. Due to all sorts of skulduggery and, "arse-licking," using her words, The Caldwell had wrangled some impressive research grants out of the MRC (Medical Research Council) and apparently the most important thing about government funding is to make sure you not just use it up but overspend fairly spectacularly in order to persuade the bean-counters that you need the same again and more the following year. Why you might ask, and I put this question to her; she was more worldly-wise than me, and after the usual look of withering contempt she explained that when a man is sufficiently inadequate, he feels in his heart somewhat worthless. She studied me contemplatively for an uncomfortably long moment.

"Really Sister?"

She nodded knowingly. "An enormous budget is a form of compensation." She pursed her lips. "While I've got you, Doctor, I should tell you that I caught Morris Alby using the 'N' word. I don't know where he learnt it," she looked at me accusingly and added grimly, "but he won't be using it again."

I tried to look suitably surprised, even though of course I wasn't, and made my escape. But this knowledge of The Caldwell's largesse inspired me to sneak off to his office later that day to sound him out on funding a study on Trevor.

I found The Caldwell in and available for conversation. I started nervously, expecting a rebuff, having only recently been told "not to waste too much time" on Trevor; I justified myself by explaining that his case had some atypical features. To my surprise, he appeared receptive. Sister Harris had yet again proved her shrewdness.

"Interesting idea, Dr Bartlett. Six months you say. Anything else?" he asked hopefully.

"Ideally I would like to conduct a parallel study with Morris. Both conditions typically display reduced levels of empathy and social interaction, but more pertinently, Trevor is much calmed by Morris' presence. I think it would be more productive."

The Caldwell considered. "And the title of this paper?"

I floundered. The Caldwell looked even more pleased. "Perhaps, if I might suggest: 'A study of insight in high functioning ASD comparative with Intellectual Disability'. I imagine you will wish to examine the overlap of alexithymia."

I felt his unpleasant blue eyes sweep across my face with the penetration of a high energy laser. Alexithymia is a condition which features a lack of emotional awareness, given his own spectacular deficit in this area, I was surprised he had referenced it. Somehow I expected it to have the effect on him that a crucifix would have on a vampire, which I'm sure accounted for the watchful and suspicious scrutiny of me. Paradoxically, I have often suspected The Caldwell of knowing what we all think of him.

His eyes strayed to the window and fixed with pleasurable sadism into the distance. "I assume you will wish to perform FMRI's."

I acquiesced willingly. Functional Magnetic Resonance Imaging is used to light up areas of brain activity during selected tasks. There was no way I would put either of the boys through that — the professor was a natural descendant of Mengele — but I pretended to go along with it, knowing that he would lose interest almost immediately until such time as a paper was produced.

"Splendid!" His unpleasant features transformed into a cold smile which I must admit I found disconcerting, I didn't know he could smile and I would far rather he didn't.

Breaking it to Morris, that he was to be the subject of a study, required tact. He would likely interpret this as some sort of persecution. I found him hanging around in my office on my return.

"Ah Morris, just the man. I've just been discussing you with Professor Caldwell."

"Oh yeah," replied Morris warily.

"I'm to select two of you for a psychological study. It's quite an honour really."

"Oh yeah," repeated Mo, brightening considerably and puffing himself up.

"Yes, I mean, obviously there are a few candidates but to be honest, they're a bit… you know."

Mo nodded knowingly. "Know what yer mean — doolally."

"I thought of you and Trevor; it's top secret though. Whatever you do you mustn't tell anyone."

That clinched it. I could see Mo swelling with self-importance, and moments later he slipped away. I knew where he was going. Mo claimed to have read an article in a magazine entitled 'Seven secret signs of a woman in love'. Since he can't read, this was probably relayed to him by one of his regular cronies, my suspicion lay with Albert the security man. Allegedly, the first of these signs was an excessive aversion to the object of the woman's secret affection. Morris imparted this to me with an expression that the unknowing could have mistaken for intelligence; it explained Sister Harris' animosity towards him. He was pleased, he liked Sister

Harris, and now took every opportunity to hang around her station until shooed firmly away. I guessed that this was his destination now, and Sister Harris told me later, somewhat nonplussed, that Mo had sneaked up on her and announced proudly, "I'm a psychedelic study, strictly 'ush 'ush though. We're workin' undercover, mum's the word."

Over the coming months I proceeded with my study of Trevor alongside his treatment. He made further improvement but how much due to therapy was difficult to know. His direct communication remained staccato but there was an increase in the more fluent episodes. I observed that the stock market reports and weather forecasts sounded as though they could have been verbatim, whereas the biblical quotes, from what I remembered from Sunday school, were garbled, though not so severely as the episodes of Highfalutin. I also noticed that there was a similar graduation in his visual response; the more garbled his speech, the more excessively he looked away. This was typical of autism where eye contact is diverted more determinedly during heightened periods of shyness or anxiety, matching to overactivation in the subcortical system. I theorised that the shipping forecasts and market reports were relatively impersonalised whereas the more complex utterances contained narratives that could give a glimpse into his psyche, and the scrambling of his language was to deflect any probing rays of inquisition and deny them comprehension. And perhaps due to his own remarkable perception, he would expect a higher penetration in others than existed, hence his increased defences.

It was this extraordinary perception that absorbed me; the premise of my paper swerved a little off course towards exclusive analysis of it. This is a long-standing weakness of mine, summed up in an early school report as, 'easily diverted'. My study morphed into an examination of the mechanism of exceptional perception albeit within the autistic spectrum, the very place you would not expect to find it. Autists' inability to read and understand the people around them is explained by a deleted gene resulting in overgrowth of the brain in early years and subsequent failure to prune back neural connections, but there is a theory that this is compounded by their avoidance of interpersonal engagement, eye-contact in particular. So much emotion is displayed in the eyes, so studiously avoided by those with autism. Trevor was typical in this respect, and accordingly his ability to acquire insight into the nature of complete strangers was puzzling, insight so spectacular that I had to word my postulation with great care to avoid using expressions such as second sight.

My paper wandered further, exploring the possibility that autism is in fact an alternative reality. Just as numbers are seen in colour, as is the case with Trevor, so too emotions are experienced and read differently and exist in parallel without connection, partly due to the inability of the autist to self-identify emotion.

Yes, I got rather carried away. And when my paper was finished, The Caldwell, being the repressed character he is, suggested some amendments to the more colourful sections, particularly those dealing with emotions, which he described as subjective. What he really meant was that they embarrassed him. I know this because he pointed to one offending paragraph while swallowing uncomfortably rather than read it aloud. His reaction irritated me at the time, but when I reread it, how Trevor could not project his identity in speech, Max being a counterpart of his soul, and his treatment of Max, the mirror of his own internal dialogue, I was honest enough to admit that he had a point.

My paper, when published, earnt contempt and derision from most of my colleagues, who were particularly appalled when it excited an unusual amount of interest from the newspapers, being dumbed down and twisted into some grotesque pseudoscientific explanation of the occult. How it came to the attention of the media, I never found out, although I suspected one of my colleagues of leaking it with mischievous intent, certainly it was most unusual for a medical paper with limited circulation to arouse public interest.

But after some weeks of slinking around sheepishly avoiding my associates, the affair seemed to blow over;

the newspapers moved on to other subjects and my paper slipped into oblivion — or so I thought.

It was three months later that Sister Harris announced with a sardonic cynical expression that two men were waiting in my office, high-ups in the health department she had it, with a look that was the closest I'd ever seen to sympathy. So it was with more than my usual lack of confidence that I greeted a tall, sad, severe looking grey-haired gentleman in a dark suit, and a much shorter plumper gentleman of Asian appearance, also looking severe but not as effortlessly as his companion. The tall gentleman held out his hand stiffly.

"Dr Bartlett?"

"Yes," I admitted, shaking the briefly offered hand.

"My name is, let us say, Robinson and my colleague, for the sake of argument, Banerjee."

"Major Banerjee," corrected this gentleman, pumping my hand vigorously.

"We've read your paper, Dr Bartlett."

I looked at the open copy of a certain redtop that I'm reluctant to name lying on my desk.

"Oh that's OK, it's not mine," I said defensively. "I just picked it up in reception."

Mr Robinson appeared concerned. "I refer to your recently published dissertation on the subject of exceptional perception within the autistic spectrum."

"Oh, I see. You are from the health department I understand?"

Mr Robinson puffed himself up, reminding me of the time a visitor had asked Mo if he knew the way to Godalming, while Major Banerjee grinned profusely. These two were something of a double act.

"There was an element of subterfuge, I regret to tell you, Dr Bartlett, in our introduction. We are not who we say we are, why, you cannot even trust the provenance of the names we have given. The fact is, we are from an entirely different government department, the very nature of which forbids any mention of its true activity."

"Gracious," I said. "You're very mysterious." Mr Robinson allowed a grave smile. "Anyone would think you were from MI5."

Mr Robinson and Major Banerjee exchanged furtive and alarmed glances; they only needed a nineteen twenties makeover with lashings of black eyeshadow to pass as stars of a silent movie.

Mr Robinson coughed. "Erm, our department is interested in your work."

"Very interested," added Major Banerjee.

"It has potential applications," continued Mr Robinson, "that could under certain circumstances have implications of national importance."

"I see," I said gravely, and noticed that Mr Robinson looked anxious. I rather think the idea was that I didn't see, which of course I didn't.

"We would be interested to meet the subject of your study, Dr Bartlett."

"Trevor."

"Indeed, as you say, Trevor," agreed Major Banerjee.

"No offence gentleman but you will scare the life out of him."

Both looked delighted, as if the idea of them scaring anybody was flattering to them. If these two really were spooks then they were comical ones.

"You have to remember that Trevor is autistic and socially inept."

Both gentlemen nodded so sympathetically that you did not need to be a psychiatrist to put two and two together.

"It is for this reason that my study has been conducted alongside another patient, Morris. His presence not only calms Trevor but facilitates his interaction. Trevor like many with autism has difficulty with such interaction, and communicates more readily with the insentient, often the wall or an item of furniture. Put simply, Morris, having exceptionally low intelligence, is the closest you will get to an inanimate object."

Mr Robinson looked uncomfortable. "We defer to you in this matter, Dr Bartlett. Psychology is not a subject we are versed in."

"But I have no objection to introducing you," I said, picking up the phone to Sister Harris who normally disapproves strongly of being given any instructions by me. "Do it yourself, dafty," being one of her favourite expressions, but on this occasion was suspiciously compliant. I was quite happy to introduce Trevor and Morris to these gentlemen. I had no inkling as to what their interest in my research was, but it seemed unlikely to be anything to do with a Nobel Prize or a fat pay rise and hopefully exposure to Trevor and Morris in the raw would see them off fairly quickly.

In due course the door opened and Trevor was pushed reluctantly in by the stern hand of Sister Harris with Morris sneaking in furtively behind, looking more like Gollum than usual.

Trevor surveyed the wall thoughtfully, raised his chin and pronounced imperiously, "And the Lord spake and said unto the people: 'Who is the man that is afraid and faint-hearted, let him depart and return to his tabernacle'."

Which amused Morris immensely for some reason and inspired him to do a sort of dervish dance and, since he was wearing the omnipresent rally jacket, an extremely smelly one. Trevor spoke again with what sounded like haughty disapproval.

"Thou shalt not worship graven images. Thou shalt not enquire of the dead."

I watched complacently, Trevor and Mo were on splendid form. I presented Morris to Major Banerjee. Mo clicked his heels together and saluted stiffly. Major Banerjee offered his hand, looking embarrassed. This was all going swimmingly as far as I was concerned. It would only be a few minutes I felt sure before the two gentlemen made their excuses and left.

But I was confounded. Trevor's reaction was unexpected, he presented Max to both gentlemen in turn, which was unusually forthcoming of him. Both responded by patting Max and murmuring, "Nice doggy."

Mr Robinson held out his hand awkwardly and Trevor who normally avoids all forms of physical contact studied it with a giggle, then slapped the back of it.

Mr Robinson looked uncomfortable. "Ah yes, pleased to meet you."

Trevor broke the brief moment of eye to chin contact, hung his head and announced, "Powdered egg up ninety-seven dollars."

Morris frowned with a remarkable facsimile of brain activity. "That's eerie that is."

Every now and again Morris takes to a new word. 'Eerie', was the latest, which, for the opportunity of inserting into his conversation, he allowed a vastly increased diversity of meaning.

If Mr Robinson found this remark esoteric, he concealed it admirably, replying impassively, "Quite so."

I was more interested in Trevor's unusually genial response, from which I understood that he sensed the unease in Mr Robinson and reacted warmly to it, but I also trusted Trevor's judgement, which was outside the parameters of the normal human senses. Just as a sniffer dog will root out contraband, Trevor reacts to decency and warmth.

I smiled at Mr Robinson. "Trevor has taken to you."

He gulped nervously. "Erm, good show."

Major Banerjee looked on with an expression of squashy sentimentality. I had just been reading an article on parallel universe theory and toying with acceptance, but now dismissed it scornfully; the odds of replicating the contents of my office at this moment were something well in excess of mere infinity I decided.

So it was that I found myself collected some days later in a sinister looking limousine with blacked out windows which unfortunately, due to the presence of Morris, did not open.

We drove for half an hour, entertained by a fairly constant commentary from Morris on a variety of subjects. Morris is never short of conversation, most of it derived from an apparently endless inventory of friends, all by a strange coincidence employed in fast food outlets, who I suspect in reality, he begged food from when homeless. He also made disparaging remarks about the driver, who he alleged was an amateur. Professional van drivers like Morris apparently approach corners with an initial flick of the steering wheel to throw the weight into the corner to keep the load from shifting; this just one of a succession of advanced driving tips.

Major Banerjee and Mr Robinson exchanged meaningful glances. Mr Robinson coughed.

"I think it appropriate to tell you now, Doctor, that as I hinted earlier, the names we have given ourselves are not necessarily our real names, which leaves us the vexed question of how you should address us."

"We have discussed this matter at some length," chipped in Major Banerjee.

"However, by a certain serendipity," continued Mr Robinson, "Major Banerjee is in fact known as 'Major' because of his previous position in the Indian Army."

Major frowned. "Also, because our director refuses to call me by my correct name, describing it as, so-called, 'jaw breaking'."

"Of which we disapprove," added Mr Robinson. "You can, however, continue to address me as Mr Robinson."

"Thank you," I said, trying not to laugh. We lapsed into silence, broken some while later by Major.

"I hope you won't mind me taking the liberty, Doctor, but I'd be grateful for your opinion on a personal matter."

I tried to look encouraging, wondering what was coming.

"It's my stomach, Doctor. I've noticed recently a certain bloating and effervescence after supper."

Mr Robinson leant forward. "Really, Major, you never told me this. I myself…"

"I'm not that kind of doctor, gentlemen."

"Ah, but you *were*, Doctor," said Mr Robinson knowingly.

I found this sinister. "I was, it's true, but pardon me for asking, how did you know that?"

Mr Robinson and Major exchanged conspicuous glances. By silent election Major replied, "Regrettably, Doctor, that information is restricted."

"I see. Well, since my secret is out, it's been a long time since I was in general practice, but my first question would be, are these suppers by any chance rather large and partaken of after eight thirty in the evening?"

Major's eyes opened wide with amazement; he looked across to Mr Robinson who nodded with a curious expression of encouragement.

So we spent the next hour, the two gentlemen sharing their ailments which I was pleased to reassure them were of no medical significance. By the end of our journey, I got the feeling that they had taken me to their bosom.

Eventually we drew to a halt. An electronic door whirred into life, admitting us into a bleak underground car park. Mr Robinson led to a lift and, unusually for this day and age, a uniformed lift attendant.

Mr Robinson looked furtive. "Good morning, lift attendant."

The lift attendant looked perplexed. "It's George, sir."

Mr Robinson looked flummoxed. "Yes, quite, let's call you George."

The lift attendant protested. "But I am George." Then twigged and flushed with embarrassment. "Ah yes I see, George it is."

Mr Robinson nodded gravely. "And I don't think there is any need to announce our floor number thank you, George."

"Indeed," added Major ponderously."

So we emerged at floor seven, as announced by an illuminated number which Mr Robinson did his best to obscure by fanning out his arms, immediately imitated by Morris, and we spilled out into an open-plan office furnished with desks and computers, just like any other office except for some surprisingly florid curtains, and threaded our way through to an incongruous looking oak door. A female voice responded to Mr Robinson and the door opened on what appeared to be a boardroom, a contrast to the outer office due to its plainness in decoration. A woman sat at the head of a conference table; she looked up briefly, shook her head with a groan, and lowered her eyes to whatever paperwork had been occupying her. A cleaning lady hovered behind her, officiating with a feather duster. She took rather more notice of us and alerted the woman in a loud whisper.

"Visitors, Miss Penny."

The woman screwed her head round and snapped sarcastically, "Thank you for that, Mrs T, I hadn't noticed."

Mrs T dusted a curtain pointedly and muttered sulkily, "Pardon me for mentioning it, I'm sure." At which point I could see Morris almost expanding with sympathy, recognising a fellow victim of oppression.

The woman behind the desk turned a high-intensity look of appraisal on Trevor. I winced. Trevor shrank back, using Mo as a somewhat sub-standard human shield to hide behind. She turned her attention to me, getting up reluctantly to offer her hand. I understood that I was not welcome.

Mr Robinson intervened chivalrously. "Doctor Bartlett, allow me to introduce our head of department, Miss…"

She interrupted him impatiently. "Or more directly, Director General, MI5. Penny if you must."

She directed a withering look of scorn towards Mr Robinson who had flinched at the mention of MI5.

I was in awe. This woman was somewhere around forty, six foot tall and with eyes that defied the stereotypes of steely blue or warm hazel: hers were steely hazel. She wore ripped jeans and a navy England rugby top. The lower fringes of her thick chestnut hair pointed forward in a fashion that had been successfully eliminated in the late nineteen sixties and failed to conceal an extremely determined jawline. A restless memory pestered my subconscious: had I met her before? I searched the database. It would have been someone in authority, maybe one of my lecturers, but it seemed unlikely that a medic would be running MI5. Then I got it: one of my colleagues in group practice. It was her air of authority rather than any physical resemblance. The comparison stopped there, my colleague from the past was of a sunny disposition, earning herself the nickname given to her by a patient: 'That lovely posh Doctor Ffiona'.

I continued my appraisal. She was shapely but there was something ungainly about her. On the one hand she looked the sort who had led her school to triumph on the hockey field but on the other, a suspicion that she could have lumbered up the field careering into players on the way, only to trip up and smash into one of the goalposts. I heaved a sigh of relief; the truth is that I have a long history of making a fool of myself in the presence of women I am attracted to. The effect of this is well known. Such a situation makes the man nervous, thus initiating a downward spiral in relations. But in this instance, I was unaffected by Penny's steely gaze.

She sighed wearily. "You are here, Dr Bartlett because our political masters have been taken over by soft-bellied liberals who seem to think that the enemy within, which is the particular interest of this agency, should be dealt with in some way other than being bumped off and left dismembered in a wheelie bin, which I have to admit is my preference, but then again half the government and most of the opposition are bloody fifth columnists." Her gaze fixed unseeingly, and I imagined a flickering black and white newsreel playing in her head, of a group of traitors in the Great War being stood up against a wall and mercilessly shot. Penny's eyes returned to me with a look of dislike; evidently, I was, by my calling, similarly damned.

"However," she tapped her desk in irritation with long scarlet nails. "Since I foolishly turned down an opportunity in MI6 some years ago, I have to live with the consequences, which are, that now we have certain matters threatening national security demanding a," she had to swallow twice before being able to pronounce the word, "psychological approach."

Mr Robinson and Major nodded encouragingly as if to a child that has just swallowed its cod liver oil, earning themselves a look of pure venom from the lady.

"And you, Dr Bartlett," she added with false gaiety laden with cynicism, "are apparently the answer to our problems." She laughed with a quality I recognised from patients with histrionic personality disorder.

During this speech, Trevor had been following every word intensely, and, as if suddenly aware of him, Penny darted him a searching glance. He stiffened, stared into space and announced, "I am Alpha and Omega, the beginning to the end, the first and the last."

The self-assurance which first impressions had struck me as Penny's dominant feature, faltered. It is easy to think of the mentally ill with pathos and sympathy. They are the disadvantaged, the backmarkers, the western equivalent of the Untouchables, yet at this moment Trevor's aspect expressed dignity, wisdom and something else that I struggled to name for a moment before it came to me: power. So much in that fleeting glimpse of a nature so remote from the reality of his life and situation. And in that moment, I was interested to see that Penny had seen it too; there was a break in that harsh visage which I had taken as an indicator of her disposition. I sighed, people never cease to fascinate me. The moment passed. Penny was talking.

"Some bright spark went on a fact-finding expenses-paid junket to Sweden where he learnt that the key to dealing with subversives is apparently," she spat the word, "psychology. And with this seed planted in that weak brain, he picked up a newspaper in the airport and read an article, Dr Bartlett, that dealt with your research," she shuddered with disgust. "Which I myself have been forced to read. Not only did this give that gentleman some very foolish notions but to make matters worse, when presented to my department, I was on holiday and these two, *traitors*," she indicated Mr Robinson and Major with an accusing finger, "collaborated behind my back." Mrs T paused in her dusting to frown reproachfully at them.

"So now we come to the problem that my idiot masters have deemed to be a matter of," she shuddered again, "that word I would rather not repeat."

Mr Robinson intervened rapidly. "Allow me to brief you on the situation, Dr Bartlett. A certain lady politician..."

Major interrupted, "Who shall remain nameless."

"Quite," continued Mr Robinson. "Has been having dreams."

"Dreams?" I was puzzled.

"Dreams," repeated Major emphatically.

"Dreams," continued Mr Robinson. "That threaten national security."

Penny sank her head in her hands.

I felt I was missing something. "Sorry, but I don't follow. How can dreams threaten national security?"

Without looking up, Penny proffered a mobile phone. I glanced at an extremely familiar image.

"Gracious."

Penny moaned.

Mr Robinson stirred uneasily. "To answer your question: these dreams are of an erotic nature."

Penny lifted her head with some irritation. "They are not of an erotic nature, they're fucking disgusting even by my standards and I did ten years in the Foreign Office."

When you're used to dealing with Tourette's patients, choice language doesn't come as a surprise. It was just not what I expected from the director of MI5, but then again, I suppose my expectations derive from James Bond stories.

Major crossed his arms smugly. "We've called a Code Red."

Trevor had been following this conversation keenly but Morris was struggling.

"I had a dream last night, eerie it was. Me and a mate, fish fryer, third dan, taught me the death chop," he demonstrated with a sudden violent karate chop accompanied by a remarkably authentic sounding Bruce Lee screech. "Stopped off at this burger joint on the Haslemere Bypass, just outside Godalming."

Penny looked up sharply. I wondered why. Mr Robinson evidently took it that she was running out of patience and intervened.

"If these dreams were to become public." He made an expansive gesture.

"Excuse me," I said. "But how could her dreams become public?"

"Ah," said Major significantly. "How indeed? If only this lady would keep them to herself why then we would not be in this," he beamed with pleasure, "Code Red situation."

Penny looked at me accusingly. "It's your fault." I opened my mouth to protest but she interrupted me. "Well not you personally, but your crowd. She's having bloody therapy!" She let out an exasperated sigh. "A pint of navy rum, that'd sort her out. Fucking Roedean," she added obscurely.

I was interested. "What sort of therapy?"

Major appeared lost in silently mouthed repetition of what I suspected was, 'Code Red situation', leaving Mr Robinson to reply.

"Doctor, have you ever come across a form of psychotherapy using glove puppets?"

"Well, there's Grover puppets, but I can't see how they'd be used in this situation. They are also used to regress severely traumatised patients back to the past they have blocked from their memory, allowing them to relive their experiences from the safety of a separate identity and displace their trauma through the medium of the puppet."

At which, Morris put his hand in his jacket pocket, lifted it up towards his face, wiggled his fingers at himself from inside the pocket and cowered backwards in fear. I tried not to laugh; this was far more hilarious than he had the wit to intend. I saw a flash of humour pass across Penny's face, disappearing so quickly that I wondered if I had imagined it, and startling in contrast to the thunderous aspect it had emerged from.

"Tell me, what sort of puppets are involved?"

"It started with Punch and Judy I believe," replied Mr Robinson.

"I see, with or without crocodile?"

Penny shook her head with a look of disgust. "What in God's name does that matter?"

I met her gaze with a certain frostiness. "As a matter of fact, it is a vital question." Of course it wasn't,

I was just being mischievous, which, judging from the dirty look she directed at me, I'm sure she realised.

Mo picked up on my tone. He never misses an opportunity to either empathise with or lord it over anyone being censored. He nodded condescendingly.

"Vital it is."

Penny blinked as if to dismiss an apparition.

Mr Robinson continued. "It appears to have changed to some sort of squabbling Eastern European couple.

"Ah, Martha and Mr Janos."

Penny looked at me with false sweetness. "Who presumably do not have a crocodile."

I ignored this. "What I don't understand is why you're so concerned. A psychotherapist has to obey strict client confidentiality."

Penny looked cynical. "Bit more than your average psychotherapist apparently, whose speciality is, guess what: hypnosis."

"I take it you've checked his credentials?"

"Of course we checked his credentials," snapped Penny irritably. She picked up a piece of paper lying on her desk. "Doctor Richard Hamilton M.Comm D.Clin.Psych., CPsychol AFBPsS. One of your lot."

"Not quite. Clinical psychologist, and top of his particular tree by the sound of it."

"But still a bloody quack and up to no good. He did a vanishing act ten years ago to practice in America and disappeared off the radar."

At this point, Trevor's expression changed and he announced ominously, "Biscay north-west cyclonic six to severe gale force nine thundery showers falling rapidly."

I was curious: this was one of Trevor's more ominous forecasts. I returned my attention to Penny.

"What is it you want me to do?"

Mr Robinson appeared restless and directed a meaningful look at Penny. "I think before proceeding further, there is the matter of the Official Secrets Act."

Penny yanked open a drawer wearily, withdrew a sheet of paper, slapped it on the desk in front of me, produced a pen and drew a cross.

"X marks the spot."

"But first of course you must read it carefully," said Mr Robinson.

"No, he doesn't," Penny snapped. "I haven't got all day." She turned to me with a disconcerting smile. "Let me summarise: if you breathe one word of this, Dr Bartlett…" She shook her head with authentic menace.

Morris was delighted. He drew his hand across his throat with a dramatic gurgling followed by loud moans of pain.

I signed with affected dignity and Penny snatched the paper from me and threw it back into her drawer.

She looked at me and asked reluctantly, "Who are these Martha and Mr Janos? I mean what's the point of them?"

"They are symbols of conflict. Mr Janos is a Hungarian woodcutter, he meets Martha, a beautiful peasant girl and they fall passionately in love."

"As puppets so often do," said Penny tapping her fingernails again in irritation.

"Well, this is all in the past you understand. I'm afraid to say that later in life love deserts them and this is the basis of the interplay between the puppets."

Major nodded sympathetically. "An all too familiar story." This earned him a glare from Penny.

I continued. "Martha has by then born Mr Janos fourteen children and this causes friction between them. Martha is worn out by childbirth and resentful of Mr Janos' continuing advances. He in turn accuses her of frigidity."

Mr Robinson exchanged a look of understanding with Major. "I suppose she doesn't want him any more, *in that way*," he added with significant emphasis.

Penny looked exasperated. "Another problem with puppets, keeping the magic alive."

Mr Robinson and Major appeared to miss the irony of this remark and nodded sadly as if in agreement.

I continued. "They come to blows, that's the point you see, it's all about domestic violence, so I am a little puzzled. I can't see the relevance of these puppets being used in the context you mention."

Penny reached for a remote control and a screen lit up. "We've got the place wired, see for yourself."

The screen flickered into life and I gasped at the familiar face who I shall call, Sam, normally seen at Westminster doing her best to avoid nasty questions being put to her accusingly by members of the opposition and some of her own backbenchers for that matter, here looking awkward and rather timid. Facing her across a desk was a dapper middle-aged character with long sleek black hair and dark unfathomable eyes; he did look the part of a Svengali. He leant back in his chair, a caricature of relaxation and asked with a casualness in which I recognised the artifice of his profession, "Did you dream last night?"

The lady flushed and hung her head. "Yes."

Dr Hamilton nodded with an expression designed to reassure. "The same dream?"

"Yes," replied Sam in a small voice.

"And can you tell me what happened in the dream?"

Sam flushed red. "No, I can't — really I couldn't."

Dr Hamilton smiled greasily, picked up two puppets and handed one to Sam. "But Martha can tell Mr Janos."

Sam took the puppet handed to her, a garish looking figure, complete with traditional gypsy headdress; she drew it on like a glove with an appearance of relief.

"Because Martha dominates Mr Janos, remember." He slipped his hand inside the outlandish figure of a poor looking creature with a hideous putrid face and sad world-weary eyes, and the puppet, suddenly animated, appeared to speak in a cringing whine.

"You are looking lovely tonight, darlink."

"Don't you go getting any ideas, Mr Janos."

Sam was no ventriloquist and spoke directly, without attempting to hide her mouth movements or affect an accent. I could see the distance in her eyes that allowed her to hide behind this facade.

Mr Janos convulsed as if in agony. "But darlink, it has been months, I could please you, darlink."

Sam laughed cynically and worked Martha's arms furiously. "*You* please *me*! I think you mean, *me* please *you* — and the answer is no."

"But darlink, don't you love your Mr Janos any more?"

Sam shook her head and Martha was lifeless in her hand. She spoke as if without awareness.

"No, I don't love you, I haven't loved you for years."

Mr Janos writhed as if in the throes of agony, but the voice that animated him transferred into another: charismatic and mesmeric, now directly from the mouth of the doctor.

"But you love another, and she comes to you in your dreams."

"She!" I exclaimed.

"She!" echoed Mrs T distraitly.

"Yes, she comes to me in my dreams. Last night she came. I was collecting wood in a place that is forbidden and she saw me as she rode past. She stopped, she'd been at a gallop, her horse's flanks were flecked with foam, she laughed cruelly as she dismounted, brandishing her riding crop. 'Now what have we here?' she mocked as she approached me. The top buttons of her jacket were undone, a fine mist of perspiration showed in her cleavage…" She faltered.

"Yes," urged the doctor.

"Yes," murmured Mrs T, dabbing her forehead languidly with a duster.

Sam's face contorted in anguish. "No, no. I can't go on." She tore off the puppet and ran from the room in distress, leaving the doctor staring moodily at the apparently dejected Mr Janos. His anger appeared to build, finally expressing itself as a vicious punch into Mr Janos' face, with a simultaneous curse of frustration.

The screen went blank. Penny turned to me with a scowl, which I took as an invitation to voice my opinion.

"I see the problem. I'm not sure the public are ready for that one yet, and you're right, it's all wrong, I know what he's up to and I can tell you it's not therapeutic."

Mr Robinson interjected, "I'm not sure I know what you mean."

"Just that there is nothing in what I have seen that you could describe as treatment. He's manipulating her with the intent of extracting information from her."

Penny shot me a look of disgust. "Thank you, Hetty Wainthrop, I think your average six-year-old could have worked that one out."

Mr Robinson cringed but I was not offended, it was tame in comparison to Sister Harris, besides something was puzzling me.

"Let me get this right, you suspect Dr Hamilton to be some kind of enemy agency trying to get his hands on a compromising recording of she who shall remain nameless spilling the beans on her raunchy dreams?"

Major nodded. "Exactly, he would have the so-called goods on her."

I shook my head. "I think it's worse than that. While I am not a wholehearted disciple of Freud, I accept the basics of his dream theory, which has it that dreams are about wish fulfilment and are often distorted in time and meaning in order to circumvent our internal psychic censorship..."

Penny looked at me sharply. "You mean, an actual affair?"

I nodded, impressed by her grasp of such obscure subject matter that I had not anything like finished elucidating. She gave me a look of pure venom as if I were to blame.

"Idiots! A bullet in the head, maybe two, but no, 'not an elegant solution,' they said."

"I agree. It wouldn't be a solution. I suspect he's been using hypnosis on her, maybe even controlling her dream content..."

"Is that really possible?" Mr Robinson interrupted. I was amused to see that he looked nervous.

"There is some evidence for it, research by Dr K Schrotter in 1912 but unfortunately he committed suicide before it could be verified." I ignored Penny's look of derision. "The problem is she wants to talk, she's bursting to let it out; keeping it in is eating her up."

I was aware of Mrs T in the background, staring into the distance. Penny muttered something I didn't catch, then snapped at me.

"So what is the solution, Dr Dumbass?"

"It sounds a little fanciful but the key lies with the puppets. We have to get to them, we have to possess them; in short we have to corrupt them."

Mr Robinson and Major appeared to consider this thoughtfully, not Penny though.

"As if they're not corrupt enough? Well, *him* anyway, what with the constant whinging and unreasonable sexual demands."

"Is it so unreasonable though," mused Mr Robinson, "to expect one's love life to continue after childbirth? I mean…"

"Aaah," Penny snapped. She rubbed her eyes. "If I read you right, it's only a matter of time before that slimy bastard weasels the goods out of her."

"I think so, she's resisting because of internal conflict, the pressure of the dominant social order to conform to its version of normality. In the past, minority groups have lacked social institutions akin to heterosexual marriage offering sanction for family life and intimacy. But times have changed and her feelings are gathering a new momentum; she is on the threshold of being reborn. And remember, she's a product of her generation so there will be guilt."

Mrs T dusted a plant particularly vigorously. Penny looked so appalled that I added mildly, "That would be the psychological view I think, not my discipline you understand."

"You think he'll wear her down?"

"I do. He's adroit, he's established a pathway, see how quickly she adopted the persona of Martha. I think she will open up very soon, the pressure to do so is from within; she is tremulous with fear and yet drawn inexorably towards revelation."

Mrs T's dusting of a *ficus robusta* slowed to a caress. Mr Robinson gazed dreamily at the ceiling. Morris' mouth dropped open, he was completely lost, whereas Trevor, deceptively blank, followed every word, I was sure.

Major's eyes were molten. "In 'The Ramayana', King Dilip had two wives but sadly died childless. Lord Shiva appeared to his widows in a dream and told them they would have a child if they made love together and lo and behold a child was born, and he grew into the great King Bhagiratha who brought the River Ganges down from heaven."

Mr Robinson dabbed at an eye with his sleeve. "Really, Major, a most moving story. I was not aware that…"

Penny snapped irritably, "Maybe skip the Sanskrit epics for now."

I continued my revenge for being called, 'Dr Dumbass'. "You could say that her primeval urges are in dynamic equilibrium with her inhibitions."

Penny looked exasperated. "God, give me strength. But I get the message, assuming there is one. When you talk of corrupting the puppets, how does that work?"

"It needs a little explanation." Penny prepared herself with another groan. "Have you heard of Stone Tape Theory?"

Mr Robinson shook his head, but Major lit up like a Christmas tree. "Yes indeed. Many Hindus believe in cremation to prevent the soul of the deceased from re-entering the body after death. Because the ghost that suffers from earthly lusts and addictions will seek to fulfil his satisfactions in a body. The spirit energy is called Akasha and its imprint is in the ether…"

Penny's horror expressed as a thousand-yard stare, usually seen in traumatised war veterans. "Oh God, not ghosts, please not ghosts."

Inspiring Morris to break into a tuneless chant of, "Ghostbusters!" and when he had taken in the looks of discomfiture surrounding him, added defiantly, "I ain't afraid of no ghosts."

I pressed on. "I admit it's only a theory but it is not inconceivable that human brain activity, which, after all, involves the emission of electromagnetic waves, leaves an imprint, just as Major describes, rather as sound and vision is recorded on a videotape and if so, certain susceptible people may have the faculty to recover these recordings. When you study neuroscience, you learn that the human brain has all sorts of unknown potential. For example, it is more than anecdotal that identical twins can experience simultaneous awareness from across the world, possibly by the same mechanism as quantum entanglement."

Mr Robinson, looked at me enquiringly, earning him a hostile glare from Penny.

"The process whereby a photon can be split into two lower energy photons that remain identically polarised, even a thousand miles apart."

Penny glared accusingly at Mr Robinson and Major. "So not only am I denied the simple remedy of a bullet between the eyes, but I have to listen to this mumbo jumbo."

Mo echoed the words, "Mumbo jumbo," sniggered and repeated them with a look on his face that told me he had taken a fancy to the expression. I expected to be hearing a lot more of it in the future.

I hurried on. "Like I say, it is only a theory, but it's a fact that the process of transmutation whereby the subject's psyche transfers to the puppet, is extremely fragile and susceptible to the slightest interference."

Penny redirected her glare towards me. "Any chance you could get to the point? You're doing my head in."

"If we can get our hands on the puppets or more literally, *in* the puppets, substituting their usual hosts with strangers, as alien as possible to the..."

Penny looked at me with a dawning understanding. "By alien, you mean..." She darted a surreptitious sideways glance at Morris and Trevor. Mo looked defensive and kicked one plimsoll against the other sulkily.

"Not an alien."

Penny looked irritated. "I take it we can't just pinch the bloody things and put them in a shredder?" And in response to me shaking my head, sighed with resignation.

This appeared to announce the end of the interview. She looked at me moodily and informed me with apparent reluctance that I would be called in when the situation demanded.

As we turned to go, Trevor turned to the window and announced as if in reply to a question, "Drum Utsire drey tsu finf sheyn seyklanik regn oder shaurz gut Dover teylmolik dikrising fir far a mol."

Penny looked startled and I had to turn away to hide my smile. In a certain capricious mood, Trevor is wont to make his shipping forecasts in Yiddish; a Jewish sailor might have listened without batting an eyelid but to an English audience it sounded particularly bizarre.

The next day I reflected on this strange encounter. Penny intrigued me. It was difficult to judge if ill temper was her prevailing mood or a justifiable reaction to having myself impressed upon her against her will. But as with many apparently ill-tempered people, I suspected this belied her true nature. I remembered that sudden bright smile as if of a different person, when Morris had impersonated a puppet. I admired her ease with her authority, letting loose her temper, language and in another moment her humour; it was evident that she was utterly careless of what impression she made on me.

I was curious to know if Trevor would have anything to say about our adventure. He had been unusually silent on the journey back. I knew where to look for him and recognised his voice as I approached the day room. I paused to listen.

"By my breath they will perish and by the blast of my anger they will come to an end. For I am your Lord and I will turn your cities into ruins and lay waste your sanctuaries."

I knocked and entered.

"Recovered from your encounter gentlemen?"

Trevor looked away but Morris was forthcoming. "Cor, bit posh that Penny ain't she?" He approached uncomfortably close in order to prod me in the chest. "Called you, Doctor Dumbass, cor, funny that, Doctor Dumbass." He laughed, raised both hands in the air, cranked at the elbow and did a sort of hobo meets Riverdance jig. "And used the 'F' word. Orlright for some, not that Morris though, get a right tickin' off if I say it."

"Did you like her?" My question was aimed at Morris but by proxy was for Trevor. I watched him out of the corner of my eye while only half listening to Morris.

"So so." Mo rocked his hands in a surprisingly apt caricature of weighing well-balanced imponderables. "That Mrs T, she's a bit of all right, reckon she's up for it."

Mo scored again with his uncanny ability to misinterpret any situation, but I was watching Trevor who reminded me of a character in a horror movie fighting desperately against the alien that had incubated in his brain, and finally losing the battle. His concentration increased in intensity as he finally broke the sound barrier of speech, his faltering staccato gaining in speed and fluency.

"Gibridy — obus — bobus. Stroke the purring Rutterkin, pleasure herself with incubi and succubi, grubbling for spells and horrid charms."

This speech was interrupted by Morris almost choking with laughter; I'd never seen him so elevated. After this had sufficiently subsided, Trevor continued.

"So doth she blast and eradicate the fruit of her womb and dip her husband's glove into boiling feathers ere she turns the sun into blood and pulls the moon out of sphere, prockering, proddering and jabbering, freezing his semen into ice, abulging him. A drab of the sullens, tormented long, gurning, mowing and forespeaking, sucking, pricking, closing and colling her fundament. Addicted to maleficence, covenant with devils. Rats dance on her shoulders, her grima bloated with spirals, timbrils and rattles, her hair of knotted vipers, a dead man's arm for a torch to light her loathsome way, rancouring and muttering necromancy."

Morris was now close to collapse and Trevor stopped suddenly. I wasn't sure what this all meant apart from that it was uncomplimentary and referenced witches. I knew better than to ask him a direct question but was curious and said with sly intent, "I thought she was rather nice."

Trevor's mouth worked. "Mother."

I wondered about this afterwards. Presumably he meant Penny's mother, but how could he possibly know anything about her? Unlike The Caldwell, who he'd had some interaction with, this was someone he'd never even seen. I regretted that there was no possibility of finding out. Which all goes to show that such thoughts are a provocation to the Gods.

Later that day, the telephone rang and Sister Harris put through a phone call from a Mr Williamson from the Inland Revenue, in fact, Major putting on an absurdly pukkah accent. After a rather aggressive introduction, wishing to, "Discuss certain discrepancies in my tax return," he asked in a loud whisper if I was alone and, reassured, demanded my presence at the tax office in

81

order to, "Sort this matter out once and for all." Presumably they had got wind of Madame's next therapy session.

I declined. I was scheduled for an assessment of a patient under "Section Three." These orders are for six months and consequently require more deliberation than the shorter holding sections. This was a difficult one because of contention with the patient's family. I tried to explain this but was interrupted by a cough, and Major said, with pleasurable satisfaction, "Your attendance is not voluntary, Dr Bartlett."

"Oh," I replied and the line went dead.

Two hours later a van with blacked out windows arrived. I was ushered into the back with Trevor and Mo. Mr Robinson, Major and Penny, sat on bench seats along the sides of the van.

Mo put my thoughts into words. "We're the 'A Team', right?" He stuck out both thumbs and Major responded inappropriately by shaking his hand, which Mo pumped enthusiastically.

"Fool," he said, in character.

"She's due at the clinic in an hour," said Mr Robinson. "We can park nearby and," he indicated a screen with a nod of his head, "we can pick it up in here."

We were driven off. There was little conversation apart from an announcement by Trevor.

"Ethylene-propylene-diene-monomer up thirty-eight dollars."

I stole a sidelong glance at Penny. A faint crease at the edge of her mouth showed amusement, a refrain of what I had glimpsed at our first meeting. In spite of the peculiarity of the situation and presumably the pressure she must be under, she appeared restless rather than anxious, even bored; the movements of her body were comically uninhibited like a reluctant teenager being taken on a family outing.

Hamilton's clinic was within a private hospital. We took up a position in the adjoining car park. Major switched on a monitor recording the same room I had seen before, now empty. Doctor Hamilton appeared a few minutes later. I was interested by his movements and expression: thoughtful, scheming, sly — up to no good written all over his face. But I smiled at an inner thought. Many in his profession observed in similar circumstances would fit this description; there is more than a little staging in a psychotherapy session. Penny picked up on my smile and stared at me with hostility, her eyes like ice.

"Something amusing you?"

I shook my head and straightened out my face with the thought that Penny's expression was dramatically changeable.

On screen, the therapy room door opened and her ladyship entered. There was a rather formal exchange of greetings. She showed keenness, almost anxiety, to don the puppet and, as the macabre figure animated in her hand, she exhaled deeply as if in relief. Mr Janos appeared to cower before her, his voice a whine.

"Where have you been, darlink? Mr Janos missed you, your own Mr Janos, you know how he suffers without his darlink."

These words appeared to succour Martha. Her arms expanded and her head tilted back, her voice again spoken directly by her animator.

"Oh God, don't grovel, you know I hate it when you do that."

Mr Janos' whine became even more cowering and ingratiating. "But darlink, just tell Mr Janos that you still love him, even if it's just a little, that's all he wants." At which the grotesque puppet doubled up as if in mortal pain and began to rise and fall with a bizarre snake-like rhythm, and Martha, as if herself afflicted, began to wave her arms in evident distress.

"No, no, stop that, you know I hate that and you know I can't love you. I've told you. Why do you torment us both? For God's sake, you've known for years."

Mr Janos was now silent but continued to writhe pitifully, I strongly suspected with the intent of hypnotic induction. The scene before us was charged with emotion and, true to form, Mo began to giggle. I broke in.

"I don't like this." I foresaw a crisis. Just as in those clips of newsreel when you see a trickle of water start to run down a dam, you know for sure what is to follow.

"She's going to crack," said Penny.

I agreed. "The one thing women despise most in a man is supplication."

Penny looked at me thoughtfully and replied, "Is that so?"

I felt the sting of a put-down. Her attention returned to the screen. She appeared to make up her mind.

"We're going in."

Mr Robinson pursed his lips disapprovingly, surprisingly reminiscent of Sister Harris. "And our plan is?"

Penny turned on him coldly. "Our plan is to stop this before it goes any further. We'll kick up a stink and maybe these two," she indicated Mo and Trevor, "will get a chance to put Dr Bartlett's madcap scheme into action. If not, we'll just have to break it up."

"Kick up a stink?" queried Mr Robinson.

"It's a clinic for relationship counselling amongst other things, and the doctor and I are just about to have the mother of a bust up. Come on, dumbass," she said to me with a slight lifting of the sternness of her frown.

"Doctor Dumbass," I protested faintly as I followed her out of the back of the van while thinking to myself that this was a woman of action who thought and acted on the hoof. With a gun in her hand, obviously her preferred method of problem solving, she would truly be a female James Bond. She led us through a maze of corridors into Hamilton's clinic and the moment we were through the door, turned on me furiously, taking me completely unawares, and slapped me viciously across the face as if in continuation of a simmering row.

"How dare you say that? I've tried to make this so-called marriage work."

I was strangely distracted by a peripheral image of Major nodding in apparent agreement and echoing, 'so-called', as if some kind of affirmation, perhaps because he used this expression regularly himself and was flattered by hearing it repeated. Unfortunately, this distraction left me floundering. Without any change of expression Penny dropped her voice.

"Come on, Bartlett, man up."

I was out of my depth. I saw in the corner of my eye a nervous looking receptionist rise to her feet. Trevor, struggling manfully, I'd swear tried to come to my rescue.

"Imperial Tobacco up to seventeen forty GBX, previous close," he stumbled, his throat worked but nothing came, then after a supreme effort, blurted out hurriedly, "Fourteen eighty GBX, could be a merger."

Penny continued. "And let me tell you, you don't fool any of my friends, none of them like you. Angela said things about you. Oh yes, she said some very interesting things, she had you taped right from the start."

"I bet she did."

Penny ordered me curtly under her breath, "Louder." Then shouted, "She said your eyes are too close together."

"Did she?" I thought frantically and added, "Oh she did, did she?" Penny encouraged me with her eyes. I struggled on. "Well two can play at that."

Mr Robinson and Major gathered around with expressions that were curiously out of place, for some reason making me think of priests attending an exorcism.

Penny continued. "What do you mean by that?"

"Just that I have a few things to say myself."

"Thank fuck for that," Penny whispered, and aloud, "I don't wish to hear them."

This was my unexpected chance to test Trevor's extraordinary outburst earlier, if only I could get myself into character.

"You know what? With every day, you get more like your bitch of a mother."

I saw Penny's face drop like a stone. She drew away, almost staggering. I was appalled. Psychiatrists heal people, not seek out their vulnerabilities and use them as weapons — with the possible exception of The Caldwell. But I had no choice but to carry on.

"Do you want to know what I think of your mother?"

Penny shook her head and replied haughtily, "I certainly do not."

Morris picked at his jacket. This was an encouraging sign, he at least perceived this as a real argument and was reacting accordingly, he is upset by conflict. But he perked up at this last remark, evidently it reminded him of Stanley ticking off Ollie in Laurel and Hardy, and repeated to Trevor, "Certainly not, Stanley."

At which a young lady with the distinctive features of Trisomy 21, better known as 'Down's syndrome,' sidled up to Morris, apparently fascinated.

Penny missed a beat but rallied to shout in my face, "Unless you have something nice to say."

"Ho," was my poor response, which Morris again picked up on and repeated to Trevor with superb hauteur.

"Ho."

Penny now looked apoplectic. "Excuse me?"

I gathered my thoughts. "No, I have nothing nice to say about your mother, there is nothing nice to say about your mother." I remembered a line from Trevor's 'highfalutin' and threw it in out of desperation. "Think what she did to your father."

Penny did a double take. Her mouth opened to reply but she paused before responding lamely, "I beg your pardon." Then, recovering, folded her arms with an affected flounce and twisted her head away. "And what exactly do you mean by that?" Adding sotto voce, "Actually, what do you mean, by that?"

I had an intuition of my own. Penny had looked up sharply when Morris had mentioned the Haslemere bypass in her office and it had seemed to me that she had tried to cover her surprise. Also, she reminded me so strongly of 'that lovely posh Doctor Ffiona' whose father had been something high up in the military. It is often the way that there is at least a superficial commonality fostered in siblings by parents of particular occupations. And there was the prescription of a pint of navy rum, for Sam. It was all worth throwing in.

"A senior serviceman from Haslemere," I started, but was paused by Penny's extreme reaction: a sharp intake of breath followed by an expression of grievous disconcert. I had scored a bullseye.

Mo's eyes lit up like headlights and he announced complacently to the young lady at his side.

"That's near Godalming, that is, just down the A239, used to drive a three-tonner round there." The young lady looked inordinately impressed.

In spite of the fact that I desperately needed to concentrate on my dialogue, my mind slipped away to register the utterly trivial revelation that whenever Morris discussed any road it was invariably the A239. If there was such a road then it was truly ubiquitous.

Mr Robinson apparently shared my doubt. "Personally, I would favour the A286."

Morris swelled authoritatively and announced to the young lady, "No way, A286, pfaw, don't wanna go near it — jammed solid. Naah, do the back doubles 'round Merrow, gotta know 'em though."

The young lady smiled up at Morris with an expression of pure love. Penny took the opportunity to whisper, "Where did you get that from, Bartlett?"

I ignored her, I had to keep my momentum. "She destroyed him, that kindly honourable man, that poor butterfly that snagged its wings in her evil gossamer web."

Penny heaved with emotion, apparently preparing for attack but was interrupted by an impromptu sermon from Trevor.

"Blessed are those who are persecuted for the sake of righteousness for he shall have their carcasses in abomination."

I saw a flicker of uncertainty pass across Penny's face but she recovered herself in an instant.

"How dare you!" Adding under her breath, "Poor father, he should never have let her treat him like that."

From which I realised that Trevor's insight was again unerring. Not only that, but by the sound of it, Penny was critical of her mother, relieving me of the concern that I had upset her, and encouraging me to continue with a new confidence:

"Your mother is a twisted spiteful mean-spirited embittered harridan, a vile malignant dried-up prune."

Penny's eyes danced with fire. "You hated my mother from the moment you set eyes on her." She appeared to lose control and flew at me so suddenly that

I was only just in time to catch her wrists. Past experience of pacifying violent patients develops sharp reactions and strong wrists. I was able to restrain her, which appeared to genuinely inflame her; I had the distinct impression that if I let go, she would take a swing at me.

But the distraction silenced her and it was for me to continue. Lacking further inspiration, I fell back on the usual complaints of married men about their wives.

"She dedicated herself to making your father's life a misery; she stifled his every aspiration; she alienated him from his friends and forbade his hobbies; she threw away his books and..." I was winging it with this but had another moment of enlightenment, remembering the change from the florid decor of Penny's outer office to the extreme plainness of her room — in rebellion?

"Replaced them with ghastly twee artefacts and appalling curtains, a testament to her tastelessness."

Suddenly Penny's face was next to mine and I tightened my grip on her wrists suspiciously, but it was to whisper in my ear, "How could you possibly know that?" Before I had time to reply, she twisted her wrists again, furiously trying to break free. God, she was strong. It was all I could do to hold her, and again her sudden anger seemed disconcertingly real.

"They are not tasteless," she spat. "They are mustard check."

I frowned in concentration. This detail cleared some inner fog and completed the vision of this room, remote in time and place. In the corner of my eye, I caught Trevor's expression, directed intensely out of the window and wondered fancifully if it were he, the projector of this vision. I described it as I saw it.

"Clashing violently with the tartan shag-pile carpet and the two-tone wallpaper." I drew myself up accusingly. "Avocado and brabazon plum." She opened her mouth either in protest or wonder but I continued relentlessly. "Separated by a mock Georgian plaster dado rail."

Her eyes searched mine intently. I was intrigued, in all her moods so far, she had revealed only an occasional glimpse of what I suspected to be her true nature. Now I saw into the dark depths of her eyes as if into her soul. Her mouth was trembling. For a moment she fought for composure and I almost laughed out loud when she spoke, at the surprising tone of her voice: it was conversational.

"Not quite, Bartlett but not far off, you got the dado rail, still there in all its tasteless glory." She announced in a matter-of-fact whisper, "I'm going to attack you now."

I played my part by releasing her wrists and pushing her away. She came back at me, pummelling my chest with closed fists.

"You bastard." She looked around furtively. "He should be out here by now." Then loudly, "You were always lousy in bed."

Her words were prophetic. I heard a door slam and saw movement in the background. A familiar figure fled across the hallway making for the exit followed by a flustered and red-faced doctor. He paused at the sight of Penny rushing towards me with flying fists, which I only just dodged and caught a blow on the shoulder; this was some serious play acting, a second's delay and she would have decked me. Doctor Hamilton found his voice.

"What the hell's going on here?" The receptionist looked scared and shrugged.

Penny screamed and came at me again. The doctor watched for a moment as if in disbelief, shook his head and apparently remembering the retreating lady took off after her. This was our moment. I turned to Trevor, a mistake, Penny's fist thudded into my cheek. The shock and pain made me momentarily angry. Her eyes were bright with laughter.

"Sorry Bartlett," she whispered. "You were supposed to parry." I tried to recover my dignity.

"Now's our chance if you're quite done."

She recovered herself and replied, "I see your point." Her sudden frigidity was so absurd that my moment of anger evaporated in an instant. Catching Trevor's eye is always difficult but I managed it, and where Trevor led, Morris followed with evident relief. Throughout all this play acting a subplot had developed in the form of the Down's syndrome girl developing an admiration for Morris, fledging into full-blown romance in all of five minutes. I dismissed the theory that lactic acid and ammonia could act as some potent pheromone in favour of the more plausible actuality that in Down's syndrome, sexual inhibition is often spectacularly absent. This is in itself usually harmless in men but a nightmare in women because of all the ethical soul searching about intervention in the matter of fertility. One did not need to be a psychiatrist to read the signs: the pawing of the jacket, a sweet loving smile and finally the naively obscene gesture of forming a ring between her finger and thumb and sliding the index finger of her other hand lewdly into it. Morris had pulled. Finally, his worldly knowledge of how to get to Godalming on the back roads coupled with the chemistry of his jacket had worked it's magic and he was petrified as well as putrefied and was fast on Trevor's heel as they disappeared from the room.

Penny dropped her facade briefly. "Carry on, if he gets her back in, we may have to intervene." Her right hand tensed threateningly and I had a suspicion that 'intervene' would mean a right hook to Doctor Hamilton's jaw. One thing I was sure of, events would not catch her by surprise; resourceful was the word that sprang to mind when considering this woman. I continued as ordered.

"You can dish it out but not so keen on taking it, are you? Well, I'm not done yet; it's time for some home truths. Ask yourself what your mother has done to you?"

Penny stood arms akimbo, her eyes fixed to the door watching for the doctor's return, replied distraitly, "And what exactly do you mean by that?"

Major, who had been following the argument with emphatic head nodding while whispering commentary to Mr Robinson, added in an aside, "What indeed, Mr Robinson? Clearly he has the gift."

Mr Robinson added sombrely, "Quite so. I had an aunt you know..."

"Oy, you two, put a sock in it and keep an eye on the door," Penny snapped in a loud whisper. Mr Robinson and Major obeyed sulkily with an appearance of offended dignity.

Penny seemed so distracted that she addressed me surprisingly politely. "Sorry, Bartlett, fire up again."

Fortunately, I was still in character. "She belittled you, mocked you, humiliated you in front of your friends. Worse than that she rejected you because she never loved you." I was intrigued by a peculiar expression of satisfaction on Penny's face at this, as if either she was gratified by my perception of this truth or, as was my intimation, that she gained some perverse pleasure in the knowledge that her mother had never loved her. This explanation might seem counterintuitive but is actually not uncommon in toxic mother daughter relationships.

Penny acted up, bursting with emotion. "How dare you!" she screamed, her eyes fixed with hostility on the nervous looking receptionist who was whispering ominously into a telephone. "What do you know about love? Nada, according to your ex-wife which is why she took off — that and the fact that she'd run out of men to sleep with, seeing as she was, if truth be known, no better than a prostitute."

A deep sigh at my side announced speech as Major turned to Mr Robinson. "This is the problem with domestic disharmony, Mr Robinson: so-called hasty remarks which cannot be unsaid."

"Indeed, Major, and the hurtfulness is added to by the readiness of these accusations, as if they have in fact been secretly harboured for some time, adding to their authenticity."

"As always, Mr Robinson you are most perspicacious."

Mr Robinson looked like a shy teenager who had just been kissed. "Oh, I don't know about that."

This extraordinary exchange had paused me. I pressed on. "I wouldn't call her that," I protested, feeling surprisingly defensive towards my ex, even though this was only play acting. From the periphery of my vision, I saw Mr Robinson eyeing me sympathetically.

Penny came at me under the pretence of an attack to whisper, "Don't be pathetic, Bartlett, I don't have your psychic powers, it's just some stuff I got about Robinson's wife." And back on full volume, "No, I tell a lie, prostitutes at least get paid for their services whereas your ex was on her back for a pint of cider and a bag of crisps." Her fists came at me again and I grabbed her wrists tightly. I got the impression that this was a trial of strength and again the restraint appeared to incense her.

"Let me go you great brute, you're hurting me."

She twisted furiously to get free, wincing with pain, prompting me to whisper, "Sorry."

She shot me a look of contempt before shouting in my face, "And you know why she insisted on doing it with the lights out?" I started to stammer a reply but she cut in venomously, "Because in the dark she could at least pretend you were someone else."

Mr Robinson stiffened and tottered uneasily.

"And passing out afterwards — not what you think, she had to drink a full bottle of vodka just to stand you anywhere near her, that's what I heard."

Mr Robinson now visibly wobbled and was steadied solicitously by Major. Penny seemed unaware and I didn't want this to go any further so, in spite of a massive gap in continuity, launched once again into attack.

"I see what you're doing, and fooling no one, trying to change the subject because," I drew myself up, trying to look menacing while holding her wrists tightly, "you don't want to hear the truth about that sidewinding old bitch — your mother!"

I released my grip on her and she stepped back rubbing her wrists. Her chest heaved and for a moment I thought she would burst into tears but she suddenly hurled herself at me, pounding my chest with "B-movie" enthusiasm, and purred under her breath, "You do have a way with words, Bartlett."

She caught me unawares with a stinging slap across my cheek delivered almost absent-mindedly with a sound like a pistol shot. Her eyes flashed with humour at the look of pain and surprise on my face.

"That woman is more poisonous than a nest of black widows."

"I'm warning you," she screamed.

"Oh, I've only just started."

"Have you?" she asked brightly, forgetting to shout.

"She's a suppurating pestilence, a festering necrotic harpy."

Penny closed her eyes and I faltered, concerned again that I was truly upsetting her. She opened them again and hissed urgently, "Go on."

"More venomous than a box jellyfish, more lethal than Marburg's haemorrhagic fever." I was running out of ideas now. "I tell you what I'd like to do to her…"

"Oh God," Penny moaned. I was distracted. She was breathing heavily and her face and neck flushed red. Her fists pummelled my chest so gently that it was almost a caress.

"You were saying," she murmured so breathlessly that I wondered at her oxytocin and prolactin levels — she really was flushed around the neck.

At this moment, Trevor and Morris appeared, just in time. Seconds later the doctor re-entered from the lobby accompanied by his sheepish looking patient. Penny supplied continuity to our piece of theatre by landing another stinging slap, this time to my left cheek, with another pistol-shot sound effect. The doctor, distracted for a moment, shouted angrily, "This isn't the bloody Jerry Springer Show." He turned away from us and caught sight of Mo and Trevor loitering in the passageway to his office. "You two, out. This is private."

Which is the wrong tone to use with Morris. "Yeah, that's it, 'ave a pop at Morris why don't yer? Mean ter say, where's the sign then? Bet if yer asked a million people comin' out a chip shop, ''ere mate, reckon you can get told off fer goin' down a corridor? Nar, mate — no way, not if it don't 'ave a sign.' Billion people I reckon, but oh no, not that Morris; don't let 'im in 'ere — not where all the posh lot 'ang out — don't want 'is sort 'round."

The doctor pushed through impatiently.

Penny frowned. "He's going to start on her again." She looked at me doubtfully. "And nothing personal, Bartlett, but I've no confidence in your hare-brained scheme whatsoever." She studied me intently and I recognised this as an invitation to contradict her, and I guessed that only supreme confidence would persuade her. Supreme confidence is a condition I've always tested negative for and never more so than at this moment.

My eye chanced on Trevor and Morris. Mo was still grumbling and kicking petulantly at some nearby chairs while Trevor stared intently into space, and suddenly I was overwhelmed by a strong conviction which allowed me to affect a slight hauteur as I replied, "He won't get anywhere with her now."

Penny's consideration of me remained cynical but apparently in a flash judgement was persuaded.

"OK, Cassandra, let's get out of here and if it goes wrong, we'll bust him." From her wistful look it seemed she was regretful of being cheated out of this option. Actions followed words with Penny and she turned on her heel, at which moment Morris' would-be girlfriend sighted him and made a beeline for him. Along with a lack of inhibition in Down's syndrome goes a somewhat telescoped courtship timescale. This young lady felt that there had been enough in the way of preliminaries with Morris, she was ready for the next level. She opened her arms, puckered up and accelerated towards him, and, possibly because she was rather a substantial girl, gave the strange impression that she was running in slow motion. Morris watched at first with a certain detachment. For all his talk, long experience had taught him that if a woman smiled at him, it would be because her boyfriend was standing behind him, and as for running towards him, her flight path would be diverted long before a collision was possible. I saw his expression change at the last moment as he realised his fate: a moment of naked fear followed by brief reflection, then resignation, and, finally with the inappropriateness peculiar to Morris, he attempted an impression of 'the Fonz' with outspread arms, open palms and both thumbs up. She caught him amidships full-on.

I would have liked to have stayed to watch this play out but Penny was already through the door.

Moments later we were back in the van watching impatiently as Major turned on the monitor, interrupted moments later by a flustered and excited Morris.

The screen flickered into life, my confidence evaporated, Doctor Hamilton was plying his patient with smooth words and a cup of coffee.

"Probably drugged," commented Penny cynically.

The doctor drew the lifeless Mr Janos over his hand reassuringly as if putting on a condom and Sam followed his example with a little sigh of relief.

Penny darted me a look which mixed contempt, derision and cynicism in something like equal proportions. My moment of truth had arrived. The doctor began to work Mr Janos with a sinister smile. My last remnant of confidence drained away. But as I watched, the doctor's smile was infiltrated by doubt. To his apparent surprise he seemed to struggle for mastery of his own hand, as if locked in a battle of wills, slowly losing control as the puppet appeared to wrench itself around, turning slowly but inexorably to face the wall.

Martha, now fully animated, swivelled peculiarly in the distinctive manner of Morris displaying his rally jacket. I sighed with relief: it was working. Mr Janos appeared to speak.

"German Bight south-east five to seven decreasing three or four moderate becoming slight occasionally smooth later near coasts mainly fair good occasionally poor." Then, turning to the doctor with his face bent downwards, "When me they fly, I am the wings."

Martha peacocked furiously from side to side. Sam looked horrified, let out a short cry, ripped the puppet off her hand and ran from the room. The doctor appeared to consider the now limp Mr Janos with a brooding and venomous rage, picked up a pen and stabbed the puppet viciously in the face — from his yelp of pain, apparently having forgotten the role of his own hand in Mr Janos' existence: an excellent example of projection.

I giggled inwardly at a sudden impulse to copy Morris with a Fonz impression complete with thumbs up and a long drawn out, 'Aaay', but a look at Penny's expression at somewhere below zero decided me against.

Mr Robinson was more impressed. "Amazing. I wouldn't have believed it if it weren't for the evidence of my own eyes."

Major agreed. "Extraordinary — this of course is the advantage of consulting the so-called experts, Mr Robinson."

Mr Robinson opened his mouth to reply but was silenced by a belligerent glare from Penny.

Morris supplied a constant monologue for the duration of the return journey.

"Wanted it she did, phoohar, not 'alf, all over me like a rash, mean ter say, talk about full on, sheesh." This monologue degenerated into a lecture on sex, a subject which I suspect Morris knows as much about as driving, but apparently derived from a recognised expert on the subject, 'Deep-sea-Dave', another fish-frier of his acquaintance, and eventually strayed embarrassingly onto the topic of stimulation of the Mound of Venus, demonstrated by graphic hand movements. I risked sending Mo into persecution mode by telling him that this wasn't the done thing, in front of a lady. He looked sulky for a moment, unsure whether to take offence, before grudgingly appearing to give me the benefit of the doubt.

An hour later we were back at headquarters. Penny took her seat at the head of the table with the ever-present Mrs T officiating with a duster.

Penny fidgeted. "Dr Bartlett, I think, erm, thanks," her lack of fluency was a match for Trevor, "are in order. It appears your..." She faltered again, apparently searching for a suitable word.

"Stratagem, perhaps," suggested Mr Robinson helpfully.

"Or wheeze," suggested Major even more helpfully.

Penny ignored them. "Whatever it was, it worked."

Major beamed at me disconcertingly. "I think I can safely say that Doctor Hamilton has come to a so-called sticky end, and accordingly, 'Operation Kurukshetra' is concluded." His face fell, presumably with sadness at his lack of opportunity to trot this name out again. Mr Robinson touched his arm sympathetically.

"An excellent name for the operation if you will permit, Major."

"Indeed, indeed and thank you for that, Mr Robinson, you are so sensitive." He darted an accusing look at Penny who shook her head in disgust and turned to me.

"Do you by any chance practice hypnosis?"

I took the question at face value. "Yes, I think it's underrated, particularly for treating Post Traumatic Stress Disorder; you see, by accessing the subconscious..."

Penny held up her hand. "I had more in mind self-hypnosis with the aim of making you forget everything that has happened." She looked at me pointedly. "And I mean — *everything*."

I suspect she referred to the moment when I had insulted her mother so thoroughly that she had flushed suspiciously at the neck. I have not known a woman climax from this cause but female erotic stimulation has a wide distribution; I knew of a case induced by a certain type of cheese and another by over-spending on a husband's credit card, so I couldn't rule it out.

Penny continued, "It would be false politeness to say, 'don't take it personally', when I say, I never wish to see you again." She paused, and as if feeling she had made an understatement, added emphatically, "*Ever*!"

I was distracted for a moment by the sight of Morris being expansive a little too close to Mrs T and being seen off with a can of air freshener. Trevor presented Max to Mr Robinson to pat in the way of a farewell. Mr Robinson obliged as a true gentleman.

"You've been a good boy, Max."

"It was a pleasure meeting you indeed." Major joined in the patting, and Trevor grimaced with pleasure.

My last vision of Penny was with her head sunk in her hands, her scalp being scratched consolingly by Mrs T with the handle of a feather duster.

That night I found myself strangely deflated. The truth was I had enjoyed this adventure, this glimpse into another world, and was sad that it was over, which perhaps explains the strange dream I had that night. When I say dream, I should say dreams, all disjointed, one rolling into another, starting with Major in a smart suit serving Mr Robinson in a fish and chip shop. I suppose fish and chip shops feature in my subconscious due to being one of the regular venues for Mo's anecdotal encounters with his friends.

Major turned to Mr Robinson. "Salt and vinegar?"

Mr Robinson responded frigidly, "Just a little vinegar please."

There was some tension between these two, the remark appeared to annoy Major and he grabbed the salt cellar, shook it vigorously and dowsed the fish and chips in a stream of salt; Mr Robinson growled with rage and wrestled him to the floor. Out of sight they could be heard grunting as they fought.

A fluorescent fly-killing device burst into life projecting the colours of the rainbow in roving beams across the walls. A radio on the counter switched itself on, blasting out dance music. Dry-ice smoke poured from the fish fryers onto the floor. The shop had transformed into a disco. Mrs T, in overalls and a hairnet, lifted a strainer full of fish from a fryer. Penny entered in a red hockey skirt and white shirt emblazoned with the England Ladies' shield, picked out by the rainbow lights, and accompanied by Donna Summer's, 'Love to Love you Baby'. Mrs T turned in slow motion and removed her hairnet steamily. Penny leant across to seize her by the hair and snarled in her face.

"One cod with extra batter, two skate, treble chips and," Mrs T's lips trembled with emotion, "a pasty."

Mr Robinson rose from the floor like a zombie in a horror movie. Penny turned angrily on him, drew her leg back and kicked him viciously in the crutch. Mr Robinson writhed in pain but an orgasmic smile spread across his face as he sank back slowly into the dry-ice vapour as if dissolving into the ground and obscurity, only to reappear moments later. The music changed to a Hindi classic. Mr Robinson strode across the floor to join with Major in dancing furious Bollywood. Mrs T mopped the floor laconically, Penny walked slowly past eating from an open newspaper. They exchanged hungry glances and left the shop together, guiltily sharing the fish and chips.

Then the shop was gone, replaced by a black turbulent ocean heaving under a starlit night sky. An immensely tall red and white lighthouse towered overhead, its sweeping beam lighting an endless panorama of monstrous waves with foaming white crests whipped up by a howling wind. Trevor stood on the lantern balcony waving his hands frantically at Max bobbing up and down in the waves.

I woke up with, amongst the absurdity, the strangely real and disturbing memory of Trevor's terrible distress at the drowning Max.

It took a while to wake fully, as if I were reluctant to lose the strange romance of the now departing dreams. I felt an unusual emptiness at the thought of the week before me. I enjoy my work in all its moods. It is sad, funny, depressing, and I'm often frustrated by the intractability of some conditions and the misguided intervention of others, but rewarded at times by progress, sometimes stumbling and faltering, sometimes a dramatic renaissance. Hence my feeling of flatness was unusual. It passed in the following days but I found myself wondering about that office in the city and its ongoing battle against the enemies of our country, and about the strange quirk of fate that had taken me there. One thing was sure, I told myself with a sigh, I would not be called upon again, another example of my thoughts tempting providence.

It was some two months later that the call was put through to me.

"Dr Bartlett? You don't know me, my name is Strong, Gavin Strong. I wish to arrange a consultation with you; it is a matter of some urgency."

I recognised the voice of Mr Robinson absurdly disguised by a sort of false dynamism.

"I see," I said, playing along. "Has the mania returned?"

Mr Robinson hesitated, I imagined at the offence to his dignity. "Indeed, but my colleague you understand." I heard a muted protest from Major. "We would much like to call on you at eleven o clock tomorrow morning."

I started to explain that this was not a convenient time but in the manner of a TV thriller the line went dead with a click.

They duly arrived the next day. I struggled not to laugh when I saw them both sporting moustaches. Major wore his with evident pride, almost gay pride, twitching his upper lip into all sorts of contortions to make the ends oscillate, all the while squinting cross-eyed down his nose to witness the effect, whereas Mr Robinson apparently felt his dignity compromised and averted his eyes sideways as if disowning his own face. After much fidgeting and beating about the bush I was informed that again my person was to be subpoenaed to an unknown destination and I had no say in the matter, although this time the pair of them apologised handsomely once we were on our way.

In fact, their embarrassment was such as to make me curious, and when I asked them what it was all about, they became flustered. I was treated to the spectacle of Major twitching his moustaches furiously while Mr Robinson attempted to look out of the blacked out windows. Major, after several false starts, eventually broke into speech.

"Dr Bartlett…" He tailed off and looked hopefully at Mr Robinson who reluctantly took up the baton.

"A matter of some delicacy has arisen." He coughed himself into silence.

Major smiled as if at a sudden revelation. "It is again a matter of psychology."

"Essentially," added Mr Robinson.

"Indeed," agreed Major. "And after your last — can I say, triumph?"

"I think you can, Major," agreed Mr Robinson thoughtfully.

"Thank you." Major beamed and bowed at the same time. "Triumph indeed, and now this…" He tailed off again.

"Now this?" I enquired.

"I see we need to explain," said Mr Robinson soothingly and rather patronisingly.

Major nodded. "It's this way Doctor Bartlett…"

And we were back at the beginning again and returned to it several times before I finally came to understand the cause of their embarrassment. They had a problem, a serious problem that they were at an impasse over. And being again an affair with a psychological dimension to it, Penny's political masters had suggested in the light of my success giving me a second commission. The difficulty was that no one had dared to tell Penny.

I laughed at their embarrassment. "She was a bit frosty with me, I know, but I expect she'll thaw out. I mean, it's not as if she hates me, is it?"

The nervousness in my laugh was compounded by my companions' silence and averted gazes.

Mr Robinson blustered, "No, no, I'm sure she doesn't hate you, Dr Bartlett."

Major nodded, causing his moustaches to jump up and down at the ends. "More despise," he said distractedly, his mind occupied with his moustaches to judge from his cross-eyed efforts to observe them.

I suppose this should have prepared me for my reception, but I am by nature an optimist and I had persuaded myself that Mr Robinson was a doom-monger and Major's use of English was sometimes suspect. Accordingly, the look on Penny's face at the sight of me was a bit of a shock. One of the most upsetting and disturbing aspects of my work is dealing with patients suffering from visual hallucinations, often as a result of dementia, when you see some poor soul in a state of extreme fear and you can do nothing to pacify them because your presence becomes incorporated into their psychotic delusion, whereby your smile is seen as demonic and your soothing words some vile threat. So now Penny's face registered horror at my appearance. She covered her face with her hands, opening one eye between her parted fingers as if to verify this dreadful apparition. Major and Mr Robinson fidgeted in silence until eventually Mr Robinson broke cover.

"The minister felt that in view of the psychological dimension to the current situation vis-à-vis…"

"Traitors," Penny hissed violently.

They hung their heads like disgraced schoolboys. Mrs T paused in her ministrations to direct a censorious look at them. Penny sat up straight, pushing out her chest, her eyes blazed with fury.

"Fifth columnists."

I felt it was time to speak. I was on my dignity, more than a little offended. "I'm sorry if I've intruded on some sort of internal squabble. I am in fact extremely busy at the moment and there is nothing I would like more to get back to my work if Her Majesty's Government permits."

Penny got up slowly and menacingly, Mrs T advancing behind with a duster in her hand. Penny's mouth opened and shut silently as if robbed of speech by violent emotion. An indescribable sound eventually found expression, something between a groan and a curse. Her hands twitched with frustration. Mrs T leant forward, turning her cheek submissively, I'd swear an invitation for her mistress to slap her. I think the same must have occurred to Penny from her momentary look of surprise. But this appeared to be her moment of capitulation. She subsided into her chair and Mrs T wandered off nonchalantly to continue her cleaning duties.

Mr Robinson reminded me gravely that I was still bound by the Official Secrets Act before proceeding.

"Our problem, Doctor, requires a certain amount of explanation." The slumped figure of Penny emitted a low moan and he hurried on. "This country has essentially been bankrupt, for some time now. This is not significant in itself, most Western states are. As long as we all stick together to keep rigging the global financial system to keep the Third World's nose out of the trough, we can just keep running up debt, inflating assets and printing money on the back of it. Everything is fine until it becomes so implausible that people get the jitters, usually because someone in the markets goes on a bender and wakes up in the morning with a hangover and has a brief moment of lucidity, revealing how preposterous it all is. Then they all panic and get stuck in the door on their way out and we have one of our global crashes: a load of fuss, plummeting share values and massive losses which of course is what pays for it all — until some bright spark thinks things are going to turn and they all pile back in again, like snapping up bargains in a January sale. And that's rather the point: when greed overtakes fear, the sell-off turns into a buying frenzy."

"Think of a roller coaster," said Major as if talking to a small child. "It ceases to drop and starts to go up again."

Mr Robinson continued. "It's all about confidence. However, misplaced that confidence is, doesn't in itself matter as long as people have it. You will understand then that any threat to this confidence is a threat to the very existence of our nation."

I did understand and was impressed by Mr Robinson's fluency on the subject. I guessed he had once been, by calling, an economist. He then went on to explain the nature of this threat, manifested in one man, Sir Douglas Henderson, a name I recognised as one of our top financiers. He was generally admired, and when I mentioned this, Penny's snort of derision made Major jump so violently that it started his moustaches off again. Mr Robinson explained gently that success, power and wealth, while generally admired and aspired to, were always at someone else's expense and, *in extremis*, the name of this loser was Great Britain.

"The markets are by nature parasitic but again that doesn't usually matter, they recycle wealth, provide funding and the money they diddle others out of has already been taxed, and when they spend it, it gets taxed again. The problem only comes when one of the players becomes too big, some of them have incomes the size of nations, then comes a certain moral hazard. Ministers, laws, the whole mechanism of government is bent out of shape."

Penny lifted her head. "Corruption! I think is the word you're trying to avoid," she snapped.

Mr Robinson continued unperturbed. "Sir Douglas, as you may know, is the prime mover in the Saruman Corporation."

Major chipped in. "Aptly named one might say, Saruman being the corrupt wizard in the so-called, 'Lord of The Rings'."

I began to understand Penny's perpetual bad mood, these two were hard work. Mr Robinson smiled with approval.

"Most apt if I may say so, Major. He is indeed a corrupt wizard and as such, presents a unique challenge, his every manoeuvre is at our expense. He shorts the pound and the Bank of England has to spend a fortune buying currency to shore it up, he buys copper, sugar, orange juice, anything you can think of, squeezes the life out of it to push the price up, then dumps the lot. The volumes are staggering."

Major interjected cheerfully. "He's plundering our kitty."

Penny looked up. "Sometimes, Major, you can say in a word what takes others a week." She glared pointedly at Mr Robinson. "Even if that word is some weird archaic hangover from the Raj." She turned to me brightly. "That's it Muppet-face, he's plundering our kitty, and since the happy wholesome days of assassination are now considered so non-PC, we have to come up with some other way of dealing with him."

Major looked pleased, evidently flattered. "My preference would be a honeypot."

Mr Robinson smiled condescendingly. "Trap, Major."

"Honeytrap indeed." Major smiled at Mr Robinson in a way that appeared to make him uncomfortable.

"Personally, I have nothing against honeytraps," Penny said breezily. "Or honeypots for that matter, which presumably are for the benefit of Winnie the Pooh."

And suddenly, in the extraordinary way that had so caught me unawares before, a flash of humour illuminated her face for the briefest instant before her expression refroze. Mrs T paused motionless in her eternal dusting to stare dreamily at Penny, who continued.

"But, alas, the pussies supposedly in charge of this Sceptred Isle come over all self-righteous at the suggestion, which wouldn't necessarily rule it out were it not for the fact that we have dug deep into this gentleman's past and come up with zilch."

"He has lived the life of a priest," chipped in Major.

Penny looked sour. "I wish. But it appears he isn't into women or for that matter..." She paused. "Speaking of which, why are you two dressed like 'The Village People'?"

Major twitched moustaches with evident pleasure; Mr Robinson attempted to shield his with his hand.

"We have been to Dr Bartlett's place of work and did not wish to be recognised."

"Ah, the funny farm, surprised they let you out."

"We are in disguise," explained Major unnecessarily.

Penny looked cynical. "Yeah right, that'll put Blofeld off the scent." She sighed. "But I digress. Since you are unfortunately here, Dr Bartlett, totally against my wishes I might add, what we are looking for is a way to take him out."

"I see," I said stiffly.

"Discredit him, that sort of thing," Mr Robinson explained. "But the matter is delicate because of his large presence in the States."

Major, looked inappropriately pleased with himself, explained by the announcement, "It's a Code Crimson."

Penny continued. "Who we cannot afford to upset. There's someone big behind him, and we don't know who. I smell a rat, a large furry one."

Major's eyes lit up. "I once saw a bandicoot rat in Bengal — so big." He spread his hands widely. "It was absolutely enormous."

"We know," said Penny wearily. "Heard it before, size of an elephant."

Mrs T paused in her ministrations to interject, "Dirty beasts."

Major continued. "Whereas in Kashmir, you find the loveliest little field mice."

Penny raised her head at me, rather rudely I thought. I felt considerably out of my depth but tried to sound confident.

"We need to find his weak spot."

Penny opened a drawer in her desk and handed me a grey file, with a graphic look of scepticism. "There's a summary on the first page, you can read the rest in your own time."

The file was marked, "Top Secret," in red just like in the movies. It made interesting reading, being in effect a case history only with a reverse remit: to destroy instead of cure. Penny was tapping her fingers with impatience before I'd finished.

"Well?" she asked.

"Difficult," I said. "He is perhaps a psychopath or sociopath, a loner without intimacy and probably no empathy, an impulsive risk-taker, unburdened by morality." I darted a meaningful look at Penny, getting my revenge. "Like most people in high office."

Major nudged Mr Robinson who tried to nod gravely but due to the resultant oscillation of his moustaches achieved only comic effect. Even Mrs T dusted a picture frame pointedly.

"You mean by that, directors of MI5 I presume?" Penny's expression was particularly inscrutable and I wondered if this was intended as humour.

"My point is that such a person is particularly difficult to undermine. Psychopaths are halfway to automatons; they suffer no fear of consequences and are undiverted by emotions."

"Bollocks," said Penny crudely. I opened my mouth to protest but she stopped me short. "No, Doctor, strange as it may sound, I'm not doubting you over that, which is why I said, bollocks." She brightened up. "In fact, if you tell me the job's impossible, I have no choice but to resort to," she smiled with mock sweetness, "other options."

"I'm not saying that, just that I need more information and time to think."

Penny's momentary brightness faded from her face. "Go on then, three days. Get out the lot of you."

My last sight of her was slumped over her desk with her head in her hands with Mrs T massaging her back with a J-cloth.

That night, I read the full file; it dealt with the hideously complex dealings of Sir Douglas Henderson. I discovered a grudging respect for these financial gurus, I'd always considered them as nothing but wideboys in suits, I hadn't appreciated how clever they were, shenanigans it might be but in its own way as complex as biochemistry. After two late nights and a lot of wine I acquired at least an idea of how his company operated and the figures were staggering. There was a link to a TV interview on the occasion of his being knighted, this gave an insight into his psychology. There is a commonality in seeing captains of industry interviewed, like The Caldwell, you can almost see the dark mechanism exposed, whereby they skew their answers to whatever question they are asked into a continuous stream of propaganda. Not so, Doug Henderson, there was something naive, almost childlike, about his responses. It didn't seem to occur to him to do anything other than answer questions directly, without any hint of evasion. His comprehension was strictly literal to the point of absurdity. When the interviewer suggested that his parenting had been distant and had not contributed to his extraordinary success, he replied, "Oh, I don't know, Mother told me to get out of rubber when I was three."

And another classic on the subject of his nurturing. "I do remember Father saying to me, I must have been four: 'Your mother wants me to talk to you about life, son, I'm not sure why, but you know what women are about having mixed portfolios.' I remember him looking perplexed."

"And was that helpful?"

"Not really, I mean 'life' is not a sector that has ever interested me, even at that age, nor my father. Nevertheless, he felt obliged to explain the basics, the differences between term and guaranteed issue, but I didn't grasp the concept of mutualisation until I was five."

Not what I'd expected, not a psychopath but another on the autistic spectrum, and it was hard to associate this rather likeable man with the villainy he was accused of.

I was still ploughing my way through the file at work the next day when I looked up to find Trevor and Morris in attendance. In my preoccupation I hadn't noticed their presence.

Morris had taken one of his shoes off and was studying the sole. I knew why. His plimsolls had become so high that his occupational therapist had stolen them and burnt them, replacing them with an antique pair of "Wayfinders" she'd found in a charity shop. These were embossed on the soles with a variety of animal tracks. Mo had switched allegiance with deplorable infidelity.

Trevor, as if by some sort of divine intervention, was buried in a notorious pink publication which gave me pause for thought. He was often given to utterances on stocks and commodities, on one notable occasion, right in the face of The Caldwell. "Buy bananas!" Which incidentally made me feel like a proud mother. Could it be that his extraordinary powers extended to the markets? I decided to test my hypothesis.

"Hmm, biggest riser, I wonder." I spoke as if to myself but saw the paper twitch. There was a long moment of silence as Trevor struggled with a reply. I knew well that none would have been forthcoming if I could see his face, but the newspaper screen allowed him to answer in his rushed staccato.

"Sophocles Analytical."

This stimulated Mo to reprise his newly discovered favourite. "That's mumbo jumbo, that is." He made various attempts at repeating the name, none of which sounded remotely like. But eventually with a dawning smugness and a triumphant wave of his shoe in the air, which had already acquired the pungent aroma of rotting cheese of its predecessors, he spun around a couple of times and announced confidently.

"Syphalytical."

Next day the papers were full of it. Sophocles Analytical shares rocketed on rumours of a takeover and when Trevor and Mo trooped into my office after breakfast, I collared them.

"Boys, I have another task for you if you are willing."

I was gratified by a grimace of pleasure on Trevor's face.

"Yes," he rushed out hastily. Mo was more circumspect.

"'Pends don' it, mean, could be, could be." He spread his hands as if making some invisible measurement which was so unfathomably inappropriate that I struggled not to laugh.

Three days later, armed with the intelligence that Doug Henderson, being a loner, invariably took his lunch on the same park bench, we were all duly positioned around the corner in the surveillance van. Five minutes after he had been spotted entering the park, I launched Mo and Trevor on their mission which, in spite of extensive schooling, I was aware could follow a somewhat random course, and I watched the CCTV, impressively secreted all around the park, with nervousness. Doug Henderson was in mid-frame; he was a short stocky man, intelligence written across his fine-featured face co-existing with a surprising diffidence in his pale blue eyes. If I didn't know otherwise, I would have placed him as a high-flying techy although there was some nebulous suggestion of power about him.

He was absorbed in the pink newspaper laid across his knee and absent-mindedly reached in his pocket for an apple.

"Golden delicious I would surmise," said Major.

"You think so?" queried Mr Robinson. "A little too dark perhaps, I rather fancy a Granny Smith."

They were silenced by a dangerous glare from Penny. Doug opened his mouth to take his first bite, but like a badly synched movie, a load crunch was heard off camera. Doug looked at the apple suspiciously, it seemed to take him an inordinately long time to realise that unless the universe had slipped a cog, it could not have played a part in the noise he had just heard. But he got there in the end, turning his head slowly, just as Mr Robinson, operating the VCR, panned back rapidly to reveal Morris and Trevor dressed as tramps — no disguise required for Mo — alongside.

Mo munched at a particularly horrifying looking piece of rotten vegetation, possibly once an apple, which I guessed he had found in a bin. "'Ow do."

Doug looked surprised and spoke frigidly. "Good morning."

Mo slipped off the bench and stood heavily on one leg. I groaned inwardly, knowing what was to follow. Since acquiring his "Wayfinders" Mo was constantly searching for ground soft enough to imprint, as was the path occupying his attention now. After bending his leg a few times to ensure maximum impression, he sat down in order to inspect his artwork.

"See: badger, fox, dog, rabbit." At the mention of 'dog', Trevor surreptitiously slid Max from under his jacket and caressed him. "Bear," Mo continued, causing Trevor to slide Max back protectively. "Dunno 'bout the last one, owl maybe." He frowned. "Could be a chicken. Need to know; mean if yer out an' 'bout an' yer see that an' it's a chicken, mean pfoof, yer not that bovered, got chased by one once, chicken that is, not an owl, owls don't chase bods. But bears..." He drew in his breath and shook his head. "Mate o' mine, 'tater peeler, third dan, bloody genius with the death stars..."

Doug stared at Morris, taken aback, as indeed are most people, by the unique dreadfulness that is Morris. He was distracted by the sight of Trevor withdrawing a copy of the *Financial Times* from his pocket and skimming through the section on stocks and shares with a sliding finger. Doug's eyes, already widened by exposure to Mo, were now the size of soup plates. Mo was distracted from his anecdote.

"Vestments, that's what," he whispered conspiratorially. "Summat well big in the city 'e is; richest bloke in the world they reckon. See that jacket, put yer 'and in 'is pocket, mink-lined it is."

I became suddenly aware of Penny's scrutiny at its most cynical. I looked away.

"Morris has gone a little off-script I'm afraid."

"He's an idiot," exploded Penny.

"Technically you are correct," I conceded stiffly. "His IQ measures between twenty-five and thirty-nine, which is within the parameters of what you describe, but we don't use that term nowadays."

"Fuck's sake."

"But then again if all goes according to plan, Morris' performance will only serve to heighten Trevor's," I said hopefully, praying that Trevor would not slip into a biblical pronouncement of gloom or his trusted standby, the shipping forecast.

I sighed with relief as he pronounced on cue, "Global Consolidated up forty-three." He shook his head with a grimace. "Sell."

I wondered at first if Doug had even heard, let alone considered sufficiently to respond, but he took the bait beautifully.

"Sell Global Consolidated? I hardly think so, my advice to you would be to hold."

At which point Penny burst out, "Is this for real? A tramp appears out of nowhere with a cardboard dog, sits next to the most renowned financier in the city and instead of telling him to sling his hook, he starts debating stock market tips."

Major smiled condescendingly. "Some people retain their spiritual humility for all their earthly power. In India…"

"Yes, well, thank you for your eternal wisdom, Mahatma Gandhi but… Hang on." She hushed herself, Trevor was talking again.

"Blood and fire and pillars of smoke, the sun shall be turned into darkness and the moon into blood before the coming great and awesome day of the apocalypse." He glanced at Doug's feet for an instant before turning away. "Sell."

Doug was about to speak but Mo interrupted by pointing out a new set of footprints he had just made with his other foot.

"Tha's a wombat that, don't get many over 'ere, not in the wild anyway. Saw one behind a burger bar once, might've been a squirrel I s'pose."

Trevor drew up his newspaper to hide his face. Doug stared into space as if at some traumatic experience. Mo tut-tutted and shook his head patronisingly.

"Wanna listen to him yer do — spot on 'e is every time. Yeah, 's'a wombat."

I hardly slept that night and in the dark hours it seemed absurd to suppose that Trevor's prediction would be correct again. I felt myself sweat at the thought and wondered at this. It was quite an extreme physiological reaction, why did I care so much? And the answer was Penny. Failure meant the end of our association and I felt a curious flatness at the thought of not seeing her again.

The next morning, I picked up a *FT* on my way to work. Global Consolidated featured on the front page. A glimpse was enough: 'Shares crash on rumours of fraud'.

Later, at work, the phone rang and I was treated to Major's excellent impression of an Indian call centre operative, informing me that I was due a refund on a mis-sold insurance policy and a car would call for me in an hour to chauffeur me to head office. I had a laugh at his expense by explaining that I hadn't purchased any such insurance policy, forcing him to hiss in a whisper that it was he, Major, not really a call centre.

On arrival, some hours later, I received an enthusiastic welcome from Major. "Ah, Doctor, I have named this operation 'Sama Veda — The Knowledge of the Melodies'."

Mr Robinson approved. "Another excellent name, Major."

"Thank you, Mr Robinson. What is it that you particularly like about it, may I enquire?"

"I think it is the obscurity, the casual listener would suspect nothing. I mean to say, 'Knowledge of the Melodies', it is ostensibly unrelated to our problem and yet a hint may be gleaned from..."

"Excuse me." Penny looked at them with extreme irritation, causing them to smile significantly at each other, leading me to suspect that Penny had lost a bet on the outcome of Trevor's prophecy. She looked up at me momentarily and, in an apparently connected gesture, pulled a whisky bottle out of her desk and filled a coffee mug. She drank deeply and in the process of drinking raised her eyes, as if stung by conscience she held out the bottle.

"Want some?"

I had not taken alcohol during the day since I was a teenager but some reckless mood made me accept the bottle and a mug and take a large slug.

Major and Mr Robinson now openly smirked, this time I had no idea why.

"Right." Penny slapped her desk. "We've got someone on the inside with a body-cam. Let's see how this goes down."

A monitor fizzed into life. I recognised Doug, now looking somewhat ill at ease at the head of a massive desk, surrounded by his fellow directors and subordinates I supposed. A sharply dressed young man was speaking.

"Commodities, five mill up on shorting wheat, and a killing — no numbers yet — selling our positions on three month copper. Thirty-five second oil — again, no figures yet, but it's looking good, over a hundred mill."

The next contributor was a woman dressed in a red twin-set and a hairdo that went out of fashion at the same time as Penny's. Her eyes were wide open as if with surprise, somehow, she gave the impression of being a head teacher rather than anything corporate. She blinked several times before proceeding.

"UK stocks and shares, bought all top six risers, net accrual two hundred and thirty million sterling." She paused to blink several more times before continuing. "Sold all fallers except one: net value since purchase, four hundred and twenty million sterling…"

"That's the finance director," said Mr Robinson.

Doug appeared to wake from a reverie and met the lady's blinking gaze with a frown of consternation. "Except one?"

A voice from the table interjected heartily. "I wouldn't beat yourself up about that one, Doug. Global Consolidated, who would have thought it?"

The work with the body-cam had been a bit random and, in an attempt to catch Doug's reaction to this comment, we were treated instead to a close-up of a lady's face blinking at an unnatural rate, a point that did not go unobserved by Penny.

"What's up with her?" I looked at her enquiringly.

"Yes you, Doctor, you're the ruddy psychiatrist."

"Well," I considered, "there are various possibilities. In general terms, it's a sign of stress but that can be due to a variety of reasons, a liar may reveal himself or herself in this way…"

"*Him*self," Penny cut in decisively.

"Or," I continued, "at the other end of the scale, it can be a sign of sexual arousal."

"Really," said Penny sarcastically, staring at me with open unblinking eyes, but there was a brightness in them which hinted at humour. I opened my mouth to continue but she hushed me.

Doug rose from his seat with an expression like a sleepwalker. "Global Consolidated." His voice held a loaded significance, at which point the sound and vision fizzed out with a flash and a pop.

Penny looked irritated. "Last time that happened, the operator had been shot, but I doubt that on this occasion, just more crap technology." She darted an accusing frown at Mr Robinson. "Still, I suppose it's success of a sort, got him thinking." She turned her frown on me.

"How did he know, your, erm, assistant?"

"An interesting question."

"Perhaps he's been shadowing the shares," suggested Mr Robinson. "A subtle pattern in the movements can reveal fraudulent trading, but these require supercomputers to detect."

"Well, he is a savant."

"That's someone with extraordinary intelligence," explained Major, unwisely I thought.

"As opposed to someone extraordinarily patronising," retorted Penny.

"But it's more than that," I continued, grateful for the interruption, it gave me a moment to shape my thoughts. "Human affairs are like a game of chess on a grand scale with an almost infinite number of variables. People often criticize economists because at any one time at least half of them are wrong about everything. You might forgive them for not taking into account the unpredictable, such as natural disasters, but all too often they…"

Penny was showing increasing signs of psychomotor agitation, tapping her fingers in particular, so I was not surprised when she interrupted me.

"So all the pundits get it wrong because the great unwashed don't like being told what to think, and go the other way out of sheer perversity; it's called the buggeration factor." She took a large swig of scotch.

I opened my mouth, more in surprise than preparation for speech. She looked at me curiously.

"Well, that is what you were going to say?"

"Erm, yes I suppose I was, possibly without the reference to the great unwashed." The speed of her reasoning was disconcertingly fast. My thoughts must have shown: her expression softened.

"No need to top yourself, Bartlett, go on."

Interesting. An indication of kindness, the quality I value above all others. This reflection displaced my train of thought. Penny prompted me.

"Presumably the preamble was leading to an explanation of your friend's unearthly powers."

"Ah yes, in the case of Trevor, not only does he have a seemingly limitless pool of knowledge to draw from, accessible due to his eidetic memory. But coming back to the human chessboard I started with, he has that rare insight, the so-called experts lack, that enables him to predict the forward moves."

I was not surprised to see Major nod enthusiastically at the use of his precious, 'so-called'.

Penny appeared to consider for a split second before apparently conceding. "So we repeat the trick."

Two days later found us in the same position outside the park as Doug appeared in view, approaching the same bench but this time looking around a little furtively before settling down and opening his paper. This was the cue for Trevor and Morris to appear, Mo walking backwards in a particularly dismal imitation of Michael Jackson moonwalking, in his case the better to inspect his footprints. Trevor followed with Max tucked preciously under his arm. Mo spotted Doug with absurdly over-dramatised surprise, with his hand shielding his eyes as if playing charades.

"Orlright?" He planted himself down heavily next to Doug.

Doug appeared to join in the crap acting with simulated bonhomie. "Good morning, gentlemen."

Trevor giggled with embarrassment at being spoken to and gingerly took the seat on the other side of Doug, facing pointedly away and holding Max protectively.

"Fitzroy south-east five to seven occasionally gale eight in south becoming moderate in north showers in north-west rough."

Mo leant across Doug to point at Max. "Ruff-ruff."

"Naughty Max," said Trevor censoriously.

Doug recoiled with a look that told of the full force of eau-de-Morris that assailed him. Mo mistook this for surprise.

"Used to run a lighthouse, 'e did."

Doug nodded. "I see."

Trevor looked uneasy and frowned. "And the Lord smote Ahab and was sure."

"Reckon 'e was a vicar an' all."

"Certainly, something of a prophet, but erm, now connected with the city, I think you said." He paused for a reply and not receiving it turned to Trevor with a piercing gaze.

"Tell me, how did you know about Global Consolidated?"

Always a mistake to address Trevor directly, let alone fix him with a piercing gaze. Substitute a hastily raised '*FT*' for a cloud of ink and you have an octopus. The paper quivered in silence for a long moment while Trevor mustered speech.

"Hang Seng down two per cent, all world index slid point five per cent, Topix up one point seven, Brent Crude down to sixty-two point four dollars…"

This continued for some time. It sounded as though Trevor was reading from the paper, but a look of surprise on Doug's face grew into bewilderment, reflected in Mr Robinson's expression alongside me.

"Those aren't today's figures…"

"Shush," said Penny mildly, concentrating so hard that she forgot to apply her usual caustic inflection.

Trevor continued. "Sovereign bonds unchanged, 'S and P five hundred' falling nought point four per cent, Fanshawe Metcalfe in receivership."

Doug started as if stung by a wasp. "Fanshawe Metcalfe! What are you saying, man? One of the soundest fund managers in the world."

At which point Mr Robinson interrupted. "Indeed, they are, Doctor, with all due respect I have a feeling Trevor may have gone astray with this one."

"Shush," Penny hissed with her usual irritation this time, causing Mr Robinson to pout petulantly. I was pleased to not have to answer him, the truth was, I had repeated my questions to Trevor the day before and he had blurted out in his hurried staccato, while shaking his head.

"Fanshawe Metcalfe, bad." Adding with a giggle, "Naughty men."

Doug appeared lost in thought. Morris, who has a short attention span at the best of times, was distracted by one of his animal tracks, and announced proudly, "Ocelot that is, bet you can't spell it, right tricky, got a "C" in it, bet if yer stood outside a pie shop and asked all the bods comin' out, 'do us a favour mate, spell ocelot,' they'd say, 'wiv an "S" mate' and argue the toss to boot; mean to say, cod's got a "C" in it."

Doug appeared not to hear: he was lost in a reverie, his lips mouthing silently what I suspected to be 'Fanshawe Metcalfe'.

I had another restless night but awoke to the reassuring headline on the TV: 'Fanshaw Metcalfe call in receivers'.

"And that isn't the half of it," imparted Mr Robinson in a hushed whisper after phoning under the pretext of wishing to offer me a quotation for gardening services.

Duly chaperoned to London, I found Mr Robinson and Major almost fizzing with excitement, in stark contrast to Penny who had a face like thunder, which became even more ominous at the sight of me but she admitted grudgingly, "Henderson sold out before close of business, and this morning Fanshawe thingummy went for a burton. People are saying he knew, and of course he did but from a loony tramp on a park bench."

I opened my mouth to protest but she raised a hand to pre-empt me. "I know, I know. So now you feed him the bum steer or more to the point, we do. Tell him, Dritharashtrar."

Major's eternal smile died a short death, evidently, he did not like this name, so why did she do it? First insulting Trevor, now picking on Major. My ex-wife was passive aggressive, this woman was just aggressive.

Mr Robinson adopted a look of gravity that appeared unnatural. He puffed out his chest and made an expansive sweeping gesture with his right hand.

"A certain company has come to the attention of the SFO."

"That's Serious Fraud Office," explained Major, earning him a glare from everyone including myself, even I knew that.

Mr Robinson continued. "Due to certain reporting irregularities…"

"Fitch Spanner are about to be busted." Penny had run out of patience.

"You've heard of Fitch Spanner, Doctor?" asked Major.

I shook my head. "I'm afraid anything outside the *Diagnostic and Statistical Manual of Mental Disorders*, Edition Five, tends not to hold my attention."

Mr Robinson struggled on. "Certain irregularities which will result in," he smiled significantly, "an intervention."

Penny got up abruptly. "So your man has to get this across Henderson is the measure of it; you lot can twitter on all you like but I have a meeting that started twenty minutes ago, so do your bit, Bartlett and we'll call you once we're ready."

The telephone rang and Penny snatched it up impatiently. "Yes, what?" she asked rudely. A look of irritation spread across her face like an accelerated storm cloud. "I've no idea what you're selling but whatever it is I don't want it." As she replaced the receiver her expression changed to what I can only describe as rapture. She got up slowly and breathed in luxuriously.

"I know it's childish but I so enjoy doing that."

"The minister?" enquired Mr Robinson.

Penny nodded with a sunny smile. "It's his own fault for murdering the English language — his revolting use of what Orwell called exhausted idioms in particular — utter bollocks."

I caught her perfume in the flurry of her leaving, it was exquisite.

The phone rang again and Mr Robinson picked it up. His face was inscrutable. "Yes, yes, she's on her way. I couldn't say, a misunderstanding perhaps. Very possibly, who can say. I see, if you say so, sir. Would you like me to tell her that? No quite. Thank you, sir."

His manner, as he replaced the receiver, was the best depiction of 'Jeeves' I've ever seen. For a moment all three of us were silent. Mr Robinson studied his shoes, Major his fingernails and I, their faces. Mr Robinson broke the spell with a slight snigger and suddenly we were all three crying with laughter. It was one of those great comedy moments, inexplicably funny and a revelation to me because even as I laughed, I was aware of how these two had revealed themselves. These men from the ministry, these stooges, the apparent conventional architecture of government, were in fact not at all as they appeared, for some reason more unexpected to me than Penny.

Work occupied me for the rest of the day. A conference with The Caldwell on a report I had prepared for the parole board, an important one because in the case of sentences over fifteen years the board's recommendations are made to the secretary of state. The prisoner in question was a psychopath and I was cynical about his supposed redemption. He had attended a Cognitive Behavioural Programme, which I considered to have been entirely inappropriate. It was this opinion that had raised The Caldwell's eyebrows; he had a liking for reports so shrouded in terminology that they were completely devoid of sentiment: mine was not. He

137

was also unhappy that I appeared to be turning my nose up at the Offender Behaviour Programme itself rather than just the selection of this prisoner for it, earning me a tedious and patronising diatribe on the various longitudinal studies that evidenced a reduction in reoffending due to these courses. The professor then accused me of being biased by the nature of the crimes themselves, all the time wearing his most sanctimonious expression, of a patient Gandhi imparting sagely wisdom to a young hot-head. I nearly lost my temper, it was only the thought that if I did so I would probably be impressed into an anger management course, that kept the lid on it.

I had a moment of bonding with Sister Harris in the corridor afterwards who correctly diagnosed the rare exhibition of pent-up fury in my face.

"Let it out, Doctor," she whispered.

"The professor is a… I mean, he's…" She encouraged me with a circular movement of her hand but the words wouldn't come.

She shook her head as if at a schoolboy that has underperformed in his exams. "I'll say it for you, Doctor, he's a …" and she used a word rarely used by women, even medics who have a particularly choice vocabulary due to all the anatomical terms at their disposal.

"There now." She rubbed my back just as a midwife soothes a mother after a difficult birth. "You'll feel better now."

I like Sister Harris.

Later, I mulled over my assignment. It was all well and good for Penny to talk of how, 'my man has to get this across Henderson'. But Trevor is not my man, he's very much his own man and, our relationship, developed over a period of time now, is based on trust. Trevor trusted Morris, not because he told the truth — Mo rarely told the truth — but because he was essentially good-natured, his dissembling was transparent, and he was incapable of malice or treachery. As for me, I think he knew that I was truthful to him as well as having affection for him.

So I told him the truth now, in the belief that he would not be a party to deceit, however valid the cause. And so it proved. He sat sideways across the desk from me and, long before my words could possibly have given any indication of what I was to say, those mysterious precursors gave him premonition, expressed in an increasing agitation and, when I finally explained what had been asked of us, he shook his head with an anxious frown.

I comforted him. "It's what I thought you'd say, and that's an end to it."

Trevor stroked Max as if passing on this reassurance to the dog.

I looked thoughtfully at Mo, who as ever completely misunderstood the situation.

"Yeah, that's right, pick on Mo," he sucked his teeth. "Mean, that's a nasty job, that — give it to Mo — sorted, job done." He frowned. "What is it anyway?"

I looked at him doubtfully, it hadn't occurred to me to involve him in anything other than a minor role, but it was a thought. More to the point, I couldn't think of an alternative. I shook my head at him doubtfully.

"It won't be easy, Mo. It needs someone with special qualities."

Morris looked doubtful. "What, like Superman?"

"Little bit. Let me explain."

The park bench scene was repeated two days later, only this time it was just Morris who sauntered into the park and plumped himself on the bench next to Doug. In the van I was sweating. I knew he would do his best, that was the problem. One of the many features of Mo's intellectual disability is a tendency to overemphasize any statement with extreme and absurd embellishments, and whilst this had provided the hospital staff with some sublime comedy, it was this trait that I particularly feared just now.

"Orlright?" Mo opened with.

"Erm, fine thanks, where's your friend?"

Mo looked around cautiously as if suspicious of being overheard and whispered loudly, "'E's up to summat; strictly 'ush 'ush though."

"Oh, I see."

"Down the bank, 'e is, loaded 'e is, betcha didn't know that did yer?"

"Erm, you did say, something big in the city as I remember."

"Sentric millionaire, no, billionaire, that's it, and tell yer what…" Mo paused dramatically until Doug obliged with:

"What?"

"I tell yer what, putting the whole caboodle 'e is on…" Morris frowned, desperately trying to recall the words I had repeated dozens of times. I prayed to a deity that I only summoned in such extremes.

"Fish Spanner," Mo blurted out proudly.

"Fitch Spanner," repeated Doug thoughtfully. "That's most interesting, there's a lot of profit taking going on at the moment, most people seem to think that now the share value has tripled it's time to cash in."

At which point Mo excelled himself, purely by accident, I was sure. He wagged his finger knowingly and said, "Knees and…" He frowned in concentration, desperately trying to recall his lessons, raised his arm in frustration which evidently triggered his almost retentionless hippocampus to come up with a memory, even though, as ever, an incorrect one.

"Armpits," he said proudly.

Doug shrunk away as well he might, Mo's armpits are particularly deadly and he had taken one at point blank range.

"Buy at the knees and sell at the shoulders, I think you mean," he said distractedly.

Mo frowned, he hates being corrected and can be relied upon to protest. I held my breath, I could see him swelling with wounded pride.

"That's where yer wrong, see." He nodded patronisingly. "Ask the Queen if yer don't b'lieve me, she'll tell yer."

"Oh God," I muttered under my breath. This could go anywhere now but at this moment divine intervention manifested itself in the humble form of a honeybee diverted from its usual business by the strange aromas emanating from Morris, thought better of it and continued on its way, but Morris was sufficiently distracted to announce authoritatively, "African 'ornet, that was. Dunno what it's doin' over 'ere, must 'ave got lost. Bloody lucky we was cos, cor, if one of 'em stings yer, mean yer right for it."

Doug appeared not to hear, apparently still mulling over Mo's last utterance. "Are you telling me that your friend thinks that Fitch Spanner is going to run?"

Mo was gratified by the attention of his audience and acted up splendidly. "S'right." He tapped his nose knowingly. "Keep it under yer 'at though."

Doug nodded absent-mindedly. "We sold our holding a while ago." His thoughtfulness took on a new intensity as he stared at Morris. "It's an interesting one; all my instincts tell me the stock is already considerably over-valued."

This was beyond Mo's comprehension but he obviously felt the need to make a response.

"Armpits," he replied confidently, and coming from someone of such low intelligence that up until the advent of the *Diagnostic and Statistical Manual of Mental Disorders* would have been labelled an imbecile, this response sounded almost pertinent.

I was chauffeured to London the next day. I knew that Fitch Spanner were due to be busted but of course had no idea what was going on at the Saruman Corporation.

Robinson and Major also knew nothing, and when Penny arrived, she told me to sit down and shut up. She did not look in a good mood and I feared the worst. She turned on me accusingly.

"So much for your brilliant scheme."

I attempted a wry smile but saw Mr Robinson wince and decided unheroically to turn it into a look of concern. Penny was bristling.

"What makes it worse is that the home secretary has just had the bare-faced cheek to try and blame me, at which point I had to remind him, rather pointedly actually, that this whole crackpot scheme of bringing you in was his idea."

I looked at Major and Mr Robinson hoping for some support after our bonding moment earlier but saw that I was wasting my time. Major stared fixedly at the window and Mr Robinson with equal studiousness inspected a potted plant. I frowned and as if they sensed my disapproval, they switched roles: Mr Robinson took over the plant and Major took the window. I resigned myself with a sigh.

"They didn't buy in then?"

Penny gave a short bitter laugh. "Oh, they bought in all right; they've caught a packet, it's your bloody psychology that's up the spout. Here, see for yourself."

In a matter of seconds, we were viewing the covert recording of what was evidently a special board meeting. The opening scene was a close-up of Henderson's face. I was interested to see that his mouth was not open in horror, his head did not hang in shame, rather he looked like a scientist whose hypothesis has failed to be supported by experiment: absorbed by academic curiosity. I rather admired him. He was the only one standing apart from the finance director whose blink rate appeared to be multiplying out of control. She spoke in a strangely detached voice.

"Losses approximately four hundred and seventy-eight million sterling."

Doug appeared to wake from reverie. "Well firstly I owe you all an apology, with hindsight I see that I should never have made this recommendation on such a poorly founded basis. One could almost say it was a whim, in fact I will say it was a whim, and of course I must offer my resignation."

There was a tense silence. The finance director patted the back of her nineteen fifties hairdo. An elderly gentleman got up and slapped Doug on the shoulder.

"That's the chairman," whispered Major.

The elderly gentleman seemed overcome, dabbed at his eyes with a handkerchief and after several attempts managed speech, although with a breaking voice.

"Come now, Doug, it would be harsh of us to ask for that, and ungrateful. For years now you've never put a foot wrong, everyone is allowed a mistake," he laughed wolfishly. "As long as they don't make a habit of it."

A burst of nervous, hysterical laughter broke the tension and they were all up on their feet applauding. Some were crying.

Major looked puzzled. "I didn't know they were like that in the city."

"It's a fucking love-in," said Penny in disgust.

The blinking lady's face appeared to boil, convulsed by a myriad of unfathomable emotions.

Penny seemed to read my thoughts. She looked at me with a curious expression.

"Haven't you got it yet, Dr Dumbass?"

I shook my head. "Not quite."

"She hates him but hates herself even more because she's in love with him." She looked at me thoughtfully.

"Of course, how did I miss that? It seems so obvious now you say it."

Penny's expression softened momentarily, there was no hint of triumph at besting me. She appeared to notice Major staring studiously at the ceiling and treated him to a glare.

"So that's it, blown out of the water."

I was thinking. "Unless of course we can engineer another failure. Reading between the lines, I don't think he'd survive a second one."

Penny turned her glare on me. She had striking eyes, strange I hadn't noticed before.

"And how are you going to manage that? He's hardly going to pay any more attention to your tramp double act."

I tried to look far more confident than I felt. "Give me forty-eight hours."

"You may find that some unfortunate accident has befallen him by then, if not…" She shrugged.

I wrestled with the problem that evening over rather too much wine. My mind kept wandering. It was only in the night, on the edge of sleep that the background disturbance troubling me stepped forward from the shadows and revealed itself, the same as before only this time stronger. If I failed in this task, I would lose contact with Penny and this thought upset me.

I took a hectic outpatients' session in the morning and had no time for further consideration of the problem. Aware that the clock was ticking, I resolved to stay up all night if necessary.

I returned to my office to find it cluttered up with Major and Mr Robinson dressed unconvincingly in boiler suits. Even what sounded like a bruising encounter with Sister Harris could not dampen their enthusiasm, they were full of it, Major in particular was fizzing like a squib.

"We've got it, Doctor, the so-called solution."

"Really."

"We came to tell you ourselves," added Mr Robinson unnecessarily.

"In order to save you troubling yourself," said Major.

"There is in fact no need now."

At which they paused in order to smile condescendingly at me. It took me a moment to work out that they awaited my congratulations.

"Excellent, gentlemen, I have to admit that I have as yet come up with nothing."

They looked delighted. It was Mr Robinson's turn to flame up.

"It came to me in my bath this morning. I always read the financial news in the bath."

Major sighed wistfully. "The eccentricity of the true English gentleman."

This continued for a long ten minutes. And irritatingly, even after this, they were still coy about the plan itself. All they would tell me was that there was some kind of shindig for the Saruman Corporation to be held at 'The Ritz' that weekend, and we would be there.

It was only the next day when I had been taken back to London that I learned the details. Apparently, the scheme was news to Penny as well. She listened impatiently as always. The big idea was for us all to sneak into this 'do' but, before explaining the plan, Mr Robinson slipped in casually that Penny and I would be attending as man and wife.

"Excuse me?" She put a finger in her ear and waggled it. "Now say that again."

Mr Robinson and Major shared a glance that I would describe as inscrutable. Mr Robinson repeated himself. Penny let out a short screech.

"Stop you there. No!"

I was slightly offended. We had used this incarnation with Dr Hamilton and that had been her idea so this seemed a bit of an overreaction.

Major and Mr Robinson nodded at some mutual understanding. Mr Robinson detached himself and whispered something in Penny's ear. She looked at me curiously.

"Really? Oh, I see." She shrugged. "OK, we'll give it a punt."

A complete volte-face in a matter of seconds. Apart from my surprise at the amazing speed of this, I wondered what it was that Major had whispered to her.

Saturday evening found myself, Penny, Major, Mr Robinson and, to my surprise, Mrs T, entering 'The Ritz.' We booked in. Penny and I made for a room while the others adjourned to the bar. My nerves were in shreds which Penny appeared to divine, she produced a bottle of single malt from her bag. I accepted gratefully.

"You never know what women keep in their handbags."

"Bet you don't," she said grimly. She shook her head critically. "Look at the state of you, Bartlett. You weren't this bad before. I think you need another, doesn't matter if you make an arse of yourself, in fact that seems to be the extent of your participation. If anyone's got a right to be nervous it's me, in spite of hours of cramming from the permanent secretary of H.M. Treasury, probably the most tedious man I've ever met in my life; it was like Girton all over again."

"And are you nervous?"

She lifted an arm contemplatively, inspected underneath and shrugged.

"Apparently not."

I laughed. There was something superbly comical about this powerful woman checking for a sweaty armpit. She spun around to face away from me and struggled impatiently with her zip.

"Give me a hand."

I hesitated. This was an extraordinarily inappropriate level of intimacy, not only because of the nature of our relationship but also because we were almost complete strangers, although there was no suggestion of anything sexual in her behaviour, far from it. I felt mildly offended by the realisation that she would not behave like this if even the thought of such a possibility between us occurred to her. Even so, she had yet again floored me with her unpredictability. I could not help but muse on the analytical. Such inappropriate behaviour could be due to a variety of causes, most of them associated with trauma and dysfunction, which didn't seem to fit, although experience has taught me time and again that those who have suffered childhood abuse are often remarkably adept at concealing it, as if the shame was theirs. There was another possibility though.

"Penny?"

"Bartlett."

"Did you go to public school?"

"Cheltenham Ladies College, although not many of them turned into ladies."

I smiled, bullseye. There are times when life experience is worth more than any number of books or lectures.

"Bartlett?"

"Yes," I said, fumbling manfully.

"Any time that suits you but soon preferably."

"I'm not good with zips."

"Evidently."

"No wonder you didn't make it as a medic."

"I see you've been checking me out."

Her dress dropped, revealing an incongruous match of a matronly bra strap and rather more fashionable stockings. She kicked the skirt away as if in irritation and moments later I heard the sound of her running a bath, but she kept the door open and continued our conversation.

"Oh yes, we know all about you, Bartlett, have to you understand." She sounded almost apologetic.

"Quite," I said dryly, taking a seat outside the bathroom door.

"You were married for seven years, why did that break up?"

I thought about this, such a simple question but not easy to answer. "The old cliché, we grew apart, but I suppose it would be more truthful to say that neither of us knew each other in the first place."

"Sounds disingenuous."

"I'll tell you if you like but don't fall asleep in the bath, it's dangerous."

"You're OK. I like hearing about people's marriages. I had one myself."

"Well, it's rather commonplace I'm afraid."

A loud splash was followed by, "Fuck."

"Was that a comment or is the water hot?"

She sighed pleasurably. "Mainly the water, but you were saying."

"I think what attracted me first was her quirkiness, her use of strange droll expressions, her dizziness, always in a muddle. When she came to my flat, she invariably left something behind, gloves, hairband, a book, all sorts."

"Did you ask yourself why?"

"Not at the time. I was young and, if I'm honest, naive for my age."

"Marking her territory." This was followed by further splashing and, "Ooh that's nice."

I continued. "It sounds overly critical, because it wasn't her fault, but all those things that so captivated me were actually nothing more than vapid gestures and mannerisms distorted by sexual chemistry into a beguiling mirage and when that had dissolved…"

"You were strangers," she interjected. This was followed by more splashing and it occurred to me that this, from the distance of the next room, facilitated a conversation that would be too intimate for comfort face-to-face, which demonstrated a form of shyness. This was an odd thought to have about a woman whose prime feature appeared to be supreme self-confidence.

"Strangers," I agreed. "With nothing in common, and I was a disappointment to her as well."

"I can imagine." This time with no splashing. I found it a surprisingly hurtful cut.

"She left me, found someone more her type, more impulsive, less predictable."

"And less honest."

"You're being nice again, but yes, as a matter of fact, he was."

"Was?"

"They're still married."

"But disillusioned?"

"Yes, well she is. I've never had anything much to do with him."

"You don't like him?"

"Not even as strong as that, just not my type."

"And maybe not hers as it turns out?"

"You really are very good, exactly that. All the impulsive romantic gestures, the quixotry, underneath it all there's not much of substance."

"Jealous?"

"Contemptuous. When she left, I was hurt. She had a car accident, a bad one, and I said, 'good' to anyone who cared to listen, which was rather shocking."

"And I suspect out of character."

I was intrigued by this remark; it revealed that she had formed an opinion of me.

"And now?"

"Now I know her, the real her, and care for her in a different way. I'd like her to find happiness."

There was a long silence and then splashing followed by the sound of the plug being pulled. Penny emerged almost immediately, engulfed in a bath towel, rubbing herself vigorously. I turned away. She laughed.

"Such modesty, but stay that way a moment, it's that sort of dress." And only seconds later, "You can turn around now."

I obeyed. "I think you'd make it as a quick-change artist."

She rummaged in her handbag and withdrew an elaborate necklace that I didn't understand the significance of at that moment. I observed her surreptitiously. The dress changed her appearance, somehow, she seemed a little older, more voluptuous and more comely, but again I was aware of a feeling of deflation. Her movements, her attitude, everything about her was completely removed from our situation: a man and a woman together in an apartment.

"According to your research…"

She anticipated me. "I know, I'm not a bloody honeytrap, or even honeypot for that matter, thank you, Major, for that, but with all due disrespect to you both, I'll make the call on this one. Now hurry up."

She was half out of the door with me hurrying to keep up. She led through the reception area to a door marked, 'The Saruman Corporation', and whispered in my ear.

"Get the drinks."

After ordering two double scotches, I spotted Mr Robinson in remarkably animated conversation with none other than Doug Henderson alongside Mrs T in an evening dress, looking little different from in her overalls; she had one of those figures that left you unsure as to where one bit ends and the next starts. She was eyeing her glass suspiciously for grease marks.

Penny had joined them. She frowned as I approached and gave me what I can only describe as a dirty look as she introduced me.

"My husband," she shuddered. "Raymond."

Major chose this moment to appear from nowhere and pump Henderson's hand enthusiastically.

"Ah, Sir Douglas, I am most pleased to make your acquaintance. Gagandeep Bhattacharya."

Doug attempted a smile but succeeded only in looking nervous. "Do I know you?"

Major beamed. "No, no, dear sir, I am on the so-called Indian Desk but I am well acquainted with Mr Forrestor." Major gazed over-significantly at Mr Robinson, I suspect he took his acting inspiration from early Bollywood films.

Doug nodded. "Oh yes, from Foreign Exchange I understand. We were just talking about where the dollar's going, Forrestor seems to think the Fed's not going to tighten after all."

There was something wrong with Major's face, it took me a moment to work it out: he was wearing eyeshadow. I wondered if this was a case of thought fathering action, I remembered thinking when first meeting him that he only needed lashings of black eyeshadow to pass as the star of a silent movie. He fixed his rather ghoulish smile on Doug.

"Yes, yes, all very interesting but pedestrian don't you think? I think you'll find conversation with this lady more interesting, she specialises in… well don't let me talk for her."

Penny somehow turned a look of irritation into nonchalance. She shrugged laconically.

"Depends what you're interested in."

"And what are you interested in, may I ask?" Doug gave the appearance of a man going through the motions for the sake of politeness and Penny followed suit.

"Credit default swaps, naked shorting, IPO's, volatile currency pairs." She darted a contemptuous look in my direction. "All of which seem to scare the hell out of my husband, but then again some men have the souls of mice."

Mrs T turned her head towards me with a harmonised look of disgust and ran her finger pointedly along an adjacent dado rail, holding up a finger with a 'tut' of disapproval. Doug's eyes had gleamed at the mention of these instruments but looked uneasy at the suggestion of marital disharmony. Penny acted up beautifully. She drained her glass in one and handed it to me.

"Get me a proper drink this time."

"Yes, dear." I wandered off, turning my face away quickly because calling her 'dear' had brought me dangerously close to laughter.

I went for eight shots in one glass for Penny and contented myself with just the four. A row was brewing and I needed to be ready. As I returned, Penny fixed her eyes on me, dark, brooding and, taking me unawares, beautiful. I braced myself with a mouthful of whisky before my final approach and handed Penny her glass meekly.

"You took your time." She continued her conversation with Doug. "Double risk really because the market is poised for flight; it'll only take one of the big stakeholders to pull out or the slightest whiff of trouble and it'll all come tumbling down like a pack of cards."

"And you?" I noticed that Doug looked interested now.

Penny appeared to sneer at him. "Me? I'll wait for the building to start collapsing before slipping out the back door."

I prepared myself with another swig. "It'll all come down on your head one of these days, you mark my words."

Penny gave me a look of seething contempt before turning to Henderson. "See what I'm married to?"

Doug looked uncomfortable again and glanced at me with unmistakable sympathy. I remembered my earlier instinct about him, that I liked him. Behind his back Mrs T lifted her head contemptuously in order to look down her nose at me; I suspected her of taking everything her boss said literally.

Penny almost spat at me: "All you've ever done is stifle me, in case you've forgotten, let me remind you of Blackbeard Securities."

Major's eyes lit up, absurdly theatrically in my opinion. I wondered, not for the first time, how on earth he had ended up in MI5. Doug pricked up his ears.

"Were you in on that?"

"Got out with seconds to spare."

"Or to put it another way, had an extremely lucky escape." I tried to sound sanctimonious.

Penny's eyes flashed with anger. "No, not a lucky escape: judgement." She nearly drained her glass in one angry gulp and swayed unsteadily but this was in the script, whereas I was beginning to feel genuinely shaky now, which was not and I'd only drank about half of what she had. Penny fixed on me belligerently.

"Seriously though, why did I marry you?"

Major and Mr Robinson exchanged a sympathetic look of glum understanding that was so comical that I had to look away. Her anger was superbly visible.

"What you don't understand, what you'll never understand, is that there are wolves and there are sheep, the strong and the weak." She turned to Doug. "Don't you think there is something magnificent about the strong preying on the weak?"

"Magnificent!" I laughed as derisively as I could manage. "Oh, spare me that, predation is the new nobility I suppose."

Penny turned away from me in disgust and looked appealingly at Doug who evidently felt pressured into comment.

"Ah yes, the ethics debate. I'm sure you know we have a committee that deals with all that sort of thing nowadays, I believe the PR people run it."

For once I was ahead of Penny. "I'm sure Sir Douglas' interest is an academic one. I doubt if he is one of your slavering wolves delighting in the demise of the herd."

Doug agreed hurriedly, "Oh yes, definitely, not that sort of thing at all."

Penny moved unsteadily towards me and her words were low and menacing. "How dare you. I doubt if that pretty little act fools anyone, certainly not me." An open hand darted out at stunning speed and delivered a vicious slap across my cheek and then even harder with the back of her hand. I recoiled in pain. She was working herself into a frenzy.

"You horrid, horrid, demeaning bastard."

Mrs T pushed forwards to comfort Penny with a look of disgust aimed at me that nearly set me off laughing. This was not scripted but Penny allowed herself to be comforted with a matronly hug and played along with a sudden fit of sobbing followed by, "I've had it with him. I'm going to my room."

She rounded on me, convincingly furious and emotional. "And I tell you what, I'm going to kiss the first person I see, not just kiss, you'll see." She turned to go, only to find herself, to her evident surprise, only a few steps from the elevator. For the past five minutes Mr Robinson and Major had been absurdly obviously shepherding us in that direction. Penny pressed the lift call. Doug watched her in stunned silence.

She turned to me. "I will, I mean it."

Mrs T quietly seethed with suppressed emotion. The lift arrived with a 'ting', Penny entered. For a moment I thought Mrs T was going to break ranks and make a dash for it, and apparently Mr Robinson thought the same, for I noticed his restraining hand on her wrist.

Meanwhile Major manhandled Doug suddenly and deftly towards the lift and elbowed him inside. The doors closed on his surprised face. I was impressed.

"You look rather handy at that sort of thing."

"Some things you never forget, Doctor. I served in the Mahar Regiment." He moved close to whisper in my ear, "I was in 'Operation Brasstacks'."

Mr Robinson released his grip on Mrs T who attempted to recover her composure but was pink with embarrassment. I looked away, almost overcome by a wave of pity, this was a terrible crush she had on her boss.

We all watched the lift panel. I half expected the doors to open again but the light proceeded inexorably upwards: two, three, four, finally coming to rest at five. Mr Robinson nodded knowingly.

"Penthouse Suite, that's a good sign."

We finished our drinks in thoughtful silence. Mr Robinson looked at his watch.

"Might as well break it up I suppose, nothing more we can do here."

I headed for my room. Too much drink had knocked me out and I dozed off almost instantly, but my sleep was troubled by another strange dream, presumably inspired by the encounter with Dr Hamilton, or at least my memory of it, Freud being adamant that the stimulus for a dream must have occurred in the preceding twenty-four hours.

Martha and Mr Janos were squabbling. There were no hands to animate them; I realised with a shock that they were sentient beings with human features. And irrationally arousing horror and revulsion, they had grown to the size of small children. Curiously, I had the feeling that they were familiar to me, that this was their true embodiment awoken from their comatose mannikin state. Mr Janos, this new real Mr Janos, was disfigured by deep lines across his face, carved by some terrible sadness. And Martha, so ugly, I was surprised to find that she was behaving sexually towards me, for I was Mr Janos. We were embroiled in some bitter argument, but it was a mime with no words, it's meaning obscure. Emotion was simulated, our true feelings for each other concealed, but as if at the twist of a kaleidoscope, reality took on a new shape. Now that our performance had ended, Martha washed and scraped away her hideous make-up and another face emerged from the ruin. She was beautiful, I could smell her perfume, I breathed it in with a catch at my heart, she had become Penny and even in my dream I was aware of a parallel transformation — from how I had first appraised her, now to something else.

And then I was awake, for a moment Penny's perfume provided continuity. She was sitting on the bed, looking at me cynically.

"Didn't take you long to nod off."

"How did it go?"

She tapped at her necklace. "All on camera."

I sat up in bed. Penny turned away from me to work at her phone, her face in profile lit silver from the screen. I felt a sudden strange rush of emotion for her. It came out of nowhere, something unbearably touching, plaintive, almost forlorn, about her face bent forward in concentration. How strange.

The screen was between us, revealing an image of the lift doors opening.

Doug lurched into view looking flustered and nervous.

"Top floor?" Penny sounded matter of fact.

"Yes, I suppose so. That chap pushed me in you know."

"It's rough in the playground today."

Doug appeared to shrink backwards.

"What's the matter with you?" Penny sounded annoyed. I was impressed by the fact that within such a short while of meeting one of the top financiers in the world, Penny, though posing as a minion, had already adopted a dominant position.

"Sorry, it's just that you said…"

"I know what I said. I was angry, but so what? Don't tell me you've never been kissed?"

162

"No, well, just the once, a most unpleasant experience. I don't, erm, you know — not with women — not with anyone. I'm curious about you though, the naked credit default swaps and other instruments, all so high risk." The lift arrived with a 'ping' and the doors opened. "My floor, would you care for a coffee?"

"Sure, why not?"

"Rather exciting," continued Doug "That type of investment."

A door opened and closed. Penny replied, "It's what gives me a buzz, but I admire what you do, the way you mix it up, futures, options, currencies, stocks and shares."

Doug sounded pleased. "Oh, I don't know. There's a joke in commodities, can't have all your powdered eggs in one basket. But I don't recollect seeing you around."

"Ex-staff, used to be on the Indian Desk with Gagandeep."

"Ah, the Indian Desk, I see."

"So you're not interested in women then?"

Doug sounded puzzled. "Women?"

"Yes, women."

"I'm not sure what you mean. Should I be interested in women?"

"I think you should. I mean there are certain differences."

"Oh, I see, yes, they do tend to be steadier in the medium to long-term sector, being, no offence, generally more risk averse, present company excepted of course."

"Amazing the things that get you noticed. Don't suppose you've got any scotch?"

"I don't drink."

"Didn't think so."

"But I believe there are various things in the cabinet over there."

The cabinet came into view.

"Glen Mc Duffie. Oh, this you must try, in the world of drink this is a high-risk derivative."

"Really?" Doug sounded excited.

Penny's hand was seen handing a glass to Doug. "Now *this* is living on the edge."

"I think I will." The tone of Doug's voice announced that he was throwing caution to the wind.

The sound of cautious sipping was followed by, "Wow, it's rather strong."

"That's the rye, it tastes stronger than it really is."

"I see." And after a long gulp, "Gracious."

"Gagandeep told me that a huge portrait of you hangs over the Mumbai Stock Exchange trading floor."

Doug was heard to sip again. "Really?" He sounded pleased. "Golly, makes your toes warm, doesn't it?"

"Renowned for it. And he says you're mopping up on the Dow Jones at the moment."

Doug produced an i-Phone with a flourish. His voice was slightly slurred.

"Number two in contacts is the American desk, manned all night of course. By the time the staff get in in the morning we've traded millions, often billions, in the night."

The bottle reappeared into view and hovered over Doug's glass. "Oh no, really, well just a little then — it does make you feel, well — braces you up doesn't it. When, when, whoa," followed by a surprisingly girlish giggle. "Gosh."

The i-Phone appeared in Penny's hand. "This is flash, I've never seen one like this."

"No, you won't have, it's a prototype, there are only three in the world and…"

Doug's finger wavered ponderously and I thought to myself, 'If his finger's that drunk, the rest of him must be a mess.'

"I'm not supposed to even show it to anyone. It was a present from… Ooh, just remembered, I'm not supposed to tell anyone that either." He drank again and hiccupped. "Whoopsy, tastes of oranges, doesn't it?"

Penny was seen to handle the phone deftly. "What you were saying about women being steadier in the medium to long-term; that's the thing you see, I'm not a typical woman."

"You certainly aren't."

"Do you know what really excites me?"

Doug swayed into view and said thickly, "No."

"Collateralised loan obligations."

Doug's delicate sipping had regressed to a loud slurp, followed by, "Bloody hell!"

"In fact, that's what started the row with my wimp of a husband."

A crimson lacquered fingernail was seen to press button two on the phone. "You know De Toilette and Nephew are going down the pan?"

"Doug giggled. "Down the toilet pan one might say."

I winced, people with no sense of humour always make the worst jokes.

"But there's the chance of a buyout, I'm going to go for it."

"I wouldn't."

"Wouldn't what?"

"Buy De Toilette and Nephew."

The lacquered fingernail could be seen working busily through this exchange and I guessed what Penny was up to.

"So you don't think I should…?" Her pause invited him to complete her sentence.

Doug obliged. "Go for it. How much were you going to stake?"

"Thirty mill. It's on behalf of a client you understand. What's that in rupees?"

Doug, in spite of being three sheets to the wind, came back immediately with: "Two point seven billion."

"But you sound like you're sure it's a bad move?"

"I'm quite sure," said Doug.

Penny tapped the screen off. "That's about it apart from getting him so pissed that I had to put him to bed."

"And kissed him goodnight, I expect."

Her face lit suddenly. "I should have. I agree with you, there's no harm in him. Damn bad luck him stopping himself just as he was going to spill who that phone was from. That would have given me a name. He's just a puppet."

"Martha or Mr Janos?"

"More like your friend, Trevor." I opened my mouth to protest but she interrupted me. "Don't get your knickers in a twist, all I mean is that he's a bit special, takes everything literally, brain the size of a planet but really just a child. Someone is using him."

"Who?"

"There's the question, the Saruman Corporation is opaque, HQ in Milwaukee and when you try and find out who actually owns it, you go round in circles. The shareholders are listed as holding companies in the usual places, Bahamas and the like, classic profile of a criminal empire." She paused thoughtfully. "Poor man, he has no idea of what he's just done."

"I think I have a clue. I saw some suspicious hand movements during that phone conversation."

"As you say, and when traced by those busybodies at Cheltenham, that phone conversation should make interesting listening."

Which after a call and a call back, I was privilege to.

"American Desk. Good evening, Sir Douglas."

"Buy De Toilette and Nephew."

"You surprise me, sir. I understood we had sold our holding."

The slightly thickened voice, ordered, "Go for it."

"If you say so, sir. How much do you wish us to place?"

"Two point seven billion."

"What? I mean, did I hear you right, sir? De Toilette and Nephew. Are you sure?"

"I'm quite sure."

Penny switched off the phone. "That should do it, providing Robinson hasn't fucked up and De Toilette and Nephew do the decent thing and go under." She yawned. "I guess we can get a couple of hours. Turn the light out."

I did as ordered. She disappeared into the bathroom to reappear almost instantly in a nightgown. She got into bed, turned her back to me and sighed luxuriously.

"Night, Bartlett."

Extraordinary! I lay there for some time wondering if this behaviour met the criteria for a diagnosis of disorganised behaviour and fell asleep with this in my mind, probably explaining my second dream of the night.

Trevor danced on a disco-lit dance floor, his outstretched hand joined with Max's paw in a polka. Morris rocked to and fro with the Down's syndrome girl in perfect nineteen fifties rock and roll harmony. The music changed to a loud Hindi classic and Major and Mr Robinson jumped forward from the shadows, writhing gracefully in the style of Indian classical dance, Mr Robinson's hands clasped as if in prayer, snaking his head elegantly from side to side.

I danced with Penny. The music subsided. I was alone in a vacuum slowly invaded by her presence, I breathed in the sweet scent of her hair and felt her weight on me. The dawning twilight of consciousness slowly gave definition to the vision of her asleep on my chest with one arm sprawled across me.

As if with premonition, I felt apprehensive. Her face was turned towards me, her eyelids fluttered before her eyes opened. It seemed that she studied me in her sleep, then came a gleam of animation and a deep breath that pressed her against me.

"Bartlett," she murmured, still half asleep. This amused me, I could not imagine this if she was fully awake. I became guiltily aware of a soppy expression on my face, shamed by the memory of my ex-wife telling me that this was, 'one of the things about me that revolted' her. I tried to straighten out my face, but too late, Penny jerked out of bed with astonishing speed.

"Bartlett!" she hissed the accusation. I was startled by the extremity of her reaction, her expression was a mix of anger, shock and another curious emotion that I couldn't place.

I muttered an apology but she was not satisfied.

"What was that?"

"You, close against me like that."

Her eyes were sombre, as if a matter of importance troubled her.

"But you're…" She left the sentence unfinished.

"No. I'm not," I replied, rather disgruntled.

"No?"

"What made you think I was?"

Her face clouded with anger. "Well, those two pranksters for a start. One thing you might not know about senior civil servants is that they are gifted with a sense of humour, it's not something they're known for."

"I had sort of guessed."

"I'll kill them for this." She looked as if she meant it. "They got me, I admit. I've had you vetted." She looked at me grimly. "Should have had you vetted in the true sense as it turns out. And growing apart from your wife, you said yourself it was a cliché."

"But true," I protested mildly.

She shuddered. "I was in bed with you half naked."

"I'm still the same person."

"That's just it, you're not. I thought I was, well, you know…"

"In bed with a girl?"

"No, well yes, that's it isn't it." She relaxed. "You're quite perceptive sometimes."

"Thank you, but that actually says more about you, a really old-fashioned public-school attitude to your own sex, and homosexuality for that matter."

"Probably," she conceded, then after a moment's thought. "Mrs T thought you were and she should know. 'As a coot,' in her words."

"Interesting, why do you call her that by the way?"

"Because I refuse to call anyone Lavinia, besides, she's rather right-wing, even by my standards."

"An MI5 cleaner who attends her mistress on operations?"

"You know far too much already, Bartlett — I mean apart from seeing the director in her undies — you might as well know: Mrs T is an extremely valuable member of our agency."

"So not just a cleaner?"

"Yes and no. She came from GCHQ, they were trying to hack into the MSS, that's the Chinese intelligence service, the benchmark of all inscrutability. After they'd gone home, Mrs T came in to clean and flicked over one of the keyboards with a feather duster. In the morning they came in and found the screen alive with military protocols in Mandarin, detailing the order of battle in the event of an invasion of Taiwan. They were all mystified, then it happened again a few days later. It took the numskulls six weeks to work it out. No one knows how she does it, not even she: feather duster for the Chinese, dry sponge for the Russians, J-cloth for… Well, I'm not going to tell you that one."

"Because we don't spy on our allies."

"Quite," she said primly. "Come on, Bartlett, we've got to get moving."

We were driven back to HQ in time to witness Robinson and Major at their most innocent, only a whisker away from whistling, although Major betrayed himself with a smirk.

"Pleasant night?"

Penny opened her hand threateningly. "I'll deal with you two later."

Mr Robinson interjected hastily. "They've called an emergency meeting."

"Are we in on it?"

"Unfortunately, not," replied Mr Robinson. "It's main board only, but our man managed to wire the room." He pointed to a nearby monitor. "They should be in any moment now."

"And De Toilette and Nephew?"

"Sunk like a ship in the so-called Bermuda Triangle," said Major, still smirking.

Penny opened her mouth to speak but at this moment, our attention was diverted by signs of movement on the screen. A door opened. Doug entered, followed by the elderly gentleman I recognised as the chairman.

"The chairman," whispered Robinson unnecessarily, adding, "and the finance director," as the lady with the rapid eyelid movements followed in behind.

Doug was in mid conversation. "Of course, I'm not used to scotch but I don't think it was that, apparently, although it tastes strong, it's not potent alcohol-wise."

The chairman closed the door. "Doug, this will be a surprise to you — not to us, not one bit — but apparently to you. 'D.T. & N' have gone under."

Doug shrugged complacently. "No surprise to me at all, I was only warning off one of our people last night, ex-people actually, she used to be on the Indian Desk, I told her they were going down."

Doug appeared unaware that he was surrounded by a growing hostility, revealed by an impressive increase in blinking from the finance director, but more conventionally from the chairman who now looked decidedly bellicose.

"Don't try that Doug, not with me."

Doug looked surprised. "Sorry, not following you."

The finance director responded by racking up her blink rate even further, the chairman by twiddling with a smartphone and thrusting it accusingly in front of Doug.

The conversation I'd heard last night was repeated, to the apparent amazement of Major and Mr Robinson, and also Doug. His mouth opened in surprise.

"But-but, that wasn't me, I mean it was, but I didn't say those things, not like that. I've been scammed. It was that damned woman, the one from the Indian Desk."

The chairman shook his head belligerently. "You can't talk your way out of this one, Doug. You've just lost the firm two point seven billion sterling, and it's no good blaming the scotch of fictitious sirens. There is no Indian Desk — not now, not ever."

The finance director had been slowly closing in on Doug during this speech. She was breathing heavily, her nostrils flared and her blink rate had gone critical. She looked angry. I thought she was going to slap him, and slap him hard, but as he opened his mouth to reply, she gave a short scream of frustration and passion, and kissed him full on the mouth.

The chairman looked on flabbergasted, did a double-take, turned on his heel, exited the room and, absurdly, closed the door really softly behind him.

I looked up to see Penny staring directly into my eyes contemplatively. She appeared momentarily flustered.

"Told you so." But this remark did not tally with the muse in her expression and left me puzzled.

Monday, having been told by Sister Harris that I had a particularly full patient list, interrupting her speech several times to purse her lips, I made my ward round, followed by several community visits, and finally settled at my desk to catch up on paperwork. Of particular urgency was a report to be returned to Her

Majesty's Courts Service by the end of the week. It fell to me because it concerned one of my ex-patients. Reading the notes, I recalled the patient to mind: Martin. His was a troubling case, an ex-soldier traumatised by bloody action in Afghanistan, and, I suspect, adversely affected by an anti-malarial that has since been withdrawn, then addicted to alcohol, exacerbated by opiates prescribed by an unenlightened GP leading to the belligerence and derangement that goes with a failing liver. His rapidly deteriorating condition finally manifested itself bizarrely in his digging up a body in a cemetery in order to have an argument with it. The justice system is disproportionately offended by such behaviour, just as by Morris dropping his trousers in public.

The report demanded an assessment of Martin's level of culpability, for which I needed to read the case notes in detail, but as I did so, my mind pottered off like an errant child on a nature walk, as it so often does, in my case following a stream of consciousness rather than a beetle or a butterfly. I found myself wondering if Penny would be sympathetic or not to Martin's plight. Was she truly as hard-boiled as she represented herself? And that name uttered in my thoughts had a sudden and unexpected effect. As though a smile were wiped from my face, my mood swooped down at the realisation that I would probably never see her again.

I was rescued from becoming maudlin by the appearance of Brian. He poked his head around the door closely followed by Morris, who announced in between oafish giggles, "'E wants to ask yer summat, don't yer Bri?" He prodded Brian encouragingly. Brian smiled at me beatifically, rather as a vicar at his congregation.

"Has anyone died today?"

I sighed wearily. "I don't think so, Brian."

"I see." Brian looked disappointed, before brightening up. "You will let me know if they do, won't you?"

"I expect you'll get to hear of it, Brian."

Brian nodded earnestly. "I see."

Morris was almost apoplectic with glee. "Anyone died, 'e wants to know." He sniggered loudly and I shooed them gently out of the room.

I succeeded in banishing Penny from my thoughts for long enough to finish my report but she returned that evening. Why was this parting so unsatisfactory? I had been dismissed by her with perfunctory thanks and no suggestion that my services would be required again, and I cared. I repeated my first impressions to myself as a test, 'she's not my type,' but the words now carried no meaning. All I knew was that the thought of not seeing her again gave me a strange feeling of desolation. And if I was uncertain of my feelings towards her, what about hers towards me? That was the greater mystery. A psychiatrist is no better equipped than anyone else when it comes to self-analysis. All that schooling in reading signals: the smirk that tells you an anorexic is laughing up his or her sleeve at you; the lack of authenticity in the simulated emotions of a psychopath; a hunted look that warns you a schizophrenic is humouring you because he is afraid, in the distorted reality in his head, you are threatening him and in turn you are in danger of his attacking you in defence of his own life. I had all these perceptions, but with Penny they were of no use to me.

Over the coming days I recovered. My work recaptured my attention. A rather attractive oncologist smiled at me. The colour that had drained from my life began to return.

The phone call when it came caught me at my most absent-minded. The adage that men can't multitask has always irritated me because at times I can. This wasn't one of them. I had a clinic in half an hour, I needed to talk to the GP of one of my patients and couldn't get through, an Alzheimer's patient had found her way into my office and I was waiting for someone to come and shepherd her away but I was keeping close to her because she was another victim of The Caldwell's psychotropic medication regime and unsteady on her feet.

So when the phone rang, I answered it with my attention elsewhere.

"Bartlett?" A woman's voice enquired.

"Yes," I said irritably. "Who is this?"

My irritability was returned in her reply. "Penny."

"Oh."

"Exactly," she said dryly. "Can we meet tonight?"

"Oh."

"I'm glad I'm not one of your patients, Bartlett, not if it involves talking therapy anyway."

I recovered myself. "I'm just rather surprised to hear from you."

"Evidently."

"Well yes, I suppose I could."

"Good." She named a restaurant in Hampstead and rang off. My heart was beating curiously fast. I took my pulse. My average resting rate is around sixty, but at this moment was up to one hundred and seven, a most impressive response. I found myself taking a long deep breath, I had stopped breathing, interesting.

I supposed it to be another problem requiring my assistance but why should she contact me directly, and why a restaurant in Hampstead? I toyed with the idea that she had been thinking of me as I had been thinking of her, but this just caused further excitation of my poor over-stimulated sympathetic nervous system, resulting in sweaty palms this time.

As the hour approached, I wondered how much more I could take. Why should I put myself through this? I didn't work for her, I didn't even get paid. But I knew that I would go. When the time came, I ordered a taxi to the station and arrived two hours later Hampstead Village.

She was there before me, half getting up to announce her presence, wearing perfume I noticed.

"For the benefit of any prying eyes we're on a date, however unlikely that might appear."

And suddenly I was self-possessed; this last remark was unnecessarily rude and I wondered why she made it. The answer I suspected was that she was ill at ease, and this — human nature being the perverse see-saw that it is — restored my possession. I made no comment. She looked around, apparently casually.

"I've already changed tables, which will probably have you sticking a nasty little label on me marked, 'paranoia'."

A wine waiter appeared and I went along with a bottle of something Sicilian.

"Thing is, Bartlett, something a bit strange is going on."

"Something you can't tell Robinson and Major, or whatever their real names are?"

Penny looked at me curiously. "What have they been telling you?"

"I rather got the impression from Robinson that his name at least was an alias."

She rolled her eyes. "This is what happens when you let civil servants off their leads and let them play at being operatives, which they're not. They work for me but they're not my people, which brings me back to your question. Don't get me wrong, I trust them with my life but not to keep shtum to the minister."

The wine waiter reappeared at a run, making me suspect that Penny was a regular and that he anticipated her impatience from past miserable experience. This made me smile and earnt a frown from Penny. She downed half a glass distractedly. I followed suit.

"Where do I start with this? These two affairs you've been involved in were unusual, by which I mean more subversive, sophisticated and malicious than mere criminality. You get a feel for these things, they have the mark of a state intelligence service all over them. The first one made me uneasy, the second, suspicious and now we have another situation, again targeting the very heart of the state, which I would not in the normal way dream of telling my own family, let alone an outsider, but I am going to confide in you."

"Very trusting."

She gave me a curious look. "You'd be surprised, yours is not necessarily a safe profile but what makes it so is that we approached you, not the other way round; that simple fact trumps the most sophisticated vetting."

"But you're making an assumption."

She was there before me. "I suspect I'd insult you if I offered you payment?"

"Not insult me, but you're right in thinking it's an irrelevance: it's the time." This was true, but there was also the disruption to my peace of mind. I could not tell her that her phone call earlier had acted on me like a jolt of ECT, animating my unliving flesh.

She handed me a menu. Our eyes met briefly and, in that moment, I caught a glimpse of the different internal dialogue that runs in background to every conversation, in this case, a hard piercing stare of appraisal that I had seen before but this time did something strange to my stomach and legs.

"I suppose I shouldn't have taken it for granted, taken you for granted I should say. Although I'm not in your profession I usually get the measure of the people I'm up against. Time and again the same motivations: greed, vanity, narcissism, the desire for notoriety in the alienated and the inadequate, the list goes on."

"A good summary of the profiles of miscreants."

"I've got a feel for it, even the psychopaths who are so clever at concealing themselves, and the radicalised."

"The dispossessed."

"Major likens them to The Untouchables converting to Islam to be liberated from the slavery of the caste system."

"Our class system?"

She looked at me much in the manner of Sister Harris. "I'm not a bloody socialist, Bartlett."

"And you assume I am?"

"That's just it, just what I was coming to, I don't know what you are. I can't make you out. For starters," she gave me a look as though she had just eaten something unpleasant, "why did you give up doctoring to get into this…"

"Witchcraft?" I supplied helpfully.

"Well," she considered. "Going back a few years to when I was in the FO, they made me go on a course." She shook her head as if at a bad memory. "It was bollocks. I particularly remember Freud's theory that Medusa turning men to stone symbolised a little boy getting a hard-on at the sight of his mother's bush. I mean, I went to boarding school and I've seen some fairly untidy ones but that's pushing it, I think it was more about his own fear of women."

"First of all, I'm not a psychologist, and secondly, that's Freud, the master of suspect methodology. We've had Jung and Adler and Watson since, although actually, I think the debunking of Freud has gone too far. Modern psychodynamic theory has borrowed more than it cares to admit from him, it accounts for pivotal early life experiences, explaining the tensions within us, our strangely inconsistent feelings and the role of the unconscious in…"

"Maybe later, Bartlett." It was a gentle put-down that made me laugh rather than be offended. She continued. "You didn't answer my question."

"You have to be a medical doctor first anyway, but in my case, it is true that I did two years as a GP before specialising."

"So what changed your mind?"

"Far be it for me to further the cause of feminism but it was down to a woman. I had just started in a group practice and one of my patients presented with a distinctive lump at the base of her nose, a small tumour, not dangerous unless left too long, but a tricky bit of surgery because the skin is thin just there and it's a notoriously disfiguring type of lesion, not something you would normally tackle in general practice. But when I showed it to the 'lovely posh Doctor Ffiona', as she was known…"

"F-f-f-fiona?"

"Yes, for real, two F's. And in spite of the fact that she'd only qualified a year before me, she glanced at the thing, gave the patient a reassuring pat and said, 'I'll nip that out for you, dear.' And she did, with incredible deftness and hardly a scar to show for it. It was one of those defining moments; somehow, without real thought, I had always seen myself as destined for surgery. I'm not saying I couldn't have made some kind of a surgeon, but I would only ever have been way behind the likes of Ffiona."

"I can understand that," said Penny almost sympathetically. I guessed that in her career, achieving anything but the very top would have been out of the question to her.

"But I came to realise that I was good at understanding people, or, more accurately, how poor at it most of the other doctors were. It's not difficult. If you like people, care about them, are interested in them, they open up to you and you get to read them. You need that because patients are deceptive, they may over-report symptoms because they are what we used to call highly strung, or the reverse. I had one old man with stage-four stomach cancer apologising for making a fuss about a bit of pain. And then there are the ones that come to you with a complaint, but some gut feeling alerts you to look under the floorboards. I had one young girl, suddenly blind in one eye. She'd been referred for numerous tests, when they came in, she asked particularly to see me, I suspect because the other doctors were becoming impatient with her. But what was peculiar was that when that last test revealed no organic cause, I could see from her expression that it wasn't a surprise, somehow, she knew! And that fascinated me."

"Faking it to get off school?"

"No, completely genuine, known as psychogenic blindness, quite rare, but it revealed a disturbing lack of sympathy and understanding from my colleagues. Doctors are as varied as the general population, most of them are kind and well-intentioned, and some have empathy, but all too often it is limited to behaviour in which they recognise themselves, they only see others in their own image."

This seemed to strike a chord with Penny. "We have some of those."

"But the ones that really bug me, and I've known a few, don't actually like people and should never be doctors, however good they are academically."

Penny considered me thoughtfully. "Shame you didn't stick at it."

This remark cut like a knife. "If that's just a jibe, fine, but if you meant it, then it's ignorant."

Penny stiffened. "It wasn't intended as an insult."

"Well, it sounded like one, and I'm touchy on the subject."

"Apparently you are," she said dryly.

"Because I've heard it too often. Like I say, a consultant psychiatrist has to have a medical degree, that's five years, followed by six more in psychiatry, then, in my case, a residency in a psychiatric unit. And that's the starting point."

"Perhaps I'm prejudiced."

I relaxed. "Perhaps you are. Not all my patients are like Trevor and Morris. I will admit that there are times when I feel defeated; so much mental illness is intractable compared to physical illness. Take eating disorders. They have their own category but there's an element of psychosis…"

"You are talking to a layman, Bartlett, a laywoman anyway."

"A break with reality; the false self-image that fires aberrant eating in order to gain control that has been lost. Of all the conditions I treat, it is the one where I feel most unwelcome and the one that upsets me the most when treatment fails. I lost a patient recently. I watched her slip away in front of my eyes, a drowning girl I couldn't save because she didn't want to be saved. It was different when I was a doctor, the gratitude of the patients was embarrassing at times. But my patients now — so often sensitive, intelligent decent people but emotionally so impoverished that they have nothing to give. I saw one of my patients in the street recently, and she crossed the road to avoid me. The nearest I've had to an accolade was when an autistic child threw a sausage roll at me."

A waiter appeared looking nervous which Penny justified by a hostile look of irritation. She rattled off her order. I asked shamefacedly for fish and chips. The waiter stiffened with disapproval and translated my order disdainfully into the description on the menu. I tried to placate him with a grateful smile with only partial success.

Penny shook her head. "Fuck's sake, Bartlett." But in a fraction of a second her attention had passed on. "To get back to where we were, before I insulted you and you threw a tantrum." I opened my mouth to protest but she interrupted me. "Which was actually interesting to me because, like I say, I don't know what makes you tick; you're not my usual subject matter, not motivated by all those nasty vicious venal things I understand."

Something in the distance of her expression told me she had slipped into the past. "Because of your mother?"

She looked at me curiously. "You see this is what I'm talking about. When I first caught sight of you…"

"You sank your head in your hands, I remember."

She mimicked the action but her eyes looked up at me brightly which made me laugh.

"I thought you were what my grandmother called a, 'Gawd help us', but I have come to suspect you of being on the case, which I find disconcerting. That remark you just made is uncomfortably perceptive. I think you understand me better than I understand you; the boot's on the wrong foot and I don't like it."

Inwardly I was gratified by this speech, vanity tempted me to nod knowingly and significantly in the manner of The Caldwell, but honesty won the day.

"Not a clue if you must know. You're the most enigmatic woman I've ever met. I mean, yes I pick up on certain things."

"So much of what you said when we were play-acting was bang on. I'm not going to tell you what you got right and what you didn't, but enough to spook me. I'm one of a few you can't possibly know anything about."

I recognised this as a question. "I deal with abnormal psychology. I need to be able to diagnose, to medicate, to provide therapy, and it's true that there is a huge no man's land between normal and abnormal. The classic students' mistake is to diagnose everyone as mentally ill. In some ways we are, it's just a matter of degree. Move the line one way and most of us are normal, move it in the other direction and we're not. Normality is an average." A wry look on her face made me smile. "But I've wandered, as I see you've noticed. What I was leading to is that you can learn academically how to identify mental conditions but that doesn't make for understanding people, normal or abnormal. In fact, perversely, many practitioners chose the career because of their frustration at that very deficit. They don't understand the people around them, and so fail to predict actions that hurt or confuse them, coming apparently out of nowhere. They are lost in a fog of perplexing human behaviour that they yearn to penetrate, and these are the ones who will never be any good. Some people have it, some don't. You've got it."

"Get to it, Bartlett."

"You're so impatient." Inwardly, I interpreted her words as cover for her discomfort at the compliment.

"Only because you're so slow."

"Well, what I was getting to is that an important part of the process of understanding relies on behavioural recognition, seeing patterns and adding them to your database, and the problem with you is that the drive is empty. In a word, you are not like anyone I've ever met."

"From the long-winded to the obscurely concise."

"You are extremely intelligent, spectacularly decisive, abnormally so and, for no particular reason, call it instinct, I suspect that's also from your mother."

She looked at me thoughtfully and nodded, apparently reluctantly.

"At first, I thought you were capricious, but I don't think that's it. I suspect you make up your mind so quickly that the problem-solving part of the brain, that's the frontal lobe…"

"Thanks, Bartlett," she said acidly.

"Is already engaged elsewhere, while the speech centre is still stacking the work in progress."

Her eyes were dark. "I don't know how you worked that one out, it happens a lot, I can feel my thoughts running ahead and I can't catch up." She looked at me mildly. "It's frustrating at times."

"So, I have some intuition, but all that about your mother came from Trevor."

"Trevor!" I was gratified by her surprise. "That's extraordinary."

"He *is* extraordinary, and way out of my league. If you'd read my paper, you'd know."

She pulled a face, simulating shame with comic insincerity.

"And that look is almost certainly a hangover from childhood, possibly even infancy."

She flashed me a smile, so momentary that it made me think of the particles created by the large hadron collider that exist only for a nanosecond. Then, it was gone and I was closed out again.

The question of my acceptance still hung in the air. I resigned myself with a sigh that I intended her to interpret as reluctance.

"I suppose I could find the time."

"It will mean several days away from work, can you manage that?"

"God help me. More disapproval from Sister Harris, who I should explain is actually the ward matron, and although technically my underling, in reality treats all consultants as dirt beneath her feet, myself as the very filthiest."

"She probably fancies you."

I enjoyed this remark. I knew it wasn't true but I liked the idea that Penny thought it a possibility.

"Sister Harris," I replied emphatically, "once told me that the reason patients tend to gravitate towards me is because they recognise me as one of their own; she despises me." And suddenly her eyes were laughing into mine. Her meaning was clear, she was reminding me of the irony of this remark, of the finance director with the rapid blink rate crushing her lips hard against Doug's.

But just as before, her humour was short lived and was replaced by an uneasy frown. "In spite of you accusing me of being a high-speed processor, I don't actually know where to start with this. Another pillar of the state under attack, this time the Archbishop of Canterbury, and he is in grave danger of being seduced." She reacted to my surprise. "No, not what you think, not like that, not your average temptress. How can I put this, he is being seduced, not sexually, but by piety."

"Gracious."

She shook her head and repeated mockingly, "Gracious," before returning to seriousness.

"This all started a few months ago. I got pulled into a meeting with, well let's just say the highest of the high, and told that there were serious concerns about the amount of time the archbishop was spending at a charitable mission run by what sounded like the bastard child of the Archangel Gabriel and Mother Teresa."

"Pious, you said."

"Ultra, but worse, far worse, she's a nun and like most nuns, but apparently not all — I've had the lecture — she's of the Catholic variety, originally from Mexico."

"I'm probably going to get my head snapped off for this but why exactly does that matter? I thought there was all sorts of interdenominational fraternisation nowadays."

"Naive, Bartlett, very naive. It's all window dressing, you watch those do's and they're all as nervous as a straight in a gay bar. There's a chapel attached to the mission and he's been there a few times, right on the edge, eyeing up the saints and the icons, fiddling with the rosary beads, and she's whispering sweet nothings in his ear about transubstantiation and the Virgin Mary, but it's the Eucharist that really gets to him. You see him do it in Canterbury Cathedral and he tinkers with it looking bored, but amongst the left-footers, his eyes gleam with ecstasy, the silly old goat's just about to make an absolute arse of himself."

"And what are we supposed to do, some sort of smear campaign?" "Upskirt him, there's a thought. But there's more, you don't know the half of it…"

At this moment our food arrived, earning the waiter another scowl from Penny and we adjourned our conversation. I ate my fish self-consciously and observed Penny with amusement; she had no such reserve and tucked in with schoolgirl gusto. She shot me a suspicious glance.

"What are you sniggering at?"

"You eating."

She shook her head in mock despair and refilled our glasses. "Like I said to you earlier, there's something behind all this, and what you said to me jokingly when we were in the hotel was uncomfortably true, about not spying on our friends across the water."

"The special relationship."

"As you say, which at times makes HM Government nervous as kittens. The deal is supposedly collective defence but in reality, they hold the umbrella, and keep a watchful eye on us."

"I suppose Philby, Burgess and Maclean didn't help."

"Maybe not, but the point is the compliment may not be returned."

"Are you saying that this nun…?"

Penny looked and sounded cynical. "That's the thing, I don't believe she is a nun. But I left the meeting I was telling you about with the distinct impression that I should somehow rescue our esteemed pillar of the Anglican church from his own foolishness without any sort of investigation of her."

"Which of course you disobeyed, but why should our friends across the pond care about a Mexican nun?"

"Exactly! They shouldn't."

"Interesting, so what happened when you checked her out?"

"There's nothing on her except that back home she was renowned for her dedication, bravery and kindness. In a way not surprising but, then again, the very fact that a nun would have no security profile makes her a perfect agent and I'm suspicious at how little there is on her, because if it's been wiped, I don't know about it, and I'm the one person who should."

"What about checking with the Vatican?"

She gave me a look of contempt. "Assuming that's not an attempt at humour, you are talking about probably the most secretive and corrupt organisation on the planet."

"I take your point."

"So I decided to plant someone in the mission, someone I could trust."

"Mrs T?"

"Makes a superb bag lady."

"And, of course, she'd do anything for you because she's head over heels in love with you." Penny looked poker-faced but I got the impression the remark irked her. I laughed. "I bet you'd give nothing away under enhanced interrogation."

"And I'm rather disturbed that you've even heard of that, Bartlett."

My mind wandered. I felt a sudden sympathy for Mrs T, imagining the immense power Penny must have over her.

Penny continued. "From what Mrs T says, if she's anything other than as advertised then she's a damned good actress, never anything other than smiling devotion."

"But you're not satisfied?"

"No, she's fake, I'm sure of it." Penny downed half a glass of wine ruminatively. "The only thing Mrs T picked up on was she thought there was something dodgy about her entourage. She bought over some helpers from Mexico, they cook and generally help out, but Mrs T says they're watchful and described them as rough types."

"Interesting country."

Penny looked at me doubtfully.

"Do you know there's a cemetery in Santa Fe with an urn on a pillar that contains the mummified leg of General Antonio Copel de Santa Anna, shattered by a French cannonball." My conversation faltered under Penny's mortified gaze as some poor creature being subjected to the concentrated rays of the sun through the magnifying glass of a sadistic schoolboy. "He had it put there, he turned up in my studies as an example of narcissism."

She shook her head as if to reset her brain. "In answer to your question, no, surprisingly I did not know that, and now you've made me completely forget what I was saying."

"The Mexican assistants, minders by the sound of it."

"That was it."

"And where do I come in?"

"I need to get in there, correction, we need to get in there, with your two... not sure of the PC name for them, but you know."

A picture formed in my mind of Trevor facing the wall, his voice struggling with the effort of communication, and Morris on a particular occasion when the hospital discharged him — the lost look on his face, his shrunken distress as he turned to leave the safety of what had become his home — and I was angry.

"I'm sure if you think hard, you'll remember their names," I said coldly.

Penny appeared not to notice. "OK, Trevor and Morris then. The idea is we're a couple of philanthropists who've taken in these boys." She stopped suddenly with a frown that was curious rather than angry. "Did you just tick me off?"

"I just don't think..."

"No, no, I get that, why you did it, I'm just surprised, I didn't know you had a spine, sorry."

"You didn't know I had a spine and I didn't know you could apologise."

She considered me for the briefest moment, before continuing.

"We took in the boys..."

"Because we can't have children of our own?"

To my surprise she considered this seriously. "No, I think we're just so humanitarian that we wanted to foster two disadvantaged boys rather than have our own perfect family."

"In fact, we disapprove of that as being self-indulgent."

"But finding we can't cope."

"Both of us?"

"No, me. This involves some serious dissembling, best you're the bit-player in this, and of course Trevor and Morris only have to be themselves, if that doesn't offend you."

"No, it's just that…"

"I know, I do get it. If you have a fault, Bartlett, it is to labour your arguments for rather a long time after you've made them."

I opened my mouth to protest but stalled at the memory of Sister Harris accusing me of the very same thing only a few days ago.

"OK but how can you be sure we'll even be considered? I mean a place like that must be oversubscribed several times over."

"Way ahead of you, we've got an appointment, day after tomorrow."

"Taking my compliance for granted?"

"I need you for this, Bartlett."

"Well, I've agreed now, subject of course to Morris and Trevor's approval, but I'm still not sure what your scheme is, you say expose her, but how exactly?"

"Now that I can't tell you because I don't know myself. I don't doubt I'll find her out if she's a fraud as I'm so sure she is, call it a hunch if you like."

"That you're staking your reputation on?"

"One thing I didn't tell you is that I saw a letter she first wrote to the archbishop inviting him to visit, and it was too damn cute."

"Manipulative?"

"Appealing to his desire for visible interdenominational cooperation, which is actually a threat."

"Of how bad he'd look if he turned her down?"

"But there was more. I can't remember the wording but if you read the news, you know how pissed off the die-hards are in the C of E about gay marriage and girly bishes. You have to remember that all religions were invented by men to oppress women. Think of Salome and Joana."

"Friends of Mrs T, perhaps?"

"Early Christian disciples, erased from history by Constantine in the fourth century." She looked at me curiously. "Are you religious?"

"Ah, do you want the long answer or the short?"

"Short please."

"Thought you might. Well, yes and no."

This elicited a groan, followed by, "Oh God."

"OK then, philosophically, I'm all for any religion or non-religion that teaches morality and mutual respect. As for a creator, I find the idea no more absurd than there not being one. But I do wonder, usually to myself because at work I am surrounded by ardent atheists, if the culminating product of evolution will in fact be God, finally in his own image, the stars and planets, the particles of his brain interspersed with dark matter instead of grey."

Penny looked embarrassed. "Yes or no would have done," she said shortly. She clicked her fingers at a passing waiter and ordered more wine. "Getting back to the point, we have to have a watertight story. The brilliant thing about you is that you're completely clean. We manufacture identities when needs must but there's nothing better than the real thing."

"And you're my wife?"

"Yes, we met on the rebound from your divorce and found ourselves soulmates, both humanists and philanthropists, a bit hippy-dippy."

"I wonder how we met?"

To my surprise, she took this as a serious question. "Motor accident. I pulled out in front of you, you lost your temper, which I wasn't used to, being what you might call…"

"Domineering."

"That's it, good, I like that, domineering. But I found it stimulating and invited you to dinner."

"Which of course is how your parents met."

And suddenly her eyes were staring directly into mine, dark, pensive and very beautiful.

"As you say."

Two hours later, I was in a taxi on my way home. My first thoughts were of the practical concerns of absenting myself with Mo and Trevor. Even though they were not held under section, I would need a cover story.

Back home, my thoughts returned to the enigma of Penny, again without resolution but undoubtedly inspiring a bizarre and vivid dream in the night.

I found myself returning home in the early hours along a Victorian mews lit from a row of atmospheric gas lamps, reminiscent of a Sherlock Holmes movie. I climbed a flight of flagged steps to the heavy oak door of my house, a magnificent town mansion. The interior was exquisitely tasteful but I stopped in surprise as I entered the lounge, met by a dazzle of crystal sidelights. My first thought was that I had left them on by mistake, but then saw that an open hearth was aglow with red-hot coals and above it an illuminated glass fireguard of pale green. It was this that startled me, it wasn't there when I had left. For the first time I felt apprehensive, this was something more than just strange. I tried the other rooms and each was the same, blazing lights and glowing fires, each surrounded by a coloured glass guard, orange, rose-pink, crimson, primrose — all very beautiful but arousing a feeling of disquiet. This wasn't a prank, some malign force was behind this, and my apprehension grew as I felt a presentiment of evil upon me.

I awoke sweating, my heart thumping. How strange that nothing more than some beautiful interior decor had led to such foreboding. I was aware that this dream would have been pounced on by Freud as being relentlessly sexual, particularly the act of climbing steps which he claimed to represent coitus. Unconvincing in my opinion but I did accept that the dream was a manifestation of my doubts about Penny, and in the still of the night these took the form of frenzied thoughts, tumbling unmarshalled through my tired mind like a flock of unruly sheep, until, exasperated, I ordered myself to tackle them systematically. First, that same question: how did I feel about her? Was I falling for her? If so, it felt different from anything I had known before, this was love in a different mood, almost non-sexual, I wanted to be with her, I felt lonely and miserable at the thought of being without her. I recalled my excitement only those few hours ago at the unexpected sound of her voice, and the physical symptoms, which if a patient had presented with, I would have ordered them to lie down, suspecting syncope. I'd found myself repeatedly thinking of situations and thoughts that I wanted to repeat to her. My mind slipped to that moment when she had sat on the bed in the hotel room and the light from her phone lit her face with a silver aura. I had struggled to define the emotion this had aroused in me. I analysed it now, and it emerged like the bloom of a moonflower that opens only at night: it was the desire to protect. How absurd! If ever there was a woman not in need of protection, it was Penny. What primal creatures are men. But before my thoughts strayed, I pulled myself up. That was one question answered but it led to another: how did she feel about me? This question too had been tumbling around, sometimes above, sometimes below, the surface of my consciousness like Winnie the Pooh on his jar in the flood. And my doubt? I was sure that she knew or suspected how I felt about her. Was she in fact deliberately encouraging me to keep my interest? I remembered her stonewalling my accusation that Mrs T was in love with her. More than that, the accusation had annoyed her, perhaps because it implied that with this knowledge, she was exploiting Mrs T. And was I in fact being used in a similar way? When our conversation had become too intimate, she had backed away. Like an orbiting moon, I was to be kept in her sphere of influence without being allowed too close. I remembered how she had apparently melted in my arms during the argument about her mother. I had thought at the time that this was adroit play-acting, but was it not in truth by design to secure my fascination? But this only made sense if she believed in my susceptibility, which was possible since the suggestion that I was homosexual had been made after that. But what about that suggestion? My mind stumbled on to the next doubt that had been gnawing at the door of my subconscious like a trapped mouse. Was it really believable that the director general of MI5 would share a bed with a relative stranger because she thought he was gay? I had wondered at the time; she was apparently so capricious that it was impossible to decide. But remembering her reaction on waking in the morning, was it not too extreme? And there was that incongruity of her expression that did not quite fit with her agitation. I struggled on without resolution and my tired mind eventually tumbled back into sleep.

My dishevelled appearance at work, late and with a hangover from too much wine and interrupted sleep, earnt me a brief but emphatic shake of the head from Sister Harris. She dropped her head to ignore my, 'Good morning', but just as I was passing said, "You've got a visitor."

I looked at her suspiciously; she was smiling, that always meant trouble. She indulged in my discomfort a while longer before imparting in a loud whisper, "Batman."

"Oh God, not this morning."

She pursed her lips; Sister Harris was the master of the pursed lips. "You were the one who insisted he was to be let out of Mulberry during the day."

I nodded gloomily. "Batman" was The Colonel's nickname, which he had earnt when in my office one day, having caught sight of his reflection in a mirror, apparently appalled at his state of undress; ties were not allowed on Mulberry Ward.

"Poor show, I'll have words with my batman over this."

Unfortunately, Morris was in attendance at the time. Mo had an absolute fascination for the dementia patients, he found them hilarious. 'Batman' had only one meaning to him and he spent the next five minutes with his arms stretched out imitating flight while singing in a nasal monotone, "Ba ba ba ba ba ba Baatmaaaan."

I remember The Colonel surreptitiously tapping the side of his head and confiding in a loud whisper, "I'd get the MO to have a look at that boy."

I didn't like this nickname, it's use seemed somehow sacrilegious for such a dignified old gentleman. It was beyond my power to stop its spread, but I continued to know him as, 'The Colonel'. In his lucid state, you could read innate honesty in his face coexisting with an air of authority lingering from his former seniority. Transcending all though was a childlike trust which I guessed had been amplified by his dotage. I remember thinking once, with a catch in my heart, that I could have led the old boy into hell and he would have followed. And here he was in my office.

"Doctor," he greeted me, to my surprise, usually I was a fellow, albeit junior, officer. "Take a seat." He led me graciously to my own chair. I managed a smile, my headache and bad mood were not the old boy's fault.

"Now can I get you a coffee?"

"Thank you, Colonel." The idea of this kindly old gentleman's intended hospitality was both hilarious and intensely sad, he being utterly incapable of performing such a task.

I managed to officiate with the coffee machine without him noticing, and he took his coffee from me with courteous acceptance, his offer to me had been forgotten within a second of his making it.

"Now then, Doctor. A few matters have come to my attention, we need to discuss." He looked around furtively. "I've been talking to the chief of staff."

I settled down to listen, time enough to drink my coffee then I'd gently move him on. Five minutes later I found myself being prodded in the chest and his words invaded my consciousness.

"Three days' supplies! I know what it is, some blessed pen-pusher on the GS (General Staff), never seen action in his life, trying to make a name for himself."

I nodded sympathetically. "Pen-pushers!" I tutted.

"You've got it, Doctor, that's exactly what they are." The Colonel appeared delighted by my perspicacity, having forgotten that he'd used the expression only a second ago. "You never said a truer word, Major, I'd top hat the lot of them."

I was just smiling at my change in profession when the door opened and Sister Harris ushered in a real Major along with Mr Robinson, both in smart grey business suits this time.

"Gentlemen to see you, Doctor, from the, erm, utility providers apparently." Adding with deep sarcasm while remaining impressively deadpan, "One might think they'd settle in a career."

For once Mr Robinson and Major appeared ill at ease, which pleased me, even these two were no match for Sister Harris. The Colonel chose this moment to shake hands with Major.

"Ah, Major, I'm glad the Fifth Armoured are in on this." He shook hands with us all courteously before making his farewell, leaving Major looking nonplussed.

I laughed. "He's blown your cover."

Without knowing of the extraordinary coincidence by which The Colonel had hit upon his name, Major was seriously spooked.

"But I've never seen that gentleman before in my life, and yet he knew me. How can this possibly be?"

Mr Robinson touched his arm reassuringly. "Anyone can see you are a military man, Major."

Major expanded his chest and looked relieved. "Ah, yes of course, it is the so-called, 'cut of the gib' that gives one away." His brow darkened. "It is a little disturbing though, after all, we are in disguise."

Mr Robinson seemed to accept this with complacency. "Indeed, most disturbing."

"Is there something I can do for you, gentlemen?"

This resulted in much humming and hawing and considerable unease. At length, Mr Robinson shuffled for a long moment before enquiring in a rather forced voice, "We just wondered how your soirée went last night, Doctor?"

"Your so-called, tryst," added Major knowingly.

"Or perhaps I might say, *date*," added Mr Robinson significantly.

"We know all about it you see." Major beamed. "You had the fish."

I tried to look non-committal. "OK thanks, but I repeat, nice as it is to see you gentlemen, was there something you wanted?"

Mr Robinson appeared to consider. "Nothing in particular, just a chat, really."

Major made an expansive gesture. "We happened to be passing, you see."

"And we thought we'd drop in," continued Mr Robinson. "I said to you, didn't I, Major?"

"You did, you did, I particularly noted it, let's pop in on our friend, the doctor."

"Because we think of you as a friend, Doctor."

"All of us," added Major significantly.

Mr Robinson coughed. "All three of us, that's myself, Major here, and Miss Penelope."

"Miss," repeated Major with heavy significance.

"Of course, she was married." Mr Robinson picked up the baton.

"But sadly," Major sighed with feeling, "it ended."

Both shifted weight uneasily, for a long moment.

"She talks about you, you know," Major blurted out.

I wondered where this was leading and decided to help them out. "Really, anything nice?"

Mr Robinson looked shocked. "No, no, nothing like that I assure you."

"Quite the reverse in fact," added Major comfortingly." And then brightly, "We made notes." They exchanged glances. "We could read some of them to you."

I shrugged. Major fished out a notepad from his pocket and read ponderously. "And as for that crackpot doctor, he's a…" He paused with a searching look at Mr Robinson who considered the notepad thoughtfully.

"Blithering, I think, Major, would be a suitable appropriation."

"Blithering," repeated Major, and evidently enjoying the sound of the word, repeated, "Blithering," while nodding enthusiastically. "Know it all and a…" Inspiration came after a pause. "Blithering bore and a…" Major pointed out another word to Mr Robinson who raised his eyebrows. This one seemed to stump him and I took the opportunity to prize the notepad from Major.

I was startled not just by the extremity of the obscenities but the volume of them, six pages in all.

"And your point is, gentlemen?"

Mr Robinson looked confused. "Is it not obvious?"

"Staring you in the face, one might say," added Major, undiplomatically.

Mr Robinson looked mystified. "You're not familiar with her ways, Doctor, but surely as a psychiatrist it is clear to you."

Major beamed. "The potency of the insults, really very rude."

"Very, very rude," agreed Mr Robinson, joining in the beaming. "And of course, there's the matter of wearing perfume, she never wears perfume, does she, Major?"

Major shook his head, grinning like a schoolboy. "We think she likes you, Doctor."

I wondered if they had been reading the same magazine article that had persuaded Morris of Sister Harris' secret admiration for him, but before I could ask, Brian entered. He looked at Major and Mr Robinson with knowing satisfaction and asked in an absurdly excited whisper, "Are these the undertakers?"

"I'm afraid not, Brian."

"I see." He looked at me suspiciously. "I'm not doubting your word, Doctor, it's just that Sister Harris thought they were. She said they'd tried all sorts of different jobs but couldn't stick at any of them and thought they'd try something different."

I considered Brian in silence. Most days I would have appreciated Sister Harris' humour, but this wasn't one of them. I plotted my revenge, appearing to concede reluctantly.

"You're right, Brian, but no one's supposed to know. There's going to be a post-mortem."

"A post-mortem," echoed Brian almost throbbing with delight. "And the deceased?"

"I can't tell you that, Brian, it's one of Professor Caldwell's patients and I'm not allowed to discuss it, but Sister Harris knows, she'll pretend she doesn't of course so you may have to press her."

Brian nodded earnestly. "I see." He paused at the door and said respectfully, "Will you pass my sincere condolences to the family, Doctor."

"Of course." The door closed behind him. I clenched my forehead with pain. "Thanks to your boss I have a splitting headache. How does she drink like that?" I answered my own question. "I suppose I should be telling you; the fact is people's tolerance to alcohol varies enormously, which is why the recommended alcohol consumption in units is so misleading. There are a variety of factors involved that I won't bore you with but a lot of people are unaware of the genetic component. The non-synonymous variant 1148M in the patatin-like phospholipase domain containing the PNPLA3 gene is a major risk factor for…"

Mr Robinson held up his hand. "If I could stop you there, Doctor. This is one complaint Miss Penelope makes that I think is more than just the mating posture."

"You mustn't bore her, Doctor," added Major. "It'll ruin everything."

"Ruin everything?"

Mr Robinson placed his thumbs in his waistcoat pockets. "We have hopes for you, Doctor."

"Me and Penny?"

"Exactly."

"Precisely," Major chipped in.

"Why? I don't wish to be rude, gentleman, but what's in it for you?"

They shared a look of injured innocence. Mr Robinson looked particularly hurt. "You may not know it, Doctor, but we have a sentimental nature, Major and myself, as a matter of fact, this is not unusual in civil servants."

Major nodded in agreement. "We'd like you to be happy." They both stared at me for a long soppy moment which looked so authentic that for a moment I believed it, before I twigged.

"I don't suppose by any chance that her ladyship has made your lives a misery since her divorce?"

They exchanged a meaningful look. Mr Robinson tapped his fingers on my desk nervously.

"Coincidentally I'm sure but her mood did seem to deteriorate slightly, wouldn't you say, Major?"

Major's face was a mask of nonchalance. "Now you come to mention it."

"Lame, Major, very lame, so you want me to make love to your boss to take the heat off you two?"

Mr Robinson's, "Certainly not!" was preposterously overdone. Major's look of pained distaste was barely more credible.

"Indeed, quite so, certainly not."

There was a long pause eventually broken by Mr Robinson. "She likes the theatre, Doctor, then maybe, I don't know, say a walk by the Thames."

"It's atmospheric at night, don't you think, Mr Robinson?" chipped in Major. "Not quite the Ganges but…"

"Indeed, I do, and who knows, perhaps in the dark you could take her hand to steady her."

Major frowned as if this were far-fetched. "Maybe the other way round, Mr Robinson. I observed at the Saruman Corporation function that the Doctor is not too steady on his feet after a drink, and I think he might have had a few drinks."

Mr Robinson looked at me hopefully. "Do you think you might have had one too many, Doctor?"

Major sighed. "Love is a wonderful thing."

They exchanged conspiratorial glances, then Mr Robinson leaned forward and whispered, "We've found out what aftershave her father uses."

"It would give you the so-called, head start," added Major.

I shook my head in exasperation but they persisted in staring at me with a peculiar look of stubborn optimism. And as if a last throw of the dice, Major voiced forlornly, "We think you'd make a lovely couple."

My doubts of the night came back to me, there was something suspect about all this. Penny was supposedly playing a lone hand and yet these two knew all about it, and in detail. How else did Major know what I'd had for dinner unless from Penny? She was manipulating me. I felt suddenly hurt and angry, I was not to be made a fool of. I made a charade of wearying of the subject.

"This would all make a nice rom-com, gentlemen but I'm afraid it can only ever be fiction. Penny is simply not my type."

Mr Robinson nodded sadly. "Oh, I see." There was a certain pregnancy in this remark that made me look up in time to see glances being exchanged, the significance of which did not escape me, written in bold neon in the air from Mr Robinson to Major: 'I told you he was gay.'

When they had taken their leave, I went to find Trevor and Morris. I found Mo first, in the common room, informing a patient with traumatic brain injury that, because his boss had recently acquired an operator's licence, Mo had been elevated to driving four tonners which apparently sorted the men from the boys due to their having air brakes. Not easy at first but to the experienced driver, emphasised with a knowing tap to the head, "A piece of piss."

Trevor chose this moment to walk in patting Max on the head and judging by the, "Good boy, Max," in a conversational mood. They followed me willingly to my office where I asked them outright if they were willing to help in a bit of play-acting with Penny, pretending to be our children. Mo computed this for a while before cracking it.

"So I reckon that makes you my dad." He broke off into prolonged sniggering. "An' that makes 'er…" This was much trickier but after another long bout of processing, he announced proudly, "She's my mum, she is."

"That's right."

"Mummy." He giggled. "She's my mummy." He considered. "So I can 'ug 'er an' that."

An inner vision of this flashed before me, why should I confine my revenge to Sister Harris?

"I think you should." I turned to Trevor who looked thoughtful. "Are you all right with this, Trevor?"

He nodded to the wall and announced hurriedly, "Yes," after which he addressed the coffee machine in a hectoring voice. "And the bramble said unto the trees: 'in mine ears said the Lord of hosts, of a truth many houses shall be desolate even great and fair without inhabitant'."

Which words left Morris unusually thoughtful. I saw, 'mumbo jumbo', forming on his lips but he remained silent. I have observed that Mo is much more careful how he talks to Trevor than anyone else, it is hard to believe due to sensitivity because, if so, it is way beyond his usual emotional facility, but you never quite know with Morris.

Later that morning, the phone rang and Penny's voice made me wince with an even more extreme effect than previously. However much you explain it away, as a rush of dopamine, adrenalin and norepinephrine, it still gets you in the heart.

"Bartlett," she commanded, rather as I felt HM might order around a footman. "We need a rehearsal, preferably tonight at your place. Can that be arranged?" I was still stammering when interrupted curtly by, "Seven o clock," followed by the dialling tone.

As the hour approached, I resisted the temptation of the drinks' cupboard and consequently was a nervous wreck by the time she arrived. I was modestly proud of my house; my ex had taste and we'd kept it as original nineteen thirties which gave it an Art Deco feel. I'd been happy for Caroline to take whatever she wanted, so apart from the quantity of books it left the decor minimalist which was how I liked it. Just the one framed enlargement of an elegant silver tabby with intelligent and soulful green eyes. And it was this picture that caught Penny's attention. She stood before it and I was surprised to see that she reached out a hand to trace a pattern on the glass almost as if she was stroking it.

"Friend of yours?"

"Family cat, used to sit on my work when I was doing my degree, never disturbed me, just liked the company."

She turned away. "To work, Bartlett."

Three hours we were at it, covering all the details of our lives together with the boys. There was no caprice about her today, she was business-like to the point of brusque. I smiled wryly to myself at the thought of following Major's suggestion and asking her to the theatre: the idea was laughable. As she prepared to leave, she said suddenly, "You had visitors this morning, I understand."

"I thought you weren't supposed to be in the know."

She looked cynical. "Oh, I'm in the know all right. They turned up looking like a couple of schoolboys caught scrumping apples." Suddenly her eyes zeroed in on me like some deadly piece of ordnance. "Did you tell them anything about this?"

I couldn't hold her eyes as she searched my face coldly, reading, calculating, intense without being hostile. I felt the power of the woman as never before.

"No." I was glad to be able to tell the truth, certain that she would divine any falsehood. She nodded in acceptance and relaxed; in that fraction of a second, she had reached her verdict on my truthfulness with that extraordinary confidence in judgement that defined her.

She turned to go, paused at the picture. "She is beautiful, and such a long tail."

I was amused at her assumption of gender, but she was right. "Notice how it curls up at the end? My mother told me that she was told to do that to make it fit into the picture, and I believed her for years. Mind you I grew up with all sorts of implanted nonsense. I think I was four when I asked her, 'where's America, Mummy?' I was an inquisitive child. 'Behind the Post Office, sweetie, and eat your greens.' I think the idea was to fill my head with as much rubbish as possible for as long as

215

possible. It doesn't feature in the current *Diagnostic Manual* but I'm hoping she'll get a mention in the text revision when it comes out.

Penny looked at me curiously. "Your mum said that?"

After she had gone, I tottered to the drinks cabinet feeling like I'd just survived an interrogation, which in a way I had: she was MI5 after all. But that last expression I had surprised on her face was easily analysed, when she had asked, 'your mum said that?' Evidently, she could not conceive of a mother behaving like that, but more than that she had expected me to be talking about my father because by sheer chance I had hit upon the nature of her own father.

By arrangement I was collected with the boys in a family saloon. Penny drove through dense traffic into London. I winced several times at the cut and thrust of city driving and was impressed but not surprised that she drove fast and confidently with no sign of emotion. Her mind was turned in. I was apprehensive, far more so than on our previous adventures, somehow this one seemed more serious.

The hostel was in Northolt, a rather run-down West London suburb, and it was larger than I'd expected: a complex of buildings connected to a church. I shepherded the boys and followed Penny. A great coming and going of all sorts of people made me feel comfortingly less visible. Penny's expression had undergone a transformation, she looked vague and fussed up, like a harassed mother ferrying her children to school, with an extra helping of anxiety to reflect our harrowing situation.

Signs directed us to a reception desk and Penny announced us to a rather insipid looking bearded individual. He invited us to take a seat and spoke into a telephone. Half an hour later we were led down corridors and ushered into an office. I tried to look anxious, partly following Penny's lead but more urgently to hide the extreme curiosity that the figure before us aroused. She was in some ways what I'd expected, dressed in a nun's habit with immaculate black and white headdress. As she rose to greet us, I saw that she was tall, and her movements were slow, graceful and lithe. I wondered what sort of figure was concealed under the habit. She looked tired, her eyes were uninterested, almost opaque, and did not smile along with the rest of her face when she made the effort of a rictus of welcome.

"I am Sister Teresa, welcome to the Sacred Virgin Home of Compassion."

Penny cast her eyes down and bobbed in a sort of half-curtsy, awkward and flustered, brilliantly done.

"Thank you so much for seeing us. I'm Penelope, my husband Peter, *Doctor* Bartlett," she added with an excellent simulation of pride. "And our boys, this is Morris."

"'Ow do." Mo waved inappropriately and announced with supreme confidence, "Yer a nun I reckon."

Sister Teresa broke into a real smile, her eyes smiled; she appeared an effigy of beatification.

"I am, dear, and your other boy?" She smiled at Trevor.

"This is Trevor," I announced.

Trevor bowed his head, a gesture that could have been taken as appropriate in anyone other than Trevor.

"And I saw an angel standing in the sun, clothed with a vesture dipped in blood, and the sea gave up the dead which were in it and death and hell delivered up." He stopped suddenly as the nun looked up sharply, as well she might. I wondered myself at the unusual portent of this utterance but concealed my curiosity. Did I imagine a fleeting moment of suspicion in her expression, before it melted into concern and compassion. Her voice was soft.

"I think you are a little confused, my dear." She turned to Penny. "I know your case; I wanted to meet the boys to check they would fit in here. I'm afraid that, much as we would like, there are some we can't accommodate."

Penny's face was a mask of anguish. Sister Teresa stretched out a reassuring hand, a well-manicured and shapely hand. Her smile was pained as if she feared her words had caused distress, and she hastened to reassure.

"I'm sure your boys will be happy here."

Penny was apparently broken by this kindness. "We can't cope you see." She grasped my hand as if for support and, in spite of the bizarreness of this charade, I was overtaken by sensation. I tried to calm myself with a dispassionate analysis. That feeling of euphoria would be the flood of neurotransmitters, an FMRI scan would show my insula and striatum lit up like a Christmas tree, I could almost feel my prefrontal cortex disengaging. This persuasion was in vain, the feel of her hand in mine was electric. I had to override all the sensations that were overwhelming me to tune back in. Penny broke into a confession.

"It's me that can't cope, not Peter, is the truth."

I felt it appropriate to put my arm around her waist and she leant her head against mine. My senses were now on overload at the closeness of her and the unexpected softness of her waist. I breathed in deeply and tried desperately to demonstrate my distress at our situation, difficult when you're in ecstasy and just want to dance. Penny's anguish expressed in her voice.

"I can't go on, but I can't bear to let them go. We thought of adoption but what if their new family didn't want us in their lives? Then Peter got to hear about you and your work, how we can visit and stay over; that is right isn't it?" Her eyes pleaded. Sister Teresa's face was a mask of sympathy.

"Of course, you can come and go as you please, I like to think of us as one large family."

At which Penny burst into tears and buried her head in my chest.

Sister Teresa was tactfully silent for a moment, then spoke kindly. "I'll show you and the boys to their room." She picked up a telephone. "We'll start them in a private room until they know their way around and make friends, then if all goes well, they can move into a dormitory." She smiled at the boys.

Trevor announced thoughtfully, "Lundy Finisterre Irish Sea, cyclonic six mainly north occasionally three at first good, occasionally poor." Then, fixing his eyes on my chin with unusual directness, announced in a rushed voice, "Daddy."

This surprised me, I hadn't asked for or expected this. On the contrary, I had explained to Trevor that he would not be asked to participate in any deception. Morris took this as his cue to throw himself at Penny in what must have been an extremely smelly hug.

"Mummy, Mummy." Then warming to his theme, "Mummy, Mummy, Mummy."

I questioned my judgement now on this suggestion. Morris tends to get a bit handsy with any female contact and lacks the instinct of an actor in the part of a son hugging his mother. I doubted that any scruples about betraying his role would prevent him from 'copping a feel' as I've heard him reference the activity. I suspect Penny was up to this, she improvised superbly, grasping him firmly by both shoulders and holding him safely at arm's length, apparently in order to study his face with tearful maternal affection.

The door opened and a dark-skinned, white-toothed Latino appeared. His smile would probably have got him shot in a bar in Dodge City, he truly looked like a bandit, but with the redeeming feature that he was too much of a cliché to be taken seriously, like a badly made-up extra in a spaghetti western.

His sinister smile was directed at the boys, and while Mo, with his Labrador nature, looked ready to embrace him as his best mate, I noticed that Trevor clutched Max closely to him.

Sister Teresa introduced us. "This is Ramon, one of our staff." And gesturing in turn. "Penelope."

Ramon showed even more of his remarkable dentition as he picked at his teeth, apparently baffled. Eventually he decided with a look that suggested any contradiction would be an act of foolish heroism. "Paquita."

"And this is Peter."

"Ah, Pedro."

I smiled and was rewarded with a whiff of heavily chillied breath.

"And Trevor."

This was apparently another puzzler, but Ramon cracked it in the end. "Tercero."

Trevor stared at the floor and slid Max stealthily behind his back.

"And Morris."

This was another easy one. "Mauricio."

Mo giggled. "Pocahontas."

I glanced casually at Sister Teresa as we turned to follow Ramon and surprised a gleam in her eye that was somehow peculiarly evocative, but I couldn't put my finger on the aetiology. Ramon led us through a maze of corridors with signs indicating numbered and lettered dormitories, kitchen, chapel, medical facility, the place was enormous, and finally room D5 which was actually two rooms. Ramon took his leave with a farewell.

"*Hasta luego.*"

Morris looked disdainful. It was evident to him from his extensive knowledge of action movies that Ramon had got this wrong, inspiring him to rectify the mistake:

"Hasta La Vista," he said jubilantly adding, unwisely I thought, "asshole."

Ramon paused to stroke his stubble murderously before turning noisily on his heavily metalled heels to go.

"Please don't do that Morris," I protested mildly, but still elicited a look of hurt and persecution on Mo's face.

Penny looked around warily. She had briefed me beforehand not to converse freely anywhere indoors, having invented the alibi of being a smoker for us to have a private conversation, and in due course said that she was, 'gasping for a ciggie'. We left the boys to explore and slipped outside. Penny ignored the designated smoking area and headed for the car park. She lit up.

"Feel like I'm back at school." She offered me the packet and I found myself accepting, aware as I did so that my motivation was a rather childish notion that this act somehow increased our intimacy.

"Same with me and I'm a medic for God's sake."

I inhaled. Twenty years not smoking had taken their toll, I felt surprisingly although not unpleasantly light-headed.

"What do you make of her?" I asked.

"You first."

I was flattered that she wanted my opinion.

"Difficult. If it's an act it's incredibly well done, a demeanour of weary benevolence broken by sympathy to a specific prompt…"

"And that makes it real?"

"I was just going to add…"

"Before I interrupted you."

"I would swear she was genuinely interested in the boys, so either real or superbly acted, but against that," Penny watched me with intense concentration, "I caught a look in her eyes just as we were leaving, it was unguarded, a look that was wary, brooding, dangerous and reminded me of something that I couldn't place until just now. That look was, in a certain mood, you."

"I see." If she was surprised by this, she didn't show it. "Anything else?"

"Yes, something that weighs above all others…"

"Trevor didn't offer her the dog?"

"Exactly. And one more thing, she looked up sharply when he did his Bible thing. I wondered what she made of that."

"You don't think Trevor was testing her?"

"Probably not, his Biblical quotes are always scrambled, but I think she suspected it, and it was an unusually ominous and explicit one. Either way, I think it got through to her. Now your turn."

"Fake."

"You sound certain."

"Because I am."

"But you still wanted to know what I thought?"

"Yes, because I'm me. I see it clearly but I see people in a certain way, differently from you. You might disappear up your own arse with contradictions and digressions, but you do see from different angles, unusual in a man."

"Thanks very much."

"And Ramon, an enforcer."

"Mrs T got that right, wonderful dentition though. I saw right back to his upper eights when he gave that wolfish smile. No visible gum recession, not a facultative anaerobe in sight, possibly just good oral hygiene but I read an interesting study on polymorphism in inflammatory mediators and its relation to the risk of periodontal development…"

"Bartlett!" Penny stubbed out her cigarette with a pointed twist of her shoe. "Shut the fuck up."

"Fine way to talk to your husband."

"Come on, remember if I'm right the place is probably wired so keep up the act at all times."

"Can we just check the boys first, I'm worried about them, not so much Mo as Trevor. I don't think he liked the sound of dormitories."

"We'll have made our excuses and left before then."

We headed back in and came across Trevor and Morris in the corridor outside the room. Mo was sitting on a bench with what appeared to be a gentleman of the road. He outdid Mo in the way of dishevelment and was engrossed in a can of super-strength cider, which ironically was specifically proscribed by a poster directly facing him depicting various images of alcohol, all with a large red cross through them. Mo had taken his preoccupation as an invitation.

"Thing is with a big rig, right, yer 'ave to swing out real wide round the corners; sorts the men from the boys it does. My lot, when we had a big load, the gaffer'd say, 'I want Morris for this job.' Insisted on it 'e did. 'Sixty-foot pole trailer, I want Morris.' Every time..."

I was amused that Mo had progressed from a four tonner to a big rig, which I had a feeling belonged to the American freeways rather than the countryside around Godalming.

"Are you OK boys?"

Mo, in the character of a laconic trucker, shrugged casually and stuck a thumb up, and Trevor nodded energetically with a hurried, 'yes,' that told me that he was truly OK. It's a surprise to me how content Trevor is in Mo's company; it's hard to see what benefit he derives from it, particularly his conversation that only reaches banal on a good day. I was reminded of an artist in the Hebrides who had observed an encounter between an orphaned dolphin and a golden retriever, and how they became lifelong friends. I was struck by the parallel in relative intellect and smelliness; retriever's are not terribly bright and infamous for their scent when wet. Just now I was relieved.

Penny led through a maze of corridors following a sign to 'chapel'. An ancient looking wooden door opened into a much older building that must have pre-existed the rest of the complex. Chapel was far too modest a description, cathedral would have been more appropriate, complete with all the Catholic trappings: niches, icons, crucifix and what looked like tombs in the aisles. Penny stopped to bob down on one knee and cross herself. I followed suit as best I could. The place was deserted, she led to the left-hand front pew, lowered her head, and inexplicably took my hand. I had that feeling of before, that electric excitement not felt since a teenager. I assumed this to be part of our enactment rather than the Catholic ritual of which I was ignorant, the expected behaviour of a couple in distressing circumstances. We knelt as if in prayer, but I was aware of some deft and furtive movements alongside. I guessed that this was the spot where Mrs T had observed

Sister Teresa and the Archbishop, and Penny was bugging it. We knelt in silence for a further few minutes, hand-in-hand. I supposed her to be in private thought rather than prayer and as an abrupt punctuation, she rose without warning, pulling me by the hand.

"Time for supper," she explained as we left the chapel. We collected the boys en route and followed the signs. This was the part I was dreading. I am not adventurous in matters of cuisine, only prized away from meat and two veg by the dogged determination of my ex-wife and, since our divorce, I'd sunk back into strict adherence to an extremely limited diet. The refectory was spotless, even if the same could not be said of the clientele. There was even a menu, in which corn on the cob featured in a variety of formats, each of which announced proudly that it was drenched in Mazola. We took our turn in a queue. Trevor appeared to read the menu.

"Dogger rising fair to middling south-east force five, woof, woof. Good boy, Max."

I understood that he wanted me to read it aloud for him. In spite of his advanced reading and comprehension, these faculties are disabled by the presence of strangers around him, probably due to sensory overload. I called out the dishes, watching his face which registered an agitated frown until I reached spaghetti Bolognese at which he nodded his head vigorously.

The place was busy and manned by five chefs. I recognised Ramon, and alongside him four more variations on the same theme, all speaking broken English with the sort of smile that you would expect from an executioner as he opened the trap from beneath you. My turn came. I had studied the options, none of the Mexican dishes appealed, potatoes seemed safe. I had in mind boiled or baked, but was informed by a dangerously moustached face, "Ze Gringo want cheeps."

"Boiled if possible."

"Ze Gringo want cheeps," he repeated threateningly. 'Gringo.' I didn't know this word existed outside the movies. Morris immediately went into spasms of delight.

"Hey, Gringo, pow, pow, pow." He shot me mercilessly with an imaginary six-shooter and blew imaginary smoke from the end.

Penny looked away expressionlessly, I would swear to hide laughter, and later as we sat down whispered in my ear, "Ze Gringo want cheeps."

And again, that feeling of romance and intimacy. Surely, I was not imagining it and yet, I reasoned with a feeling as if someone had poured a gallon of iced water down my neck, the more likely explanation was that this was just part of the play-acting, a deliberate but casual flirtation in order to help enable my role as husband. My problem as ever was my lack of insight into her sphynx-like nature.

We returned to the rooms and played the part of distraught and emotional parents, settling our adopted children into what was to be their new home. I didn't have to act; I was concerned for Trevor who is ritualistic in his routine and upset by any departure from it. He forecast bad weather in the Rockall and Malin in an authoritarian tone and somewhat more gloomily pronounced that three-month copper positions were down by two hundred and forty-seven dollars, then settled into bed, ticking off Max for being noisy. I was reassured: these prognostications were not extreme.

Penny disappeared into the toilet. I undressed and got into bed; this was one preparation we hadn't discussed. I can't bear pyjamas but wore a shirt as a concession to modesty. Penny reappeared in a long white nightgown, a womanly apparition.

"They seem fine don't they, better than I'd expected," she said as she got into bed alongside me.

I agreed. "They've got each other." In spite of the role-playing, I guessed she had picked up on my concern for Trevor. She turned to face me.

"He's OK," She smiled at me with unexpected tenderness. It was not the expression itself that was a surprise — in fact her smile was much as I'd imagined it. No, the shock that was causing a hollow feeling in the pit of my stomach and a contraction of my leg muscles — adrenalin and acetylcholine I analysed out of sheer force of habit, was that I had not imagined this directed, apparently so artlessly and without any trace of self-consciousness, towards me.

While all this coursed through my mind, Penny leant across and kissed me, a peck on the lips in the sexless way of a wife married to her husband for many years. The problem was that we weren't married, had never kissed and the kiss was soft and exquisitely sweet and sent my already charged nervous system into overload. I found that I had closed my eyes and, when I opened them, was startled to find her face only inches away. She studied me thoughtfully and intently, not coldly and analytically as when questioning me, nor with that tenderness of a few moments ago, this time with an expression that, as so often with Penny, I could not fathom.

We awoke to hear Trevor talking in the next room, almost certainly to himself, Mo would be asleep.

"All ruling heaven, his own dark designs to heap damnation on him, seeking evil to others, enraged all his malice served to bring forth infinite grace and mercy. Tempted by the serpent and how thou art lost, guarded by Medusa, a living wight. Thou art cursed above all beasts, upon thy belly shalt thou go — for the lord will execute judgement by fire — all the wicked shall be slain. With expanded wings he steers his flight aloft the dusky hair and all hell trembles under his ghostly advance."

His words were lost to agitated muttering; they were not familiar to me and my mystification must have shown. Penny spoke in something other than her usual matter-of-fact tone.

"*Paradise Lost*, well, sort of... so beautiful."

Trevor entered the room, turned to the wall, pressed himself against it and, unusually, slid sideways with his nose touching. He stopped and banged his head several times.

"Cromarty — violent storm — force twelve — veering north — very high — becoming phenomenal."

He turned away from us quickly and returned to his room. I looked at Penny in silence, shaking my head. I had never seen him this agitated. His shipping forecasts were usually fluent, but this not only sounded like a prophecy of doom but had slipped back to the clipped staccato of his everyday speech.

Penny simulated nonchalance. "I need a ciggie."

After we had dressed, I followed Penny outside. She lit up and handed me the packet. Her expression remained placid.

"What was that?"

"He's spooked."

"I got that, but why all of a sudden?"

"Just what I was wondering. It sounds fanciful but he lives in a different world to us. You say something to him and it's as if he responds to your thoughts rather than your words. I remember one time telling him that I'd been called out and wouldn't be back for a while. On my way out I had promised to leave a prescription with the pharmacist. As I turned to go, I noticed him grimacing in agitation. He struggled hard to meet my eyes — an extremely rare occurrence — and in that moment I understood, he was alerting me. I had forgotten about the prescription, and he knew!"

Penny digested this thoughtfully. "What do you want to do?"

"See if he settles down, I suppose, if not…"

She forestalled me impatiently. "We go."

At this moment I noticed a car parked nearby. It had been fussing me subconsciously for a while and the question emerged: what exactly was it? The colour was a nondescript dirty brown but not a shade I'd seen before, and the shape was familiar yet unfamiliar. I'd have said it was an old Ford Escort were it not for the peculiarly bulbous front wings, almost phallic. I moved to read the badge but couldn't see one. As I did so, one of the chefs, Pedro, approached. Judging from the look he gave me, looking at a man's car was a throat cutting offence in his culture. I attempted a smile.

"*Muy bonito.*"

"Si." He contemplated me darkly and I suspected I had compounded my crime by admitting that I admired his car. I attempted to break the stand-off.

"I don't think I know this model."

His eyes narrowed to slits. "*Esta Sombrero Fandango.*"

"Oh, I've never seen one of those, erm, how many gears does it have?"

Pedro seemed engaged in some inner struggle. Honour and testosterone competed with a man's desire to show off his car. He swallowed and relaxed slightly. I was winning.

"Twelve gears, Gringo."

I wondered if this answer was due to machismo or faulty translation. He fidgeted for a while, the external manifestation of an inner debate.

"You want to see inside?"

"Oh yes please." My enthusiasm was genuine and when he opened the passenger door for me, I looked inside eagerly. I'd never seen anything like it. Once it had undoubtedly been a Ford Escort but now somewhat modified, the seats had been replaced with brightly striped deckchairs, the upholstery ripped out leaving the unpainted inner skin covered in rust. A large cactus sat on the dashboard, to remind the owner of home I guessed, and replacing a cup holder in the centre console, was a bottle of tequila in a wicker basket. But topping the list of indictable motoring offences was a row of holstered guns strapped to the dashboard. The owner pointed to them proudly.

"*Ocho pistolas. Si el Sombrero Fandango es un auto magnifico.*"

He now definitely smiled which was perhaps even more disconcerting than his apparent hostility, his dentition bore poor comparison to Ramon, but I returned his smile and he grasped my hand.

We were interrupted at this touching fraternal moment by some form of commotion. A black limousine was pulling up. A chauffeur opened a rear door solicitously and a familiar figure emerged looking for some reason a bit sheepish: his Right Reverend the Archbishop of Canterbury. I was at this moment vastly relieved that Mo wasn't in attendance, he would almost certainly have introduced himself and I was grateful not to have to witness this.

Sister Teresa appeared smiling benevolently with a peculiar sort of primness. I remembered Penny's words at the outset, 'seducing him with piety', a perfect description of her demeanour now.

She ushered the archbishop inside with a courteously outstretched arm and I was again struck by the grace of her movements. The moment they were inside, Penny indicated with a movement of her eyes for me to follow her; she led apparently casually across the car park to an empty area.

"I'm going to face away from the building, stand as if we're talking and shout if anyone comes near." She rummaged in her handbag. "Better light up again." She did so and handed the pack to me with a look of disgust.

A hiss of white noise emanated from her handbag. Then after a long moment, the sound of footsteps grew louder and a voice grew from an indistinct whisper:

"Thank you, Sister, that would be most welcome."

The sound of rustling and clattering was followed by a long silence and then a sigh.

"I have thought a great deal about our conversation, Sister, and I will confess that my prayer just now was for guidance. I feel my faith tested as never before."

Sister Teresa's voice was soft, conveying that same curious impression of piety. "We have but one faith, Archbishop. You must not torment yourself. I am but a simple nun, I know only one way, one truth, my path is clear, but I do not have the burden of office upon me. My prayer was to The Virgin Mother to guide you at this time of tribulation."

"Thank you, Sister. It is your very certainty that so impresses me and makes me understand why so many of our priests, some of the best I must say, have crossed over to the Roman church. We live in uncertain times in the Anglican community."

"You say the Roman church, but truly it is the Catholic church, all-encompassing and once the very same. The departures made from it were through the politics of man rather than dictation of the Scriptures."

This was followed by a deep sigh. "Indeed. There was a time, Sister, when I would have argued with you, but it is undeniable that the Anglican church was the invention of Henry in order to marry Anne. However, it is more recent developments that make me uneasy, the acceptance of homosexual marriage and female priests, even bishops now."

"As a woman myself I have always understood the teachings of our church, and indeed the Scriptures, that it is not for women to occupy these positions. It is for us to serve in our own way, that is our limitation."

"You are too modest, Sister. Your works here are truly wondrous."

"You flatter me, Archbishop."

This was followed by an even deeper sigh. "Well, I must come to a decision. I understand of course the importance of the Rosary, the veneration of Saints, the seven sacraments..."

Sister Teresa interjected with a note of disapproval. "It is not for us to pick and choose, it is the seven that confer God's grace not just two."

"I admire your rejection of the semantic manipulation that plagues the Anglicans. Your confidence that in the Eucharist, transubstantiation means truly the blood and body of Christ, and your belief, not just in the immaculate conception but also the perpetual virginity of the Holy Mother."

"It is not my intent to convert you, Archbishop. As you well know, it was the Holy Mother who instituted the Rosary."

"Ah, that certainty again, how I envy that."

"Envy is a sin, Archbishop."

"Indeed," he sighed. "How can it be that the leader of the Anglican church harbours such doubts?"

"Your doubts are not of the essence of our faith, Archbishop."

"I know but think of the implications. If I were to embrace your denomination…"

"Why then you would give leadership to a great host who would follow you across the divide, and our churches would once again become one. And who knows," her voice was now like honey, "you have expressed your doubts about the Papacy, how could it be otherwise with your instruction since birth? But the Father is a successor of the apostle, Peter, an unbroken chain of consecration, infallible, uncorrupted by the politics of man…"

A loud snort from Penny startled me and I lost the conversation for a moment. When I rejoined it, Sister Teresa was still talking, her voice like silk.

"And you are a much younger and fitter man than El Papa."

The archbishop's sigh was now more of a groan. "If the good Lord would only give me a sign. I have prayed for it continuously."

"Pray with me now, Archbishop."

There was a moment's rustling, then came the nun's voice, apparently as artless as a child but somehow mesmeric and sinister.

"*Ave maris stella Dei mater alma atque semper virgo felix…*"

Penny's growing irritation broke out. "That's for lost ships. Well, I suppose he is a lost ship, and heading for some fucking big rocks the way he's going."

The nun's voice ceased. The archbishop continued. *"Virgo singularis inter omnes mitis, nos culpis solutos mites fac et castos..."* Then a sudden gasp. "Sister! You see it. The Stigmata!"

Penny's hand reached into her handbag and the device was silenced. "I've heard enough. The old fool is being seduced by flattery and what is undoubtedly some kind of cheap conjuring trick."

"And an element of hypnosis I think, but like His Grace, I am no longer beset by doubt."

"You've done your bit, Bartlett, I need to get cracking."

"What will you do?"

She frowned, giving me the impression that only a few weeks ago she would have told me to mind my own business and probably less politely than that. This almost autonomic reaction animated her expression for a moment, before she relaxed.

"He has to be stopped before he goes over. If I had my way he'd trip over his cassock on the steps of Lambeth Palace and break his stupid neck." She sighed. "But I suppose something more diplomatic will have to be cooked up." She moved suddenly with her characteristic restlessness. "Come on."

We returned to our room, I had to walk fast to keep up. She was the anxious mother once again but the facade nearly cracked on finding that Mo and Trevor had disappeared. In silent concert we started searching the corridors but to no avail.

238

"Try the canteen," I suggested. "Where there's food there's Morris."

Sure enough, I spotted Max the moment we entered the canteen. Mo, as predicted, was stuffing his face. As we moved towards them, my eyes alighted on two figures only yards away. There was something familiar about them, two disreputable tramps, their faces covered in dirt, their trousers splattered with mud. Both had identical straggling grey beards but, as I looked, I saw that they were staring intently at me with some furtive message in their eyes, and I noticed that the colouration of one of their faces was not due to the outdoor life: it was Major alongside Mr Robinson. A whispered curse from Penny announced her recognition, and at that moment another figure alongside them came to life as a disreputable old bag lady with blackened teeth and broken glasses. She shook with what I took to be delirium tremens but revised to uncontrollable emotion as I saw that it was in fact Mrs T stirred by the recognition of her mistress. With a yelp, she lost all control and lurched forward.

"Miss! Oh, miss!" she sobbed and threw her arms around Penny. "Oh, miss." Her bosom heaved. Penny tried to break free. I could see the titanic mastery of self-control that kept a torrent of oaths bottled up. Time seemed to stop still and for some strange reason, in spite of everything happening around me, I became aware of a small movement in the background, a door opening slowly. Sister Teresa appeared at the entrance. I saw her stiffen at the sight before her. She moved swiftly forward with something cat-like and lethal about her movements. I don't know what had alerted her but the look on her face told me that our cover was blown.

A flash of her eyes summoned Ramon and a snap of her fingers bought Pedro and another of the chefs, a rather backward looking individual I had heard called Miguel. In a moment we were surrounded and manhandled to the exit, two more of the chefs appearing from nowhere to gather up Morris and Trevor. Sister Teresa stood to one side, apparently agitated.

"You must go," she pronounced with apparent sadness, presumably for the benefit of the few around us who were aware of the disturbance. I was relieved. This woman frightened me and somehow I had expected something worse than just being chucked out, but my relief was short-lived. With the exit in sight, we were bundled forcibly into a side passage, through a door and down some forbidding and ancient stone steps, opening into a chamber that belonged to the set of a vampire movie. I presumed it to be a crypt under the chapel. Sister Teresa appeared moments later and I was amazed at her transformation; her face was hard and hostile, her eyes no longer opaque but sharp, alert and cruel.

"Search them, pockets, clothes, shoes, everything." She fixed on Penny with an evil stare. "I'll do this one." She seized Penny and marched her off.

The Mexicans set to work. I saw to my alarm the butt of a large gun in a shoulder-holster revealed as

Pedro leaned forwards. My mind started working again. My first thought was for the boys. Trevor's face was a blank mask, he had returned to the condition in which I had found him. As for Mo, he was at that moment being searched by Miguel, but both of their expressions were somehow inappropriate. It seemed they were eyeing each other up. It took me a moment to identify it: a sort of harmony. I fancied this came from the natural affinity that exists between those of low intelligence.

Sister Teresa returned with Penny. A fire burnt in Penny's eyes but she was silent. Sister Teresa photographed us all in turn on a phone, except for Mo and Trevor. She pointed a long finger at Morris, Pedro grabbed him by the arm and followed her to a door. Mo was so obviously simple, it would not require sodium pentathol to get him to talk, just benzodiazepine to get him to stop.

And sure enough, when he was returned a while later his babbling soon revealed the awful truth.

"Nice bird she is, got thing 'bout truck drivers she 'as, fancies me I reckon." He ruminated for a moment. "Only what with bein' a nun an' already married an' that — didn't know they were allowed, but s'orlright in Mexico she said — bloke called Jesus, prob'ly works in the kitchen." Mo zeroed in on me. "Reckon 'e cooked yer chips."

"Someone has cooked our chips for sure," said Penny grimly, at which, much to my surprise and admiration, Major and Mr Robinson sniggered. Of us all, I was apparently the most scared.

"And what else did you chat about?" asked Penny with false sweetness.

"Loads of stuff." Penny groaned. "She reckons you're the sort o' mum who spends all 'er time at 'ome cookin' and lookin' after kids an' that. 'Well, that's just where you're wrong,' I told 'er. 'Got a big job up town ordering loads o' bods 'round: do this, do that — pow, pow.' Fact I told 'er 'alf this lot work fer you an' all. That told 'er I reckon."

Sister Teresa reappeared and addressed our captors. "Tie them up and keep a close watch on that one." She pointed at Penny and the menace of her contemplation was chilling. "Even when she goes to the can, two of you go with her."

Ramon stroked his moustache and swallowed with pornographic pleasure and, as if infected by the proximity of such thoughts, an unpleasant sadistic expression crept across the nun's face.

"In fact, tie her to him." She pointed at me. "She might not find it so pleasant, tied to…" she paused to emphasise with cynicism, "*her husband*."

I was aware of movement out of the corner of my eye, Mrs T squirming in agitation like some enormous larva trapped in a spider's web.

"Oh please, me, let it be me."

All eyes were on her and, as if aware at that moment of how she had revealed herself, she appeared to shrink

242

with embarrassment, which struck me with almost unbearable pathos.

Sister Teresa watched Penny and me being bound together with apparent pleasure. The fact that rope was readily to hand suggested that we were not the first to be imprisoned in this place. We were tied front to front. I wondered if this was some kind of Mexican tradition for the damned. I have to admit that the feeling of Penny so tight against me was intensely pleasurable and it wasn't just the fear mechanism at work, which can heighten sexual response, it was Penny. I felt ashamed though and whispered to her:

"Sorry."

Her thoughts were elsewhere and she turned to me blankly.

"It's not your fault."

This remark was revealing. Since my first encounter with her, Penny had been quick to blame those around her, including myself, for any shortcoming or failure, but it had never been convincing. I guessed that her true nature was to take responsibility for her subordinates' actions. Perhaps, even, this was another echo from her upbringing, the blaming of others from her mother which she emulated as a vaccine mimics the real pathogen but without its potency. So she disowned this trait, her true nature being akin to her father's. My thoughts were interrupted by a cough announcing speech from Major.

"Well, Mr Robinson, it appears we are in something of a jam."

"Indeed, Major, you sum the matter up most succinctly."

"Thank you, Mr Robinson, and while we yet have time, I'd like to take this opportunity to express my gratitude for the great kindness you have shown me since I came to this country. I am sad to tell you it has not always been thus."

"It would be usual to say, 'not always been so'."

"You see! Yet another example of your consideration in helping me perfect my English, such a difficult language." He paused in a graphic facsimile of philosophical contemplation. "It is as though I see my life appearing before me." He sighed. "I was not loved as a child you know."

"Indeed, Major, you surprise me."

"My father had many children in all sorts of so-called dubious circumstances and he took no interest in any of us; quite commonly he would forget our names and several times he muddled me up with the servants."

Mr Robinson sighed. "Allow me to sympathise, Major, I too had a problematic childhood, the truth is, I irritated my father. He would constantly find fault with me and I became nervous in his presence, and of course this just irritated him all the more. 'Stop fidgeting boy,' he'd say."

Major nodded gravely. "It is the chicken and the egg, Mr Robinson."

"Quite so."

"My father enlisted me when I was seventeen. I had done well in my exams, you see, so I gained my commission as you know. But I didn't like the army."

"Really?"

"No, my regiment was sent to Kashmir, a most unsanitary place, no running water for the erm…"

"Ablutions."

Major beamed with pleasure. "Exactly, you put it in the nutshell. So I came back home. I was not welcome. I found my mother had changed."

"I'm sorry to hear that, Major. Had she become depressed perhaps? My mother was depressed."

"No, no, you misunderstand me, my father had changed her for another woman. And worse than that, he himself had become very queer, eccentric in fact. On one occasion he made me smoke his pipe."

"Most distressing for you, I imagine."

"He had developed the persecution complex, I'm afraid. You see, we had a Sikh servant and ever since the assassination of Mrs Gandhi, my father was convinced the poor man was out to get him, and made his children taste his food and smoke his pipe before him."

Mr Robinson nodded glumly. "My father was a cruel man, he worked in the Surtax office."

Major sighed. "We have so much in common, you have been a shining example to me of an English gentleman."

Mr Robinson opened his mouth to reply but was interrupted by Pedro spitting venomously on the floor. I had noticed him listening with an increasing darkness in his expression.

"English gentleman!" He snorted. "English, what are the English? Bloody parasites, snobs, friends of America."

"America!" Ramon joined in the spitting with arguably even greater venom. "They build a wall."

"We hate America," added Miguel as if explaining to anyone who might not have cottoned on, reinforcing my suspicion that he was from the Mexican branch of Mo's family.

"They have offshore earnings," said Pedro obscurely.

"Billions of pesos," agreed Ramon.

"They make TV documentaries about us," added Pedro with brooding hostility.

"And trade disputes," said Ramon, unholstering his gun ominously.

"They think we're stupid," added Miguel, and then apparently unsettled by a stare of inescapable scorn from the other two, shouted, "They call us *Pajaritos*."

Pedro spat again. "And bandits," he said angrily, his mouth working, a particularly pronounced example of psychomotor agitation, so that I should not have been surprised when he pulled out his gun and fired into the ceiling — but I was. The noise was appalling. Ramon pulled out his noticeably larger gun, which I suspect signified the pecking order amongst them, and fired twice. Miguel followed suit in a parody of a bad-guy in a western and emptied six chambers into the ceiling, earning him a frown of disapproval from the other two.

Sister Teresa appeared suddenly, looking annoyed. She folded her arms like a schoolmistress and demanded, "Who did that?"

Pedro and Ramon pointed accusingly at Miguel.

"And who started it?"

Their fingers stabbed again towards Miguel, but I noticed that Ramon swallowed hard with a noticeable movement of his Adam's apple: a classic indicator of lying.

Miguel opened his mouth to protest but a murderous look from Ramon silenced him.

Sister Teresa gave Miguel an impressively filthy look and announced imperiously, "Three Ave Maria's and six prostrations."

She turned to go, leaving Miguel reluctantly lowering himself onto the floor while muttering what sounded more like a Morrris-type whinge than a Hail Mary. Morris in fact was predictably outraged.

"That's out of order that is, 'e never started it."

Mr Robinson ignored all this and continued serenely. "You were kindly saying, Major, that I had influenced you in acquiring the attributes of a gentleman, and I was about to respond, before the rather unseemly interruption, that I would say the same of you."

"But an Indian gentleman, Mr Robinson, it is hardly the same."

Mr Robinson appeared to concede the point. "Well, I believe there is a residential course that can be taken for that sort of thing, in Tunbridge Wells if I remember rightly."

I could feel Penny becoming restless and found myself being rotated in order for her to address Major and Mr Robinson over my shoulder.

"Oy, you two, put a cork in it and explain what you're doing here."

Major and Mr Robinson looked jointly pained at this.

Mrs T burst out, "It's all my fault, Miss. You see what with you being away and no one knowing where you were, I was worried and the Major, he noticed. 'You look worried, Mrs T.' Those were his very words, he's so thoughtful, the Major."

"Thank you, madam." Major bowed his head.

"And Mr Robinson, he was worried too."

"Because they're girls," snapped Penny spitefully.

Mrs T looked doubtful. "Well, we got to talking and I have to admit I told them about you sending me to this place, and me having promised I wouldn't tell for all that. I'm so sorry."

"Yes, and we know why, because they wormed it out of you."

Mr Robinson opened his mouth to protest but Penny cut him short. "Oh, yes you did. Don't even dream of denying it, I know you two, and I know why! Because you're both so fucking nosey." She was getting worked up. In novels and drama, you hear of bosoms heaving with emotion, being tightly roped to a rather imposing one made me an intimate witness to the phenomenon, and an almost unconscious sigh must have betrayed my thoughts, because Penny broke off suddenly.

"Are you all right, Bartlett?"

"Nice of you to ask. Perhaps you could give me a bit of notice when you're going to inhale deeply, just to give me a chance to prepare."

"Excuse me for breathing," she replied huffily. She had misunderstood my remark, taking it as a genuine complaint, and she yet again surprised me. This beautiful, as I had come to realise, woman, seemed quite unaware of the fact.

Mr Robinson raised his head and sniffed, as if to check that this unpleasant interruption had wafted away.

"I was just about to say, Major, that it is I who am indebted to you. Before I met you, I was somewhat reserved."

"No, no, don't say that," Major protested.

"I assure you I was. I have learnt a great deal from you. I do so admire how you are able to reveal your feelings." I felt and heard Penny snort in my ear. Mr Robinson continued. "Your example has been an inspiration to me, allowing me to reciprocate without the fear of censure that has debilitated me since

249

childhood. Unfortunately, my mother was a cold woman," he sighed. "As indeed is my wife."

Major nodded sympathetically. "Ah yes, the so-called lie back and think of England."

"Quite so," agreed Mr Robinson.

"My mother beat me on the back of the legs with a spoon."

"Most distressing. Would that be for sniffing?"

"It would."

"Ah," said Mr Robinson with deep significance.

"A most bad-tempered woman," said Major sadly.

"I don't know which is worse, cruelty or coldness? I fell off my bicycle once and broke my leg. I'm afraid to say I cried."

"Understandable, surely."

"Thank you for that, Major, you are most consoling. I remember my mother clicking her tongue with disapproval, she considered it bad form to cry. My father complained that she was an emasculating woman. He used to breed fox terriers and she had his champion sire neutered. She did it without malice, just her instinctive reaction to the sight of the male apparatus. She even muffled the chimes of the grandfather clock. You could hear the stifled clicks as it attempted to strike. On one occasion, I caught a tear of sympathy on my father's cheek."

Major nodded glumly. "I couldn't do anything right for my mother. If anything got broken, somehow fault would be ascribed to me, even when she knew perfectly well it was the servants."

Morris had been following this with growing outrage and broke in suddenly, "Yeah, well that's typical that is. My mum used ter blame me fer everyfink even when I dun nuffin'. 'It'll be that wretched Morris, no wonder 'is dad left.' 'Useless boy,' she called me, 'never add up to a can o' beans.' Eat 'er words she would if she saw me now. Coo, not arf, like to see 'er face when I'm leanin' mi elbow out the cab of a big rig."

We were rescued from this conversation which, with the addition of Mo, had sunk to a new level of dreadfulness, by the arrival of Sister Teresa smoking a cigarette. She approached Penny with a look of casual malevolence.

"MI5, as I thought, poking your nose in where it doesn't belong. I picked up on your stooge last month, and now you turn up with your circus act." She turned to our captors. "Watch this one real close." A flicker in her expression was familiar to me. I realised with interest that she was more than just wary of Penny, she was afraid of her.

A sudden burst of organ music made me jump, Bach's *Toccata and Fugue in D minor*. For a sinister moment I thought the chapel organ had come to life but the source was revealed when Sister Teresa withdrew a mobile phone from within her habit and glided from the room with that peculiarly fluid movement.

I whispered in Penny's ear, "What do you think she'll do with us? I mean if the archbishop crosses over it'll be too late, won't it? And we won't be a threat to her so she might let us go, do you think?" I added hopefully.

Penny whispered back, "Sorry, Bartlett, not a hope in hell. We're witnesses. Yes, she'll disappear but so will we. She'll probably try and find out more from us first, which won't be pleasant I'm afraid."

I felt the sensations of deoxygenation in the gut as my sympathetic nervous system kicked in but was distracted by a vision that appeared lucidly with no obvious association. A memory of passing Mulberry Ward one night and seeing the poor Colonel at the door, his mouth open in terrible distress, trying desperately to escape from whatever dreadful hallucination tormented him. So was this thought hammering on the door of its incarceration in my subconscious.

"There's something about the way she moves."

A voice in my ear, so close that it was eerily like a reply from inside my head, replied, "I hope you're not going to sing, Bartlett."

"Sorry?"

"It's the start of a song, isn't it: 'Something in the way she moves, attracts me like no other lover'."

"Oh, I see, no, it's the nun. I'm not saying I've ever met her before, in fact I'm sure I haven't, but there is something about the way she moves that reminds me of someone and I can't for the life of me think who. You see…"

A groan in my ear interrupted me. "You're off on one again, aren't you?"

"Well, I was going to tell you about one of my theories. Would you rather I didn't?"

"Much rather but then again, I'm not going anywhere just now, and it can't be worse than listening to those two. In fact, it would be horribly true to say that you have a captive audience."

"OK. A bit of a hobby horse of mine."

"There's a surprise."

"What we were talking about in the restaurant, how there are certain patterns in people that repeat and the ability to recognise them is what makes for good people watchers."

"Oh fuck, I'm tied up to Miss Marple."

"Perfect example. She recognised templates of behaviour, for example, a furtive expression in a peer of the realm would subliminally recall a maid who'd stolen the silver. But my interest is wider than that. How is it that I passed an African girl in the street a while ago and her facial expression was identical to that of an ex-girlfriend who was ethnically white British? Is it because genetic variation is limited and patterns will repeat just as a line of cherries on a fruit machine? Or is it really…"

"Bartlett?" Again, I was shocked at the closeness of her voice, it sounded weary.

"Have you ever wondered why your wife left you? It's just that I might be able to help you there."

I was hurt by this; she sounded genuinely irritated. I lapsed into silence. I felt her move against me and to my surprise her cheek brushed briefly against mine, unmistakably an apology. I tuned back into Mr Robinson.

"I thought at the time it was my father who had insisted on boarding school but found out subsequently it was my mother."

"Dear me," said Major sympathetically.

"Indeed, and she had informed the headmaster that it would help me adjust if I was not allowed to telephone home."

Pedro's voice cut in unexpectedly: "Ees no way for a *madre* to behave. In *México*, *madres* love their *chamacos*."

This was greeted by a chorus of, '*Si*' from the others.

Mr Robinson took this rightly or wrongly as sympathy. "Thank you, gentlemen. You are of course quite right."

Major joined in and the conversation continued with Miguel and Morris taking it in turns to echo the sentiments of the others. Their voices droned and receded, Penny's chest rose and fell, and amazingly in spite of our situation a peculiar peace came over me, as if in a quiet place like a library or a museum when people speak around you in hushed voices and a tingling runs up your spine to the back of your head. It is known as autonomous sensory meridian response and is used in relaxation therapy.

My mind slowed. Without being aware of transition into sleep, I found myself in an old-fashioned red telephone box. Outside was nothing but bare grey rock bathed in silver light, the same silver light that had illuminated Penny's face from her phone in the hotel room. A voice berated me through the Bakelite receiver in my hand, not an angry voice, just concerned and loving, telling me that my dinner was ready, how long I would be? It took me a while to identify the voice as Penny's. I had strayed further from home than intended, I was on the Moon and I'd better get going straight away or I was going to miss my lunch, which didn't worry me in itself, it was just that I was late. Then for the first time came fear: if the rocket motor failed to start, I would be stranded. The fact that I must return by rocket, even though one was not in sight, was a truth that somehow avoided being twisted out of shape by the apparent illogicality of dreams. There was no escalator, lift-shaft or Narnian puddle, there was a rocket. The fear was not extreme, merely an awareness that my life depended on it firing up, just as once I had swum out to sea in the middle of the night, drunk as a lord on a Mediterranean holiday and found myself a mile out of my depth.

I was on my way now; there was the earth, blue and silver in front of me, but I was struggling to stay on course and a voice from the telephone receiver, still in my hand, registered alarm.

"Bartlett." Then again, "Bartlett." Louder and right in my ear. I awoke.

"Sorry."

"I can't believe you'd nodded off." I was amused to detect admiration in her voice.

"Strange dream," I murmured.

"Well seeing as it's you, it would be, wouldn't it?"

"I was in a telephone box on the moon, you could tell from the basalt, it was once volcanic you see, and…"

"Let's not venture further into outer space."

"You were in it too, you were telling me my dinner was ready."

"Mucky one then."

"I often dream about being on the moon, according to Freud it signifies…"

"Fascinating, but back in the real world, look what's going on with Trevor."

I jostled us around slightly for a better view. Trevor was in full flow…

"La Mancha before the Elba, the caves of Altamina, San Juan de Banos, Visigoths of Toledo, renegade Berbers in the Western Maghreb, Egilora, Aragon Parkas from the Taifas, Rodriga Diaz, Al-mutamid of Seville, Machado's lament, wretched Castile, once supreme now forlorn wrapping herself in rags closes her mind in scorn. Guernica."

During this speech the Mexicans gathered round in what struck me as comical bewilderment, as if he were some creature escaped from the castle, to be prodded curiously with pitchforks. They were stunned into silence, eventually broken by Pedro.

"*De que en el nombre de Dios esta hablando?*" Which my limited Spanish translated as: "What in the name of God is he talking about?"

Trevor's speech changed suddenly to what I guessed to be Mexican Spanish. I speak enough bad Spanish to know that this sounded different, although the puzzled reaction of our captors made me conclude that it was, as usual, garbled. Ramon approached Trevor, his movement looked menacing, although it occurred to me that the man was so heavily infused with testosterone that he was probably incapable of movement that did not look menacing. Indeed, his expression had a peculiar openness, almost shyness.

"Where the *hombre* learn *Mexicano*?"

Trevor predictably being addressed directly, closed into silence and Pedro answered for him.

"The south by the sound of it, a *Gachupines Lepero como Miguel. El no es una Comanchero como somos* — a Gachupin vagrant like Miguel, not a Comanchero like us." At which he shared a coarse laugh with Ramon which appeared to be at Miguel's expense.

Trevor reanimated from silent mode. "*Las Puentes.*"

"This was met by a stunned silence. Pedro looked afraid, more than afraid: spooked.

"You know my town, *hombre*? How you know my town? She is a pueblo, we have only a ranch, a shop, a bar, no more. How you know my town?"

Again, Trevor was silent. Ramon shook slightly as he spoke. "*No me gusta esta brujería.* I don't like this witchcraft."

Trevor glanced at Ramon's neck, looked away, and said, "Chihuahua." Inspiring Mo to bark like a dog and Trevor to giggle in response.

Ramon lurched backwards as if struck in the face. "Aaagh."

Miguel crossed himself and started praying, rocking as he did so.

"*Padre nuestro que estas en los cielos santificado sea tu nombre...*"

Trevor giggled again, he was enjoying this. "*Ocosingo.*"

Now they all sank to their knees to join Miguel in prayer. I had the feeling that they were now so overwhelmed, that somehow we should be able to take advantage of this situation, and as ever one jump ahead of me, a voice in my ear addressed Trevor.

"And Sister Teresa?"

Trevor dropped his gaze to the floor. His mouth worked. I could see that he wanted to answer but could not overcome the circuit resistance within.

Pedro answered for him with apparent reverence. "Ze Sister is a daughter of the Chinchimeca from Bajio, one of the ancient tribal areas."

Trevor stared blankly for a long moment before shaking his head emphatically. "No."

Sister Teresa chose this moment to re-enter the room, bending herself around the door with that peculiar languid grace, firing up the embers of my memory to a glowing red that threatened flame but didn't quite make it.

She pointed to Penny. "Untie her," adding with sinister menace, "let's see what she knows."

"San Angelo," said Trevor suddenly.

Pedro frowned ominously and turned to Ramon. "You know this place?"

There was an unspoken ease and shared dominance between these two that ascended the others, I had noticed it in the canteen, labelling them in my thoughts as the two alpha males of the pride.

Ramon shook his head.

Pedro turned to Trevor respectfully. "Where this place, amigo?"

I saw that Ramon darted a doubtful glance towards Sister Teresa.

Trevor battled heroically, his lips worked in silence for a full minute before eventually finding voice and rushed out the single damning word: "America."

Pedro frowned and his voice was laden with menace. "America!"

Sister Teresa appeared unaware of her danger. "What's the simpleton talking about?" she said with a sneer and a dismissive gesture, that caused her to raise her head and arch her neck, and by this movement I knew her. The smouldering embers burst into flame. I saw her in another place at another time, making just that gesture of contempt in response to a hostile question from a journalist. In my mind's eye, her dark hair transformed into a cascade of golden curls, and her pale lips blazed red.

"Jemima! Charlie Vanilla's wife."

The Mexicans turned to me, their faces convulsed by hatred of this name that was anathema to all Mexicans, the redneck US politician who wanted to imprison and return all Mexican emigres and had deeply offended them by calling them some very rude names, and his wife, although ex-wife now, erotic dancer, actress and glamour-puss who lived only for pleasure and offended the dispossessed the world over with her ostentatious display of wealth and arrogance to the poor.

"Charlie Vanilla!" hissed Pedro.

Ramon stared at Sister Teresa doubtfully.

She snorted mockingly at me, "That won't do you any good."

At this moment our fate hung in the balance.

It was Mrs T that delivered the coup de grâce. She announced her presence with a quiet cough and said, shamefacedly, "I think you'll find Jemima has a tattoo high up on her left thigh."

"Trust her to know," whispered a voice in my ear.

Sister Teresa blanched and tried to sneer dismissively but I could see that this had got through to Pedro whose suspicion had fledged into menace. He lifted the fingers of his right hand in a chilling gesture. Sister Teresa shrank back but it was too late. He moved like some beast of the jungle and her habit was lifted to reveal on her left thigh, the scarlet effigy of a showgirl dancing the cancan, not what one expects a nun to be sporting under her habit, or lacy blue knickers for that matter, evidently appreciated by Mrs T though, who let out a suspiciously low moan.

There was a moment of stunned silence broken by Penny. "Tie her up."

Events moved fast now. Pedro ignored some unholy language not normally heard from the mouth of a nun to tie up Sister Teresa, while the others set about untying the rest of us with muttered apologies; evidently an enemy of their enemy was a friend. The rope was loosened and fell away. I breathed in, a deep sighing breath, an unconscious expression of regret, but to my surprise I felt Penny still against me, held by some mysterious inertia. Time stopped still. I heard Major speak.

"Allow me to be the first to congratulate you on your timely release, Mr Robinson."

"Thank you, Major, and my congratulations extend to you also. Of course, little good ever comes to those who hinder servants of the Crown in the execution of their duties."

I felt Penny twitch as if waking from sleep and felt her draw away. "I zoned out," she explained. I fought a strong impulse to hold her in my arms and kiss her but the spell was broken. She snapped at Major and Robinson.

"Stop goofing off, you two." Maybe not the best time for Americanisms I thought. "And as for you." She lunged suddenly towards the now defenceless nun and lashed out with a vicious and professional looking right hook to the jaw. The nun slumped to her knees with a short involuntary sigh of exhaled breath; for a moment I thought she was going to pass out.

"That's for the nasty fucking body search."

Mrs T appeared to wake from reverie. "Oh, miss, did she... you know?" she asked hopefully.

"Never you mind what she did," replied Penny grimly.

Sister Teresa lowered her eyes and I was struck by the similarity of her demeanour in defeat to Penny's, she was shut down, her defiance on mute. Like opposing queens on a chessboard, one is black and one is white but they're both queens.

And that was the end of our adventure. Penny dropped us off at the hospital. Mo and Trevor seemed none the worse for their experience, in fact on the way back Morris spent some time explaining to Penny how she was holding the steering wheel wrongly, a common mistake amongst passenger car drivers, particularly women, apparently. Penny seemed distrait. I would be picked up tomorrow for debriefing, and with a curt reminder not to tell anybody anything she was gone.

I made a brief appearance on the ward, settled in Mo and Trevor and headed for home. I was hungry and thirsty but agitated rather than tired. I poured a large whisky and noticed that my hand shook, I reassured myself that it was unlikely to be early-onset Parkinson's and put it in my pocket to quieten it. I felt the unfamiliar shape of the packet of cigarettes. Penny had handed them to me and distracted, I had put them in my pocket. I had no intention of making this a habit but at this moment I had a craving to light one and, as I drew in the smoke, recognised the motivation for this as the association with Penny.

Yet again I found myself hopelessly bewildered by her behaviour towards me. The whisky lifted my spirits, there was something between us, I was sure; she had held herself against me for that long moment after we had been untied. But this moment, like others I tallied in my mind, was a lapse from her normal cold cynicism, the question was, which revealed her true feelings? This commanded my obsessive analysis but it was a complex equation that expressed the inconstancy of her mood and had too many variables to be resolved.

Weary at last, I took myself to bed where the search for an answer continued in my dreams. I woke with the knowledge of a simple truth: I was in love.

Major and Mr Robinson were shepherded in by Sister Harris around mid-morning dressed as hippies, looking uncomfortable and smiling sheepishly.

"Gentlemen to see you, Doctor, from the, erm, Social Services."

I read Penny's acidic humour behind this, her take on my profession. I was not amused, unlike Sister Harris whose curled lip was easily deciphered.

She stood back and appraised them for a long moment, announcing cryptically before she left, "Interesting if true."

"I trust you slept well, Doctor?" Major enquired politely. "And none the worse for your experience wouldn't you say, Mr Robinson?"

"I would, Major, glowing I would say. Of course, under some circumstances being tied up has its compensations."

"You took the words out of my mouth," agreed Major enthusiastically.

"Gentlemen, we've had this conversation. Shall we get on with it?"

Mr Robinson sighed. "Have it your own way, Doctor, it's just that…"

We were interrupted at this moment by Brian. I suspected Sister Harris of being behind his appearance, more than likely she had told him the undertakers had returned, but on this occasion, I maligned her unfairly.

Brian clasped his hands like a vicar and smiled at us all ingratiatingly. "Ah, Doctor. I understand there has been a mining disaster in Peru. I need to know how many are trapped."

"Sorry, Brian, I can't help you there and I have to go out with these gentlemen."

"I see."

We left him looking downcast.

The journey seemed slower and more tedious than usual and I stared suspiciously at the now familiar underground garage, imagining the staged set of an episode of *Mission Impossible*.

One look at Penny's face revealed her worst mood and I smiled inwardly at my notion of romantic possibilities the night before, but my smile must have slipped out of the confines of my thoughts because she rounded on me irritably.

"I've no idea what you're smiling at."

I was good for that one and looked at her innocently. "Just at seeing you again."

"Oh." She appeared taken aback and I felt a moment of pride at having achieved this, I doubt if in our early association anything I could have said would have had the power to disconcert her.

"Debriefing," she said brusquely. "I don't think this is going to find its way into the press but you never know, someone in the mission might have snapped something." She addressed me. "In your case it's simple, you know absolutely nothing. Just look bewildered, no difficulty for you there, and don't get involved in answering any questions about anything other than to suggest that you've been mistaken for someone else. The archbishop has been taken care of."

"Not fallen down the steps of Lambeth Palace, I trust?"

"No, unfortunately his Right Reverend Dumbass has been under a lot of pressure recently and has had some sort of a breakdown. I hear he's been sectioned. I expect he'll make a full recovery, providing he doesn't mouth off."

I protested. "But surely no doctor would authorise…"

"Bartlett, leave it. I've been here all night and I'm not good at patience at the best of times, as you may know," she added dryly.

Major and Mr Robinson nodded with an unheroic lack of conspicuousness.

"And Jemima?"

"I spent some time with her," said Penny grimly. "She should be safely on a plane by now. There will be a new appointment at the mission, a genuine one this time, and it's not in their interest or ours to go public on it."

"Their?"

"Coming to that, you've heard of the Illuminati?"

"Yes, masons, Knights Templar, the Bilderberg group, et cetera, but I thought it was all bunkum."

"And so it is, but even though they haven't existed as an organisation for over a hundred years, there is a revival in all but name of a matrix of the Western elite who club together in matters of vested interests. You'd be surprised if you knew who really pulled the strings behind the scenes in this country for instance. But I digress, I knew this was coming from the top, I just wasn't sure where. There have been rumours of Charlie Vanilla being a prime mover for some time and it seems the divorce from Jemima was just a gambit to free her from public scrutiny. We think she's his right hand."

"Curious name for a redneck's wife."

"I know I'm going to regret this, but why?"

"Because Jemima was an eighteenth-century Welsh heroine who single-handedly rounded up a group of inebriated would-be French invaders with a pitchfork and marched them into town, Fishguard I think but…"

"Stop you there, Bartlett. I want a bath, breakfast, but right at this moment, more coffee…" She turned to her omnipresent cleaning lady. "Please, Mrs T." She resumed with an ill-tempered frown. "Not a lecture on Welsh heroines. In any case, she's as American as apple pie if all the, 'goddamn mother-fuckers', she threw at me are anything to go by."

"But redneck Americans, what's their game trying to subvert the UK?"

"And that's exactly what they have been doing."

I could have done without Major and Mr Robinson's patronising smiles at this juncture. Penny continued.

"There are certain factions in the US who believe that NATO is an expensive one-sided commitment that they'd rather like to be out of, and if the UK goes tits up, they know the whole thing will fall flat on its face."

Major and Mr Robinson managed a simultaneous patronising smile.

"They have no love for the Germans," explained Major.

"And they'd ditch the French like a shot," added Mr Robinson.

I was pleased to see Penny glaring at them with irritation. "The problem is these people are everywhere, including this place. I've suspected it for a long time, suspects get tipped off, arrests get cocked up, in a word, spokes in the wheel, and I've got a pretty good idea who the principals are."

"Female intuition?"

Penny glowered at me.

"I'm not mocking, it's not without substance. Women exhibit greater activity in the prefrontal cortex as well as having enhanced blood flow to the limbic areas."

She didn't answer, apparently lost in thought. Then, with renewed attention, "Anyway, I'm going to root the buggers out and I'm going to enjoy it." Her eyes gleamed dangerously and her lower jaw extended defiantly.

Coffee arrived. I sipped mine approvingly, it was strong and dark. But somehow this seemed a symbol of finality, all was said, when I had finished, that would be it, I would be taken back to my workplace, the paths of our lives had crossed briefly and would now diverge for ever... unless? I studied her face. Her mind appeared turned in, she had left our conversation behind and moved on to the task before her. Her eyes turned unexpectedly on me, for a moment bright but instantly moody with irritation that found sudden expression.

"I don't like that look on your face."

"I wasn't aware that I had one."

Her irritation increased. "Oh yes you have, I recognise it, that psycho-bloody-analyse look. And just in case it crossed your mind to publish a crap, thinly-veiled profile of yours truly, forget it very fast."

"Absolutely not," I said curtly, irritated myself now, which earnt me an aggressive frown.

Major and Mr Robinson shifted weight uneasily, weirdly co-ordinated, further evidence of quantum entanglement I concluded.

"No?" she said sceptically. "Well try not to sound quite so fucking dismissive, because that's exactly what you did to thingummyjig and what's-his-face."

"I won't rise to that," I said coldly. I looked at her curiously. She was spoiling for a fight and I wondered why. The effect of lack of sleep on an irritable nature, or something more personal? I was trying to keep my temper, but my anger broke through.

"I'll tell you what I will rise to though, when you dropped us off yesterday, you barely managed the courtesy of a goodbye and not a word of thanks to those boys. Not so much Morris but Trevor knew we were in danger and almost certainly saved your life — all our lives."

This had dramatic effect. Mr Robinson and Major looked at their shoes like errant schoolboys, and Mrs T stopped mid-dusting, holding the cloth to her chest, curiously evocative of respect, as if she were bearing a wreath at a funeral.

Penny stared at me, her eyes were bright, her mouth slightly parted, her anger vapourised into surprise.

I was spent. I felt awkward now, tired, exposed and foolish at the memory of my romantic fantasy. I just wanted to be alone.

"If you've done with me, I'd like to go now."

Major and Mr Robinson took this as their cue to escort me. Penny crossed the room and offered her hand.

"Thank you, Bartlett."

I was confused, she was not contrite, and certainly not ashamed, but her thanks seemed sincere. Against every instinct I started to speak, for the simple but compelling reason that I knew that if I didn't, I would regret it for the rest of my life. I was still holding her hand; if I let it go, I couldn't do this.

"I did think, wondered really, if you'd…"

I caught her by surprise. I felt a tremor in her hand as it disengaged from mine, but she read my intent in an instant and cut me off.

"You'll never see me again, Bartlett." She turned. The door closed behind me.

I struggled with her expression afterwards: fierce, angry, ice-cold, all of these. And strangely, later that evening, my mood boosted by a large brandy, it was this that consoled me, her reaction was too extreme. I remembered a time so many years ago when Caroline and I first dated, knowing nothing of women, her behaviour bewildered me. Taking extreme offence over what seemed like nothing, rudeness, insults, moodiness and sulks. The explanation when it came, that she was in love with me, was a revelation. There was no direct comparison to Penny's behaviour, but the very fact that these long-forgotten memories had been stirred, made me suspicious, somewhere in my subconscious mind, the place that modern psychology is so dismissive of, there was a cue. I pictured the determined set of her jaw as if in defiance of some inner opposition as she spoke those awful words: "You'll never see me again."

I slept fitfully that night and, in the morning, determined to have a quiet hour alone in my office devoted to drinking extra strong coffee. I sneaked past Sister Harris; I should have been alerted by her, "Morning

Doctor." It had a smirk in it, and when I opened my office door, I found a young man spinning himself around in my chair. At the sight of me he decamped with embarrassed apologies and introduced himself as Sebastian.

"Sebastian?"

"Witzer."

"Oh right, and you are?"

This went on for some time, he expected me to know who he was and I didn't have a clue, and two people both shy by nature conspire to extend the lifespan of an embarrassing moment for some considerable time.

Sebastian was a rookie psychologist. He'd got his degree and had his sights set on a clinical psychology doctorate, caught up in the strange trap that besets his profession, namely that you can't get clinical experience without a job and you can't get a job without clinical experience. For two years he'd taken what work he could get, counselling and therapy on a voluntary or low-paid basis and finally landed himself a job at the hospital in my team, but no one had told me.

I've learnt to trust my first impressions but every now and again I get it spectacularly wrong, so it was with Sebastian. He was tall, lithe and intelligent looking, but what made my heart sink was the so carefully cultivated image. He had elaborately coiffured thick black hair, almost shaved at the back and sides but luxuriously moussed on top, he wore vintage, black-framed spectacles from a time when the NHS material of choice was cellulose acetate, his trousers were broad and baggy but immaculately pressed with huge turn-ups, he wore a thick black cotton shirt with only two buttons and a large collar. In short, he looked like he'd spent several hours in make-up for a nineteen fifties film. I am ashamed to say that I took his appearance as an index of his nature. My prejudice was founded on past experience, and I anticipated the arrogance, affectation, shallowness and narcissism that would accompany such a crafted image.

Sebastian followed me around like a dog and, like a dog, demanded an enormous amount of attention. He accompanied me on ward visits, sat in on assessment and therapy sessions and wanted to know everything: diagnosis, my reasoning for same, treatment options and medication, prognosis — on top of which he had an endless flow of chatter on a vast array of eclectic subjects, one minute launching into a detailed analysis of an avant-garde movie he had just watched, only to ask me moments later if I knew that a teaspoonful of matter from a collapsed star, known as a magnetar, would weigh sixty billion tonnes and, if dropped, would cut straight through to the centre of the earth, which I pointed out was quite likely — being dropped that is — since most teaspoons carrying sixty billion tonnes were likely to bend. This remark caused Sebastian to push his glasses more firmly up his nose in a characteristic gesture in order to survey me carefully. He was weighing me up.

He met Trevor and they took to each other, Sebastian being offered Max readily to pat, which he did, making a fuss of him as if it were the most natural thing in the world. This counted well with me, and I was further impressed by his encounter with Morris. Sebastian introduced himself, Mo rocked onto the outer edges of his Wayfinders and responded with, "Orlright?", then pointed at Sebastian's haircut. "Coo, look at that. Where'd yer get that? Whoever dun that saw yer comin', mate. I'd ask fer yer money back. Gone mental at the back 'e 'as — that's 'cos you couldn't see what 'e was up to — 'avin' a laugh 'e is. Then 'e gets to the top and time for a tea break, I reckon."

A fairly typical Morris monologue, followed by more pointing, an outbreak of sniggering, a few more 'coo's and a 'bloody Nora'.

I observed Sebastian and saw that he was amused rather than offended which added to my growing suspicion that I had misjudged this young man. I was pleased that I'd restrained myself from expressing my earlier irritation.

After a few weeks I suggested that he should lead a psychotherapy session with me riding shotgun. The patient was a young woman with generalised anxiety disorder. She'd been near to the end of her course when her therapist had been taken sick. The treatment was a type of cognitive behavioural therapy known as imaginal exposure. Sebastian's session started out along this path well enough, but progressively wandered off until unrecognisable as any form of therapy, becoming as rambling and unstructured as his everyday conversation. He digressed, became emotionally involved, at one point giving her an awkward hug when she became tearful. He shared his personal experiences with her. I shuddered at the thought of any of my colleagues being witness to this and yet, in spite of everything, I could see how well she responded to him. Somehow his sincerity shone through, she opened up, trusting not just in him but in his ability to help her.

I grew to like Sebastian. He'd been holding back another side to his nature; he was in fact far shrewder and more cynical than his open optimism suggested. He also had a wicked sense of humour.

We got to discussing case histories. We aired the well-worn classics: a case of visual agnosia, where a man mistook his wife for a hat and went round patting fire hydrants in the belief that they were the heads of small children; a sufferer from Clerambault's syndrome, convinced that the Queen's Christmas message was purely for his benefit, a transparent and brazen attempt to seduce him; and a bizarre case of delusional disorder, causing a man to get up each morning, don a black and white shirt with numbers printed front and back, chain himself to a metal ball and spend the day breaking rocks in his garden, singing convict songs, convinced that he was in a chain gang. Seb thought this a comment on the human condition.

We turned to personal experience. I was interested to hear that Seb had encountered a case of an 'alter', which as far as I'm concerned is the unicorn of our profession; the only case I had come across I didn't believe was genuine. An alter is a manifestation of what used to be called multiple personality disorder, a dissociative disorder whereby a person can have more than one distinct identity without either having knowledge of the other, sometimes with marked physiological differences such as different handwriting, voices, vocabulary, partners and life experience: the true meaning of living a double life. Seb's story was of one alter becoming afraid of another, and the host, or main personality, fled his home and identity in an attempt to escape the other. I accused him of pulling my leg and he admitted that it was anecdotal but maintained it was of authentic provenance.

In turn, I told Seb about a case reported to me by a psychotherapist colleague, much more commonplace but bizarrely comical, of a happily married couple drifting apart with no apparent cause. The truth, eventually prized out of the husband, turned out to be that he had become jealous of his wife's horse. This story got stranger when it emerged that the husband's jealousy was not without cause. His wife, normally careless of her appearance, had taken to putting on make-up, wearing her best clothes and washing her hair before visiting the stables. This started us off laughing. I was uncomfortably aware that although we were not mocking the distress of these unfortunates, anyone witnessing our behaviour would probably consider us to be disgracing our profession. And predictably Sister Harris chose this moment to enter the room. She took one look at us, shook her head censoriously at me, and withdrew, which just made it worse.

Sebastian, it turned out, was prone to giggling fits. Quite how he had bottled himself up for those first weeks was a mystery, but it was a zenith of self-control never to be repeated.

One morning, we were in my office when The Colonel wandered in. The old boy appraised Sebastian's haircut approvingly.

"That's better, bit more off the top next time though." He appeared to notice me for the first time. "Ah, Sergeant Major, rum goings on last night. I've suspected for a while but couldn't prove anything." He lowered his voice. "That damned grease-monkey has been tampering with the despatch bikes again. Thought I'd check up on him last night, caught the bugger red-handed in the motor pool." His voice rose with indignation. "Nicking spares off 'em, that's his game, had the tyres, horn, lights, magneto, you name it, he's had it. And what's more he's changed the registration numbers. I think we all know why."

"Why, sir, if you don't mind me asking?" asked Seb, unwisely I thought, because he was just about ready to explode.

The Colonel turned to Sebastian with a frown. "Bag snatching, that's what, handbags I'd bet. Despicable creature, preying on defenceless old ladies. Well, he'll not get away with it, not if I have anything to do with it."

At which point, fortuitously, he turned on his heel to leave, just in time before Sebastian self-detonated. 'Handbags' had finished him off. He kept repeating it in between paroxysms of giggles. When he had composed himself, I explained about The Colonel's night-time hallucinations and how they were experienced as reality. The despatch bikes were a repeated theme; another was being followed by a wasp, probably inspired by tinnitus.

"That's like, *The Voyage of the Dawn Treader*," said Sebastian.

"More of your fifties nostalgia," I teased. "But I see your point, the ship that sailed into the mists and men's dreams became reality. I would guess one of C.S. Lewis' parents had dementia."

"Ah," said Sebastian. "Actually…"

I groaned, knowing I was in for a half-hour biography of C.S. Lewis.

We became relaxed with each other. One day I was on a rant about The Caldwell's over-prescription of chlorpromazine.

"Before your time, young Seb and mine for that matter, we had wards full of tardive dyskinesia due to the prescription of first-generation neuroleptics; lip smacking, chin wagging and drooling, which the good professor seems to want to take us back to."

"Physician heal thyself. I've counted sixteen of the twenty possible traits of psychopathy." He went on to list them and I listened with a patronising smile, designed to be an imitation of The Caldwell.

"Oh, the inexperience of youth. Keep going young Seb, you're not there yet, shallow affect for starters. You should see his simulation of grief when breaking bad news to relatives, there have been many drunken reproductions by staff throughout the hospital. But far more damningly, when I attended an autopsy with him — no pupil dilation whatsoever. Were one to choose that moment to monitor the professor's insula for activity, the search for a perfect vacuum would be over. Then there's sexual promiscuity, this unfortunately, like certain other points on the checklist, is subject to a certain amount of conjecture, but Sister Harris reports that he looks at her in a way that makes her deeply uncomfortable, and being a woman, she should know."

"I heard that his secretary is in love with him."

"Strange but true and, rather naughtily, certain members of staff who shall remain nameless, deliberately engage in conversation with the lovely, delusional Veronica Kelly in order to elicit such gems as: 'He's such a talented man, and so kind.' Prizes have been awarded. I myself received a large box of chocolates for my contribution: 'The professor is really much too soft, he's always covering up for other people's mistakes, such a generous spirit.' This about a man notorious for throwing staff under buses. But I digress, you underestimate him, he's a fully-fledged psychopath and, like a few others I could name, is on the wrong side of the admissions desk."

By this conversation Seb and I crossed a line of trust to become co-conspirators.

But there was another side to Sebastian, revealed on his first encounter with Mary. This old lady was another dementia patient. We had tried several times to move her into residential care but, like Morris, our place has become home to her and she became so frightened and distressed that we ended up taking her back, much thanks to Sister Harris who has a kindly streak she takes great pains to conceal. This is not uncommon in medics. The ones who are liberal with overt emotion are often made in the image of The Caldwell: their sympathy is not real and thus costs them nothing. And the converse. Those with real sensitivity try not to show it, but all too often are overwhelmed and up to their waist in tears.

Mary was in a constant state of preparation for the visit of her son. She was perturbed because in her delusional world she hadn't had time to clean the house or do the baking, she hadn't changed the bed linen, the list went on. She was running out of time; nothing was ready and David was due at any moment. This explained her agitation when she wandered into my office one morning.

"Oh dear, now David will want a bath but the water's cold, I don't know why, and I can't find any bath towels, I know I had them." She noticed me for the first time. "Did I put them in here, dear? I think I did."

I put my arm around her, physical contact always calms her. "I'm sorry Mary, they're not in here, but they'll turn up, I'm sure."

The old lady sighed heavily with relief that was unconnected to our conversation but derived from the comfort of being hugged.

"Thank you, dear, you're so kind." She pottered out of the door, reassured for the moment.

I explained to Sebastian. "She hasn't got a son, he died as a baby. She has a daughter who has done absolutely everything for her, and she's no time for at all."

Sebastian nodded dumbly. His eyes filled with tears and he shuddered suddenly. "Oh God, that's so sad."

It seemed to me that Sister Harris smirked rather more than usual since Sebastian's arrival. I understood her first amusement at having lumbered me with him, but instead of dissipating, it seemed to be building to some sort of crescendo, and every time we spoke it was as if she was holding back on something. Sure enough, one morning it all came out.

After her usual cursory, "Good morning," she fidgeted for a bit before adding, "and how are you getting along with Son, Doctor?"

"Son?"

"Son Sebastian. That's what we call him."

"Oh, I see — San Sebastian — very good."

She was smirking again. "If you say so, but how do you find him?"

I considered. "I like him, bright lad, and this is not exactly a profile, but nice-natured. Of course, he's got a lot to learn and he can be a bit irritating."

"You think?" I should have been alerted by the wide-eyed innocence that went with this remark.

"Yes, rambles on a bit, I mean suddenly goes off on some digression and the next thing you know you're getting all sorts of irrelevant facts about God knows what. One minute, astrophysics, next, the dissolution of the monasteries, it's the Internet generation I suppose."

Sister Harris struck a pose normally seen in gay men of the camp variety rather than ward matrons with Scottish ancestry, her head on one side, resting her cheek on a pointed finger.

"Tell me, Doctor, if you go back to your student days, presumably you went to parties and maybe got a bit drunk and amorous. Is there a chance that in such a liaison you fathered a child?" I could see where this was going. "Have a good think, don't rush, there's a lot at stake: twenty-five pounds to be precise, five to one given by Vadgama."

I recognised the name of a consultant radiologist with a stage four sense of humour, who is renowned for running a book on almost anything with a bettable outcome. I had fully twigged now and was mildly offended.

"Yes, quite, very amusing I'm sure."

"I'm saying, he's you!" Sister Harris was more animated than I ever remember. "He's your son, has to be, he's decades out of fashion, he's a nerd, revoltingly sentimental, wanders off the subject at the drop of a hat and no offence, Doctor, but so, so boring. That's why you'll excuse me if I revealed the slightest irony when you said you found him irritating: *you* found *him* irritating — amazing!"

Then she was gone, leaving me I must admit feeling rather hurt. I had learnt more about myself in two minutes than in a lifetime of introspection.

At another time this incident would have stung without seriously wounding, but it went in deep now, and the reason was the relevance to Penny. It hit me like a blow between the eyes: was this how she saw me? I was convinced that there had been chemistry between us; I consoled myself with examples of it, I went to sleep at night savouring the memory of that moment when Pedro had untied us and she had stayed pressed tightly against me. Was this the explanation of her opposite behaviour, when she had denied me so harshly, and for that final mortification, "You'll never see me again". I irritated her, I bored her. Whatever physical attraction she had for me, she could never allow herself to be with the likes of me. My thoughts led to a further source of shame, burning my cheeks with adrenalin release; strange how I had never considered before the disparity of what used to be called our station in life, and how foolish not to have done so. Penny occupied a position of unique prestige, one of the super-elite, who would partner someone similarly placed, and if it were to be a medic, then surely some outstanding surgeon. I was aware of the hatching of this particular insecurity from the incubation of my inferiority complex, inspired by my early ambitions to be a surgeon.

The hurt from this revelation did not pass in the coming days. Sebastian noticed and the kindly concern on his face inspired my confidence; he had the makings of a fine practitioner. Hamstrung by the Official Secrets Act, I gave him a truthful but edited history. He thought for a while.

"I thought there was something. Sister Harris told me she thought she'd upset you. She told me what she'd said but I guessed it was more than that."

"Now there's a thing, Sister Harris is human."

"Actually, I think she's rather upset herself. She told me all sorts of things which I'm fairly sure were designed to be repeated to you, she being too proud to tell you herself. I was going to tell you anyway, but with what you've just told me I think it might be particularly helpful." He smiled. "Sister Harris actually has a high opinion of you."

"What!"

"Well, she didn't put it quite like that, more like she has a lower opinion of all the others."

"That's more like it."

"But there's more. Apparently, The Caldwell, who as we know, listens to everyone at meetings with a look of patronising wisdom as if indulging the prattling of children, actually," Seb overuses this word, "doesn't have a clue."

"That won't make the headlines."

"Ah, but this will. All he does is act on your opinion, just yours, doesn't listen to anyone else, just does what you say."

"As Morris would say, 'Coo!' That's a lot of revelations, young Sebastian. Sister Harris being perhaps the greatest amongst them."

"People with low self-esteem can be extra hurtful because it never occurs to them that they matter enough for their opinion to wound, and of course when they do succeed, they derive pleasure from returning the hurt that has been meted out to them, although I'm not accusing her of that last bit."

"Sister Harris doesn't have low self-esteem."

"Of course she does. Look at how she eats, she's obese."

"Only to fashion-conscious young health fascists; pleasantly plump to the rest of us."

"Blind in front of your nose."

"Thanks very much."

"You see the irony though. I've just been listening to you going on about not being fit to kiss the princess and it turns out you're a prince."

"Thank you, Sebastian." I meant it.

In the coming weeks, my mood picked up, apart from moments when some word or association reminded me of Penny and stabbed me through the heart.

Some months later I arrived at work to find the place buzzing with excitement. The Caldwell had gone, he'd left a note announcing his departure but gave no reason. We all assumed that in the coming days the truth would out, and there was much speculation, all highly salacious and dark. Odds were given by Vadgama. Embezzlement and armed robbery headed the list, with other bizarre possibilities: counterfeiting, planning terrorist atrocities, paedophilia, kidnapping, spying for a foreign power. The list grew longer by the hour, and probably revealed most about the characters of the theorists. But it remained a mystery. For myself and other consultants, it was disconcerting; no one liked The Caldwell but he was the devil we knew. Sister Harris approached me and asked me if I was going to apply for the now vacant post. I hadn't given this serious consideration. Admittedly Beatrice Kwame, the lead psychiatrist, was not in the running since she had been teetering on the brink of retirement for the last three years. Certain of her colleagues had unkindly diagnosed her with a rare condition known as aboulomania, which features pathological indecisiveness. I explained to Sister Harris that quite apart from the unlikelihood of my getting the job, I wasn't sure that I would want it, because of all the politics and pen-pushing in particular, which earned me a particularly disparaging display of pursed lips and a harangue that stressed heavily my loyalty and duty to my colleagues. I gleaned from this that she was petrified at the prospect of having a clinical director who might take an interest in her affairs. My amusement at this was suddenly quashed by an unpleasant parallel thought, while I got on well with most of my colleagues, there were two that I did not and it was very likely that one of these would become my new boss, leading to the blasphemous thought that I would actually miss The Caldwell.

Sister Harris' harangue had a sting in the tail. "Besides, if you don't apply, it will show a lack of ambition which will blight your career. You know they use algorithms for that sort of thing nowadays."

And after Sebastian had explained to me at tedious length what an algorithm was, in spite of my protest that I knew perfectly well, thank you, I reluctantly bit the bullet and threw my hat into the ring.

I suspect my lack of enthusiasm revealed itself at the intimidating panel interview that followed, somehow reminding me of an account I had read of the

Salem witch trials. The panel included a number of the top brass in the trust, the toppest of which was Sarah Childs, the CEO. I had only met her rarely and the experience was a reprise of school days when in the presence of the headmaster, but I knew her by reputation: she had a fearsome intellect and ability to digest facts and figures in an instant. Not only did she not suffer fools gladly but was ruthless to those who failed to produce reports on time or prevaricated or bullshitted, which is why I had often wondered how Professor Caldwell had got his job, let alone kept it. Perhaps this was the explanation for his departure that eluded us: Sarah had found him out.

There were five on the panel. I was on good terms with the medical director, had never met two of the others, who were non-clinical, but unfortunately, if not the decision maker, the conductor of the interview appeared to be the Human Resources director for whom existed a contempt that was mutual. I considered him a serial offender in using the latest meaningless jargon. What he thought of me I didn't know other than the fact that it wasn't good, at which point in my rumination I found myself in his sights.

"As clinical director you would work with the executive director of operations and senior leadership team. A prime objective would be to embed a strategic direction and vision for the directorate aligned with the trust business objectives…"

I was unfazed but stopped listening. There was a time when you would have risked a diagnosis of disordered speech for this use of language but the NHS is awash with it nowadays. It has crossed species from management rather in the way the H5N1 virus crossed over from birds to infect the human race. It stopped bothering me a long time ago when I had the happy realisation that it had little relevance to me in clinical practice. I saw that he was looking at me and switched back on again.

"And what do you think qualifies you for this position, Dr Bartlett?" asked so smugly that my irritation reached a rare high. If it was his intention to needle me, I've heard they do that at interviews, he succeeded, and I bit back.

"Nothing, actually." I'd caught this word off Sebastian. "I'm probably not suited at all."

He sat back with folded arms. Sarah frowned and the other three displayed varying degrees of puzzlement and nervousness. Back at school, an audience of enthusiasts would be circling us, encouraging, 'fight, fight, fight'. I thought I'd better explain, after all, I didn't want to lose the job I already had.

"I don't doubt my abilities as a practitioner, it's the administration and management that concerns me. Bear in mind that I was only involved with Professor Caldwell in clinical matters, so as far as the rest of his job is concerned, I don't really know what he did."

The HR director took on a frown of disapproval which I suspect was for the benefit of the others, confirming my opinion of him as a... I knew the word Sister Harris would use and agreed with it. Sarah, however, had a different expression, she was studying me curiously; she appeared to make up her mind.

"If you're saying that you would be more hands-on than Professor Caldwell," she shrugged, "then that's OK. You don't have to follow in his footsteps, in fact I'd rather you didn't," she added dryly. "But he did turn in very good stats for patient outcomes."

She looked at me directly and I got the message: she knew! Evidently what Sister Harris had told Seb was true.

Three days later I received a letter offering me the job.

I was surprised and moved by the number and sincerity of congratulations; I had not thought myself that popular. The only false smiles were from two of the four clinical psychiatrists in our team, who given the opportunity would have sectioned the whole of the selection panel I guessed. The only other suspect contribution was from Vadgama who congratulated me from between firmly clenched teeth, possibly explained by the fact that he had offered odds on my chances at one hundred and sixty to one against and, rumour had it, had caught a packet.

My first reaction was not jubilation, as expressed to Seb, "Oh, God, what have I done?"

But surprisingly after the first two or three weeks of trepidation, I found myself settling into my new routine. Apart from a higher level of responsibility and reporting, my job appeared to be little changed, or to put it another way, I found out how little The Caldwell had done.

What I hadn't appreciated at interview, probably because I wasn't listening properly, was that I reported directly to Sarah, but even this wasn't so tough. Firstly, I discovered that she had a sense of humour, revealed on the occasion of me wandering off the subject when replying to a question: she looked at her watch and yawned. Also, she was more human than her reputation, kind to the junior staff and genuinely concerned about patient care. Time revealed that we had similar likes and dislikes among the staff. She was a woman who had confidence in her own ability with a natural authority that she had rare need to assert. You knew where you were with her; she was originally from Scarborough and had the directness of a northerner. I liked her. She set out in black and white what was expected of me, zeroing in uncannily on the very things where I would have strayed from the path of righteousness given half a chance.

"Before you ask, no you cannot keep your office. You will move into Professor Caldwell's. I know your habit of having half the ward hanging out with you, about which I don't have a problem except that when I am due to visit, you will expel Morris Alby at least half an hour beforehand and open the windows. I also know your attitude to paperwork," she shook her head ominously, "which will change. The position in which you find yourself requires prompt and accurate reporting, and budgetary discipline." My face had fallen progressively through this speech, and she smiled grimly but encouragingly. "Fortunately for you, you have," she named two of the managers, "to assist you, who you will find competent in such matters but," again she appeared to read my mind, "do not think for one moment that you can dump it on them without gaining a thorough understanding of what is submitted." She sighed. "Just think yourself lucky you don't have my job."

I was aware that I was being spoken to like a naughty schoolboy. I have observed that whatever position in life a man holds, his treatment by women is determined by more native factors. In my case, a shy man with no gravitas whatsoever, a sort of reverse sexism comes into play whereby women feel universally empowered to treat me like dirt, be it Sister Harris, Penny, my colleagues, or now Sarah; even the hospital cleaners appear to look down on me, although that could be my imagination. In this case, however, I didn't mind, she was the boss, and even though I was aware that she spoke more respectfully to my colleagues, perversely I took this as a compliment, indicating a greater level of trust in me that allowed her to be her natural self. Besides, I had been promoted above them all.

After a month I began to feel secure again and settled to the point where my new position rather went to my head. For the first time in my career, I felt a real success. I had only ever been an average medic, in my mind a failed surgeon. Even after getting my MRCPsych, my position was tainted with the prejudice I had learnt at medical school: that psychiatry was on the margins of medicine. In fact, I recognised myself as a mild sufferer from 'imposter syndrome'. Now here I was, 'running the whole caboodle', as Mo had it. I held my head high, I looked Sister Harris more directly in the eye which I don't think she liked very much.

There was a strange side-effect to this new confidence, and it concerned Penny. Somehow my reasoning for her rejection of me, although no more than a theory, had by virtue of being unchallenged become embedded as truth. And now here I was, something very different to how she had known me. If I were to meet her now, surely it would be on more equal terms?

By some bizarre logic I expected this knowledge to have communicated itself to her. But the phone didn't ring and my elation at my promotion subsided. I was left sober and hungover and facing a cold reality: I had no prospect of seeing her again. I thought of writing to her but the idea was ridiculous. What would I say? Who would I send it to? And even if it reached her, I would only succeed in compromising her. So it was final now, this really was the end. Even though nothing had changed other than my perception, my sense of loss was unexpectedly violent and it must have shown. I caught Seb looking at me a few times, and eventually he asked me what was wrong. I was tempted to tell him but although by now not only did I like him but thoroughly trusted him, the thought of this confession made me feel foolish and ashamed and I passed it off with, "Oh it's nothing, just a bit under the weather."

Seb nodded understandingly and changed the subject.

I interrupted him. "Very good."

"What's very good?"

"You didn't press me, you passed on quickly and naturally without causing any embarrassment or pressure, thus transferring the initiative to the patient, who will now take it."

Seb leaned back touching his fingers together in a parody of The Caldwell and I continued.

"It's about Penny."

He listened with interest as I explained, and did not comment until I had finished.

"Funny how incapable we all are of self-analysis. You'd see that for what it was in an instant from a patient. But just in case you need me to spell it out, this is all about how you perceive yourself, with the caveat that your self-esteem, or lack of, shapes your behaviour and in turn would affect how she reacts to you, so I will grudgingly admit that there might be a change in the dynamic between you because of that, but I very much doubt if in response to your actual change of status."

I shook my head glumly. "We'll never know. There's no way of finding her."

Something stirred in the periphery of my vision. Trevor is such a regular inhabitant of my office that at times I forget his presence. He was stroking Max frenetically, a sign of agitation. He looked studiously away. I saw him working himself up for speech, finally directing his tirade at a nearby bookcase.

"TL two six four zero three eight, five two six four three six, to, TL two six four zero three seven, five two six four zero zero, east-south-east to TL two seven zero two, five two seven zero zero zero, south-west to…"

Trevor continued happily while I exchanged looks with Sebastian. He got there first.

"I think that's grid references."

"To where?" I looked at Trevor, who as ever avoided my gaze. Did this mean what I thought? And as so often, Trevor appeared to read my mind. He rushed out a single word.

"Car." He moved to the door. "Car," and then again as if concerned that I hadn't understood. "Car."

I thought for a moment, I could spare a few hours. I left it to Seb to call my secretary and accompanied Trevor to the car park. He showed signs of pleasurable anticipation, he liked car journeys. He placed Max carefully in the front seat and fastened his seatbelt solicitously.

"Max safe." He giggled and sat himself in the back passenger-side seat, always his chosen place. I smiled at the thought of what the powers-that-be would think of this if they saw what I was doing.

We started up. This had to be a wild goose chase, all our journeys had been in the back of a vehicle with blacked out windows, it was completely impossible for Trevor to know what direction we had taken. But even as I told myself this I was only half persuaded.

We reached the hospital gates and I turned as ordered, amusing myself with the thought that we'd probably gone wrong already, then at the T-junction on the main road.

"Left."

Trevor never hesitated. It was difficult to follow his commands, because they were issued at the very moment we reached whatever turning I was to make, which meant that other than at 'T'-junctions and roundabouts I overshot and had to do a U-turn. He was like the world's worst satnav. I was grateful for the fact that Mo wasn't with us; he was a consummate back-seat driver. I imagined the dialogue: 'Should 'ave done a left there, mate — wanna go back yer do'.

So we progressed. Hemel Hempstead, across the M25, Watford, Edgeware and into North London. Trevor never missed a beat. We were definitely going somewhere, the question was, where?

Our arrival came unexpectedly. We'd passed through Hendon on the Great North Way, taken a left to Islington, then a right into a maze of streets and finally into a broad residential avenue.

Trevor announced speech with a giggle before rushing out a single word, "Here."

"Here?" I checked the mirror. Trevor was nodding enthusiastically. I pulled into the side and looked around, trying not to laugh. So it *had* been a wild goose chase. To the left were some railings separating the road from a patch of green parkland fringed by trees, to the right, across the road, a row of large detached houses, once perhaps occupied by single families with an entourage of servants, now probably converted into a dozen flats, the exception being, a single tower block rising between a gap in the houses, an eyesore in my opinion that I was surprised had been allowed by the planners. I read the board with idle curiosity, 'Weber Construction and Associates Ltd.' I casually observed the driveway sloping down to a double garage door.

Suddenly, just as in a movie, everything rearranged itself in my head. I saw myself arriving with Major and Mr Robinson, turning down the slope, the door opening electronically before us. I saw through to the other side, the door closing behind us, the lift before us. I could have passed the place a thousand times without the slightest suspicion, but the longer I looked, the more convinced I became, above all because of Trevor's certainty.

I felt suddenly awkward about being parked in this place. I moved off. "You're amazing, Trevor."

I heard a snigger of pleasure followed by, "Good boy, Max."

Two hours later I was back in my office explaining all to Seb. "It doesn't seem possible and yet it happened so there has to be an explanation."

"I suppose it's something like the migration of birds."

"But surely that's genetically predetermined? That and a shed-load of navigational adaptation in the telencephalon."

Seb looked disdainful. "Reference to a bird brain is particularly appropriate, they have a form of GPS that uses intracellular iron as a magnetosensor. And that's just one of many mechanisms..." Seb was knowledgeable on this subject; his lecture ended twenty minutes later allowing me to pose my counter theory.

"I think it's to do with computation of time, speed and inertial response to movement by sensory perception with certain datum points such as traffic lights."

"Which are randomly red or green."

It was my turn to scoff. "Yes, but you can sense a green light from the driving behaviour, slowing down then accelerating."

"Like pedestrian crossings, cars turning in front of you, traffic jams."

We argued for a further twenty minutes. Sister Harris is right, we are a couple of nerds. Our area of agreement was carefully mulled over as if in preparation for a press release and stated that what had happened defied scientific explanation as far as we understood it. Seb went on to suggest that a hundred and fifty years ago, unscrupulous Victorian gentlemen with enormous side whiskers would have exhibited Trevor in a cage and prodded him with sticks.

"So what do you do now?" asked Seb. "I mean you've found her, that was your problem, that's what was stopping you. Now you ask her out on a date?"

I stared at him. His smile told me that he understood how impossible and petrifying this idea was.

In spite of my promotion, I continued in my habit of working weekends when I judged it necessary and took days off in the week in lieu. On such days, that building in North London drew me like a magnet. My first visit was just to explore, parking well away, walking up and down the road, sauntering aimlessly past and looking up casually at the windows obscured by blinds. I explored the park opposite, there was something of the 'Secret Garden' about the place, a wild wormhole of nature untouched and unchanging, protected by magic while the city grew up around it, a lush tree-lined refuge bisected by a path that led to a magnificent old church surrounded by an ancient graveyard.

I would take my lunch in the park. My hope and fear, was that in this way I would encounter Penny. There was an atmosphere of romance about the place associated with her presence like a lingering perfume. I was aware of something obsessive about these visits.

The first excitement of anticipation wore off. The sense of her presence receded as time after time I found the place deserted apart from the usual joggers and dog walkers.

So when one day I went again to the park, it was without premonition. I read my newspaper as usual, opened my pack of sandwiches, took one in my hand, paused to turn a page.

The sound of approaching footsteps slowly invaded my consciousness; they were fast and purposeful, a harsh metallic tattoo. I looked up, sandwich in hand, my mouth half open to receive it, frozen by the sight before me. I felt adrenalin flood through me with every sensation described in the textbooks and, in addition, a peculiar auditory hypersensitivity that made the footsteps increase fantastically in volume, the ground shaking beneath them.

They stopped. The echo in my head diminished until silent. She stood before me. My mouth I think was still open but I was incapable of speech.

"What are you doing here?"

I looked up into her eyes, lit by the sun, and my poor over-sensitised nervous system suffered another massive jolt. I had not remembered her as so beautiful.

"Well?" she demanded. The emotions behind her expression as ever eluded me.

"I, erm, having lunch."

"We have surveillance, you're here regularly, so I've just discovered."

"I sort of found this place."

"How?" She paused for a moment before answering her own question. "Well one of those two, I suppose, but that doesn't explain what you're doing here."

"No not them, it was Trevor."

"Trevor?" She looked momentarily surprised but apparently needed no further explanation.

"There's a thing."

"I know."

Her face lightened fractionally. "That lets them off the hook. I must admit I was surprised, they're big on the OSA, but it was the only explanation." Her eyes, her beautiful hazel eyes, studied me carefully. "Does anyone, and I mean anyone, know about this place?"

"No, I mean not where it is."

She continued to look into my eyes for a moment longer, then appeared to relax, apparently satisfied. She reached out to take the sandwich still in my hand. She took a bite and sat down next to me.

"So what's this all about, Bartlett?"

At this moment I understood why Trevor needed to face a wall in order to speak. I know that I have a high score on autistic traits, and now it was the avoidance of eye contact that allowed me to speak.

"It's just that when we last met, I wanted to ask you…"

"I know what you wanted to ask me, and the answer was no." She looked into my eyes again, this time her expression was not fierce but neither did it have the gentleness or patronisation that I dreaded. She was agitated and I exalted in this. Her hand pressed at her jaw, first one side than the other. If this was a mannerism, it was not one I'd seen before.

"What makes you think anything has changed?"

Her eyes, holding mine, were bright. This was my opportunity to speak. But, of course, I couldn't. Silence built to a crescendo. The window closed.

"Go, Bartlett, and don't come here again." She handed me the half-eaten sandwich. "That's fucking disgusting." She turned and was gone.

Something perplexed me. I found myself breathing in and caught the fragrance of the freshly cut grass but there was another fragrance, she was wearing perfume, a chemical signal that conflicted with the verbal.

Hours later I was back in my office relating all to Seb. The sandwich sat on the corner of my desk, my appetite had vanished and I'd intended to put it in the bin, but somehow found I couldn't, her bite marks made it too precious. I shook with a slight tremor which Seb diagnosed as probably dystonia or Huntington's chorea, giving me the opportunity for a revenge lecture on movement disorders.

His interpretation was that this was a final rejection. Unusually, I found myself irritated with him, but honesty compelled me to admit the possibility of this being the truth. Had I made a fool of myself? Probably, but there had been that moment of eagerness in her face while she awaited my answer, and if I had not been so hopelessly overwhelmed, if I had been able to express myself, what then? And the perfume?

The next day the sandwich was still on my desk, I still couldn't throw it away. Fortunately, the problem was solved the following day when Morris, tramp-like, ate it.

Weeks slipped into months. Work demanded my attention. Penny was never far from my thoughts but I settled down, resigned to the reality that whatever had or had not existed between us was now truly over.

One morning I arrived at work much as usual except for my office being empty, which was most unusual. Seb was attending a lecture, Mo and Trevor were nowhere to be seen, although I knew where Morris was, I had overheard him as I passed the common room. At first, I thought he was in conversation, and in a way, he was, answering a question from an imaginary interviewer, I recognised the name of a local radio personality.

"Glad you asked me that, Wilf mate. I was in the office when the job came in, just back from a TIR (Transports Internationaux Routiers) bringin' a draw-bar back from Madrid — gaffer was there, big geezer in a black 'at," — a regular in Mo's conversations — "talkin' down the phone 'e was to some bod: 'Get a ninety-tonne crane through Catteshall Lane? Only one bloke what can do that,' 'e said, 'an that's The Maestro.' That's what 'e calls me, 'The Maestro', an' 'e looked at me. 'Cor,' I said, 'you ain't 'alf pushin' it, Guv'nor, yer havin' a laugh.' Mean to say, Wilf mate, s'not like it 'ad rear steer. All cheerin' they was, after, all out in the street, callin' 'Morris, Morris, Morris'."

I had continued on my way, with the thought that all the inhabitants of Godalming needed to be prescribed nasal decongestants.

It was a rare treat to have morning coffee in peace and quiet. There was a knock on the door, I might have known it was too good to be true. I called out reluctantly to come in. A tall distinguished, grey-haired figure entered. I concealed my irritation, there was something of the night about this apparition that made me suspect him of being senior management. Some people have a certain aura about them guaranteed to inflame my inferiority complex, policemen, headteachers, NHS supremos; this was one of them. He held himself well, a tall man with a fine figure, a military haircut and arrogant features ameliorated by a hint of humour in his remarkably piercing, intelligent blue eyes which were at this moment surveying me.

"Dr Bartlett." He held out his hand. I took it and was treated to a very firm handshake.

"You're probably wondering why I'm here."

"Erm, yes, actually." I cursed Seb for infecting me with this word.

"My card."

I read: 'Admiral Sir Richard McAllister GBE KCB RN ret.' "What can I do for you, Admiral?"

He smiled and his eyes were surprisingly gentle. "Retired." He took the seat opposite my desk. "What it is, come for a spot of advice really, bit of a cheek I know, but I just saw the matron, nice woman, and she said you had half an hour to spare."

"Did she?" I said grimly. I understood all now. Normally it was harder to get past Sister Harris than Cerberus, but she has certain weak spots, one being that her father had been a commander in the Royal Navy, and another, a partiality for her own clan, any surname prefixed Mac acts as a honeyed sop. I was still puzzled though.

"Have you got a letter?"

"Letter?"

"From your doctor, a referral."

"Oh, I see. Well no. It's not about me you see, it's the family."

"OK. Tell you what. Let me get us both a coffee, tell me the problem and hopefully I'll be able to point you in the right direction, although I warn you now, it will almost certainly be to refer whoever it is in your family to their GP."

The Admiral nodded but I was puzzled by the careful scrutiny of his piercing blue eyes. It must have been a hundred years since sailors had needed to scan the horizon, but maybe over generations they had fostered a piercing blue eye gene that was heritable, a future topic of discussion with Seb perhaps.

The Admiral sipped appreciatively at his coffee. "Where do I start with this?" He answered his own question with a sigh. "Shortly after I married, my wife fell pregnant. I assumed she'd wanted to, we'd never discussed it. I suppose we both thought it was the done thing. Back then, I didn't really mind one way or the other but I thought it would please the little woman."

He looked at me anxiously, for the first time he showed signs of uncertainty and I nodded reassuringly, if I was going to hear his story, I'd do it with a good grace.

"So I was a bit bothered when I found her crying, not just weepy, the full works."

"During the pregnancy?"

"Yes, I mean they were going on about hormones even back then, I thought it was that. Then she had the baby, a girl." He paused for a moment. "Mothers are mad on babies, aren't they? But Rachel, that's the wife, never really seemed to take to her. I mean, our friends had babies and it was all, 'coochie, coochie, coo,' besotted with them, but Rachel… It's a hard thing to say but from the moment the baby was born she looked awkward with her."

"Did you talk to her about it?"

The Admiral gave me a cryptic smile. "Should have done, shouldn't I? Well, that was the start of it. Might have worked out better if our daughter had been a bit more submissive but then she's her mother's daughter, so, headstrong, obstinate, the nearest thing to a tigress amongst humans in fact."

Something stirred in the hold. "They clashed?"

The Admiral studied me and again I found it a curious look, somehow inappropriate but I couldn't put my finger on why.

"Clashed? Wouldn't be so bad in the past tense. They clashed then, they clash now, worse than ever in fact."

I considered. "If I were treating them, which I'm not," I added hastily, "if nothing else because this is the domain of a psychologist, which I am also not, I'd need to see them both separately and together but from what you've told me, you've selected as significant how your wife perhaps didn't want a child or failed to bond with her, or both. There may be a reason for this which may or may not be connected with her own childhood, but in any event, that failure can lead to guilt which finds expression perversely in anger towards the child."

The Admiral looked at me thoughtfully. "Anger you say, hatred is more like it, both ways."

"The child may repay the hurt."

The Admiral's chin tightened, giving a curiously graphic impression of determination, more than that, obstinacy, perhaps even a vestigial echo from adolescence when an independent nature rebelled against authority, providing the motivation to rise to the highest rank in the Navy, where no one in uniform could give him orders. Somewhere in my mind a memory stirred as if raking a pile of leaves had disturbed some gleaming object concealed amongst them. I returned my attention to him. After a moment's thought, he replied.

"I've heard something like this from other people but I don't get it. Guilt and hurt, you say, but they hate each other. What it is, Doctor," that stirring again, this time more profound, "she's got man trouble at the moment, my daughter that is, and the wife, I mean, she's got her pride but she's a kindly soul, and yet you can see the sneer of satisfaction on her face at it. It's a hard thing to say but she's revelling in it, taking pleasure in her own daughter's pain."

"Schadenfreude."

"Yes, but her own daughter!"

"Are you afraid of some physical harm to either of them? Is that why you're here?"

He looked at me with that curious smile again. "Not quite. This man trouble I spoke of. She's got this thing about some chap, talks about him all the time but nothing has actually happened."

"I see." I didn't.

"Of course she denies it, hasn't got a good word to say about him, lambasts him almost constantly. What it is..."

My brain took off like a whirring grouse, that smile, that use of, 'what it is', so akin to 'thing is', that determined jaw, so peculiarly evocative.

"Does she know you've come to see me?"

Now his smile spread right across his face and his eyes twinkled spectacularly. "You're there aren't you?"

I was diverted by the memory of having used just these words when I first had sex with Caroline. The Admiral continued.

"In reply to your question, good God no, she'd kill me. No, your name featured several times, sandwiched between some fairly fruity expletives, modern girls, honestly, they've got mouths like dockers. Anyway, I looked you up and here I am."

"You know it's strange, I had what I suspect is turning into a similar deputation from two of her employees."

"Did you now? The two stooges. Giving them hell, I suppose, but what to do about it, that's the question?" He looked at me archly. "She spends a lot of time at home since her divorce, doesn't like to be alone at night is what it is." He smiled. "That surprise you?"

I returned his smile. "I see your game, Admiral, trying to demonstrate her vulnerability, which probably due to the misogyny of your generation makes you think that something fragile, flapping and fluttery would be more attractive to a man."

"That's a lot of alliteration."

"Not only do I not believe it for a moment, but actually," I let that one pass as valid, "I rather like your daughter as she is."

The Admiral looked frustrated. "I thought maybe she'd frightened you off. I'm the first to admit that she's formidable, she's like a force of nature, but she is still a girl."

I nodded sadly. "What you evidently don't know, Admiral, is that I have tried, twice in fact, and she turned me down flat."

Now his eyes bored into me as if I were some distant horizon. "Let me speak frankly, Doctor. You may have attempted to woo my daughter; she herself is uncertain in the matter; but if you did…" He targeted me with a look of disgust, which passed across his face so rapidly that a blink would have missed it, just like his daughter.

"Then it was a pretty dismal effort. To woo my daughter half-heartedly is to make her as mad as a wet hen and," he looked at me in exasperation, "make my life a misery."

"But she said no, very emphatically."

"Good God man, you're not supposed to take no for an answer from a girl like that. You know what women are."

"Not that one, that's the problem. I understand women extremely well but unfortunately not when I have feelings for them."

"Ah, now that's interesting. You do have feelings then?"

"Somewhat."

"A lot?"

"Understatement."

The Admiral looked at me as though I were a tiresome piece of rigging that had got itself hopelessly knotted. "I don't understand you, Doctor, why can't you buck yourself up? No wonder she calls you names."

"I've probably heard them all but I suppose there might be some new ones."

"Let me see now: insipid, tedious, patronising, irritating and faint-hearted, that's the telling one."

I shrugged and the Admiral considered me in moody silence. "How do you think I met my wife, Doctor?"

"Car accident, wasn't it?"

"Ruddy woman turned in front of me, cut right across my bows. I was nice to her, checked her for damage and told her not to fret, but she turned on me, said it was my fault. I kept my temper which I now know was what caused her to work herself up into a frenzy, so I slapped her." The Admiral registered my disapproval. "Back then that was the accepted remedy for a woman in hysterics."

"Who told you that?"

"My mother," he said with an expression that just needed his tongue stuck out to complete.

"Urban myth, and not just the remedy, the condition itself was debunked years ago."

"Different times. She told me afterwards it was the most exciting moment of her life. Like her daughter, she is a rather imperious woman, and I don't think anyone had ever stood up to her."

"You slapped her," I said accusingly.

"Ah, but then she looked so shocked and so very beautiful that I kissed her."

I sank my head in my hands. "When you die, Admiral, the sisterhood will hold parties over your grave."

"I'll tell you something worse, there are times when that woman provokes me to such an extreme that I swear she wants me to strike her."

"But you don't?" I was curious.

The Admiral looked at me reproachfully. "Of course not, I would never hit a woman."

"You probably didn't imagine it, it does happen. Quite healthy if it's fantasy, not so healthy if she's testing you and deeply unhealthy if she actually wants you to hit her, which also happens."

The Admiral looked at me thoughtfully. "Penelope is right, you do go on a bit."

"It has been said. You were saying about how you met your wife, before this fascinating digression."

"So I was, wandered a bit myself perhaps, fault on both sides. Yes, I was just wondering if we could fix something up, maybe to show her you're a proper man."

"In which case I'll need a white charger, a battle-axe and a shield of intricate design, or maybe you had in mind seeing off a brigand with a horse whip, and then using it on your daughter."

The Admiral looked huffy. "There's no need for that, I'm only trying to help."

"I'm sorry, Admiral, I'm just not your man for that sort of thing, the horrible truth is, I'm painfully shy, always have been."

The Admiral frowned deeply. "Oh God, she hates, 'shy'." He appeared to regain hope. "But surely not, I mean you must have some balls to run this place, 'Head Honcho' that nice matron said. I mean it's full of loonies, scares the life out of me and I've been chased up the Malacca Straits by gunboats. One chap accosted me just now, walking on tiptoes and ticked me off for treading heavily, told me he was a tanker driver with a load full of nitro outside and the slightest vibration would set it off."

"That would be Morris, quite harmless."

"Harmless! Good God man. I know they use all this soft-soap language nowadays, probably call it challenging behaviour, but the man's a dangerous lunatic." The Admiral looked at me disparagingly. "Couldn't you have a few snifters, give yourself a bit of Dutch courage."

"Shyness isn't exactly lack of courage. While I disagree with your description of Morris as dangerous, I will admit that some of the patients are, and there are times when I have to be assertive, not just with patients I might add. I'm not even scared of women per se. I've never been an alpha male but in the presence of your daughter I struggle to make omega."

The Admiral looked at me with sad disappointment and conceded grudgingly. "I suppose you're not much of a man, are you?"

"Thanks very much," I said huffily. "I see now where Penny gets her extraordinary lack of tact."

"Well, it's no good beating about the bush, I mean that bloody awful ex of hers, couldn't stand the blighter, but I have to admit he was a man. He'd shave in the morning and have a stubble by lunchtime."

"How did he court her?" I asked from a sort of despairing curiosity.

"Ah, now there's a lesson there," said the Admiral with a dawning hope. "I took him on to do some work on the estate, strong as an ox but a sullen coarse cur of a man."

"Of course he was."

"Penelope asked him to do something."

"Ordered imperiously, you mean."

The Admiral smiled. "You've got it. Well, he didn't like it and told her so in no uncertain terms."

"With a sneer of contempt, I expect."

"It's almost as if you were there." I groaned and he continued. "Well, that did it, one thing led to another." He looked at me wistfully. "Surely you could manage that, Doctor, a sneer of contempt." This was the cue for me to bury my face in my hands again. "The wife said he was good looking. Are you good looking?"

"I've never been accused of it."

"Me neither, I don't trust those fellows, going around sleeking back their hair and preening themselves in mirrors like Wops."

I winced. I felt like crying with frustration but sensed this would be frowned on by the Admiral who I judged, not only to be a proponent of the stiff upper lip, but also the father of his daughter, to borrow his aphorism, I could see much of her nature in him.

Before we parted, we swore a mutual pact of secrecy and exchanged phone numbers.

"I have embraced mobile telephony, much to the surprise of my daughter, who expects me to still be using semaphore." He sighed. "Girls don't respect their fathers any more, particularly that one." He mused further on the possibility of seeing what could be done, but as he surveyed me, I could see his confidence falter and he slunk out of my office, the effigy of a defeated man.

I caught up with Seb over lunch, told him about my visitor and took a certain pleasure in the look of surprise on his face.

"She has got a thing for you then, you were right."

"It did hurt, that you had so little confidence in my sex appeal."

"Eeuw."

"The question is what to do about it?"

"Maybe he has something up his sleeve; he was an admiral after all, must be brimming with tactics and countermeasures and all that sort of stuff."

I remembered the look on the Admiral's face when we had parted and replied gloomily:

"I don't think so, I think he sees me as holed below the waterline."

Weeks passed. My promotion, which I had at first thought changed my situation very little, made increasing demands on me, thanks to Sarah, who, having eased my path by taking on much of The Caldwell's work, was now passing it back to me.

It was the non-clinical work that troubled me, the insidious pressure of financial constraints that limited the number of patients held under section. But I was grateful for the occupation. In spite of my denial to Seb, I half expected to hear again from the Admiral, and the knowledge, as time passed, that he had given me up as a lost cause, was a bitter disappointment.

I grew maudlin. Although always aware of it, the sadness that blights the lives of so many of my patients rarely infiltrates my own emotional state. This has not always been the case. In the early days I shared in the misery that surrounded me, and often went home emotionally exhausted. In time I became inured, except for those occasions when for some reason the insulation broke down and I was once again fighting back tears just as Seb had on his first encounter with Mary. To my concern I found myself returning to that emotionally febrile state.

One day brought this into focus. I was in discussion with Sister Harris when Morris came into view. Mo's crush on Sister Harris had not subsided, much to the amusement of everyone other than Sister Harris. Catching sight of her, he went through the elaborate pretence of receiving a phone call on his mobile. I'm not sure from where he obtained this artefact, probably a bin because it was an antique model with no SIM card and no life in the battery. But Morris loved it, he spent hours playing with it, pressing buttons that didn't work. He announced loudly for the benefit of Sister Harris.

"Bloody phone again." He appeared to answer it in a brusque city-magnate fashion. "Mo. What? Naaah." He appeared to listen with a smile on his face. "Special transport yer reckon, CAT 3, (Category 3 — abnormal load) phew, yeah, twenny axles, gotta' be CAT 3 that. S'pose I can fit it in; need an escort though, four yellers an' a couple o' blues, 'ave to close the Haslemere bypass an' all."

He paused alongside Sister Harris with the intention of impressing her further, but she shooed him away indignantly. In the normal way, Mo would have shrugged this off, it was a common enough occurrence, but on this occasion, I saw him turn back towards her as he retreated, his face full of hurt, and, adding a terrible poignance, clutching his precious phone upside down.

I had to excuse myself rapidly with the unworthy concern, not for Mo's dejection, but for my own emotional enervation that reduced me almost to tears.

As I reached the sanctuary of my office, my own mobile rang — genuinely — and I recognised the voice. Association produced a dramatic somatic response rather like being kicked in the stomach.

"Admiral."

"Doctor." He sounded amused.

"How can I help you?"

"Well assuming you to be a chap of constant emotions?"

"I am that chap."

"Good, never know with you young fellows nowadays. One day it's all Felicity somebody-or-other, then Jocelyn what's-her-face."

"Still Penelope."

"Good show. She on the other hand took it into her head to procure herself some other beggar."

"Oh." Strange how much disappointment you can get into one syllable. The Admiral chuckled with apparent delight.

"No, no, you don't understand, it didn't work out, insipid sort of bloke."

"Like me, you mean?"

"Yes, well, not exactly, don't interrupt and let me explain. I think she thought that if she found someone like you, well nearest possible, because there isn't anyone quite as dreadful… her words, not mine, don't shoot the messenger." He chuckled again. "Didn't work though, couldn't stand the blighter anywhere near her and, what it is, she blames you for it, says you've spoiled her. That's an admission, Doctor. You can take it from me, I know my daughter, that's a declaration that is."

"Of war?"

"Don't be silly, the other thing of course."

"What other thing?" I asked innocently.

"You won't get me to fall for that one, I know you psycho types, trying to get us to say embarrassing things to be in touch with our feminine side and all that baloney."

"Fair cop, just for fun though in my case. Presumably you suggest I take some sort of action, bearing in mind that if I go anywhere near her, she'll probably have me shot."

The Admiral tutted. "Now don't be difficult, Doctor. She's having a party, her fortieth. I'm inviting you, you will be my guest, all you have to do is present yourself, preferably bucked up a bit — I'd recommend a couple of snifters — and let nature take its course."

"By bucked up you mean…?

"Be a bit assertive, you know."

"You haven't given up on the horse whip, have you?"

The Admiral felt he was being made fun of and was on his dignity. "Just do what you can. I'm afraid I can't give you the address, security and all that. I'll send a car Saturday week. Eight thirty, OK?"

I agreed.

Over the next few days my apprehension increased. I was trapped. I knew that if I obeyed the naked fear that whimpered its plea for me to back out, I would regret it for the rest of my life and this alone drove me on.

When the day arrived, I did as ordered, and took two very large snifters, as the Admiral put it, and they did their bit in creating optimism. I must trust the Admiral, he knew his daughter. I repeated this mantra to myself, finishing hopefully but unconvincingly with: 'Let nature take its course.'

The doorbell rang at eight thirty precisely. A young man stood at the door. He was tall, extremely well built, horribly handsome and exuded confidence. My inferiority complex, temporarily cowed with alcohol, rose vengefully. It was all I could do to mutter a response and follow this modern version of Adonis to the waiting car.

I stood by the passenger door. The young man opened a rear door apologetically.

"Sorry, sir I have to take you in the back."

I understood, the windows were blacked out.

The last remnants of alcohol-induced bravado dissipated through the journey at a faster rate it seemed than the one unit per hour eliminated from the bloodstream. Adonis' shoulders seemed to grow ever wider with my dawning sobriety. My inferiority complex now hovered around burst pressure, wasn't this just the type Penny would go for? Supremely confident with a touch of arrogance and just as she had been attracted by her first husband's — 'Mellors', as I had nicknamed him — display of contempt at her flouncing arrogance, so it would be with this young man? An unpleasant hollow feeling presented in the pit of my stomach. What was I thinking of? At times in the last few days, I had persuaded myself that when the time came, I would be careless, even shamefully rehearsing an expression of laconic indifference in the mirror. Ridiculous. In reality I would slink hangdog into this party of strangers, their eyes on the alien in their midst, their contempt and derision at my awkwardness. And Penny, shanghaied into this encounter, I could imagine her anger and hostility. The unpleasant feeling in my guts turned to nausea. This was far worse than the butterflies in the stomach that labelled the sensation. I struggled for another ten minutes but the nausea now overwhelmed me. My battle was over, the decision made for me. I called out.

"I'm sorry, can you take me back. I'm not feeling well."

"Of course. I'm sorry to hear that, sir." He sounded sympathetic. I wondered how much he knew.

Moments later we were heading back home and my stomach recovered almost instantly. Now a different sickness afflicted me. Against all odds I had been given a chance and thrown it away. I'd thought it before, but this was now truly the end. A peculiar image came to me. A memory of that strange dream in the hotel room, of Trevor on the lantern balcony of a storm-ravaged lighthouse, his hands waving in terrible anguish as the sweep of the beacon picked out Max drowning in the tempest.

The car drew to a halt and the driver opened my door. I thanked him, for the first time looking him in the face, and felt absurdly grateful for the sympathy I read in his expression. 'Oh God, what have I done?' my lips formed silently as I turned away.

Back indoors, I poured a massive brandy. Misery and self-pity washed over me. Just as I had feared, I would now regret this forever. But a voice countered from within, I could not help myself, could not bear the pain of her, for this was the truth. I had never felt like this before. I was reluctant even to describe it as love. Unsatisfied, it had proliferated malignantly into some dark neoplasm. Even now I was tempted to ring the Admiral to explain, to ask the car to return, but just the thought reduced me mentally even further. I was spent.

I got up to pour another drink and my legs hardly supported me. I slumped back into my chair, lapsed into sleep, woke again, and, too tired to go to bed, dozed off again.

Some insistent sound invaded my stupored dreams and gained definition: the doorbell. I was too dazed with sleep and drink to even wonder more than in the vaguest way who could be calling so late on a Saturday night, so I opened the door blinking into the dazzle of the porch light. A dark figure stood back from the door. It took me an absurdly long moment to recognise her. I opened my mouth but no words came.

"After a long moment of bemused silence, during which I suspect my mouth fell open — it would explain her response.

"Well, are you going to just stand there gawping?"

Suddenly, miraculously, I was in command of myself, partly the drink, but more because my fear, that had festered anaerobically in her absence, was neutralised by the oxygen of her presence.

I stood aside. "Come in." I closed the door and turned to find her studying me suspiciously.

"You don't look ill."

"Better now, thanks, just nerves," I explained with a lack of embarrassment that surprised me. I suspect it surprised Penny too. The suspicion on her face matured into knowing cynicism.

"You're pissed, Bartlett."

"Very possibly."

"Well, if you haven't drunk the place dry, then get me a whisky." She undid her coat to reveal a grey top of some fine material and figure-hugging jeans. I had not seen her wearing clothes like this before, she looked stunning.

"Of course, and would you like me to take your coat?"

For answer she threw it on the floor.

"Very well," I said ponderously.

I poured her a drink, she took a large slug and considered me thoughtfully.

"Just how blotto are you, Bartlett?"

"Oh, so, so, pretty much, I fear."

"So what do you mean, 'just nerves?' That's not ill."

"I think I would have thrown up."

"I see." And after a slight hesitation, "I was expecting you."

"Your father told me you didn't know."

"I didn't, until I saw a particular smirk on his face. I always know when he's up to no good." She paused. "So why the nerves?"

The drink had done what drink is supposed to do, loosened my tongue. "I don't mind telling you that, it was the thought of seeing you, but it didn't help having a car turn up with blacked out windows driven by a cross between Hercules and Adonis, and shoved ignomin…" I tried and failed again. "Ignominiously in the back. It felt like I was being rendered, if that's the right word, for someone up for rendition."

"Restricted address, surely you understand that?"

I warmed to my theme. "It was demeaning."

"Justified though, to prevent stalkers hanging around outside munching on disgusting sandwiches." She took in my look of affronted dignity. "You're funny when you're stoned, Bartlett."

"It was not a disgusting sandwich," I replied peevishly. "As a matter of fact, I took it back to work after, I might add, you had taken a large bite out of it, and put it on my desk where it lay for three days before Morris took a fancy to it and said afterwards, and I quote: 'Coo, nice that, bit posh an' all'."

"Why did it lie on your desk for three days?" Her eyes were bright, she suspected.

"I tried to throw it away but strangely found that I couldn't."

"You should get pissed more often, Bartlett, at least I get some answers out of you, but still as clear as mud. You couldn't throw it away because…?"

I knew the answer she was eager for and supplied it willingly as if it were catharsis.

"Because I loved you."

"Go on."

"Just something that happened, not your fault you understand, you never encouraged me, just something that happened, bit like a snake that slips out of the jungle when you're trying to nip past on a path, minding your own business as it were, and bites you on the ankle."

"You're drivelling now." Then, as if just registering, she snapped, "What do you mean, never encouraged you?" And before I could reply, "That's what you told, Dad, that I rejected you."

"You did. That last time I saw you, before the sandwich incident I mean, I was going to ask to see you again, but you knew that."

"Of course I knew. I wondered what the hell you were playing at."

"'You'll never see me again.' Your words. I'm going to have another, helps me talk."

"Helps you talk a load of bollocks." She refilled our glasses. "Let me ask you something, when we did our performance in the clinic, did you think that was just play-acting?"

"I wasn't sure. I supposed it was but the feel of you against me, that was real, for me anyway. I mean I've often wondered, when actors and actresses kiss on stage, how do they actually feel? After all, they're human, they're not automatons, they're not immune to the neurological responses…"

"Yes, well, perhaps wonder that at another time. That's one of your problems, Bartlett, you think way too much. I'm talking about you and me. I don't do flirting but I thought we had a moment."

"We did."

"So that was your cue to kiss me, even in this day and age men are supposed to do that, and you didn't and I wasn't best pleased. That was before the suggestion that you were batting for the other side, so I assumed you had some other interest even though you were supposed to be unattached. Background checks aren't infallible and we all know what goes on in hospitals."

This astounded me. "How could you possibly have thought that? I didn't know what to make of you. I'd never met anyone like you. Correction, I *have* never met anyone like you. Your brain works at lightning speed, your mood switches so fast I can't keep up. You utterly confuse me. There were moments, just as you say, or I thought there were, only they were gone in a flash; it seemed they were in spite of you and you throttled them down pretty damn quick."

She considered me thoughtfully, apparently perplexed. "You got that right, but why not the rest? I thought you understood me."

"I told you I didn't."

"But some of the things you said... Thing is, Bartlett, I've never met anyone like you either. I didn't know what you were feeling. I expect to be pursued or at least to be given a clue that I'm wanted. My ex wanted me. Even after things started going wrong, I could still press his buttons." She looked at me doubtfully. "That's probably not so healthy, is it?"

"Sometimes women, not just women but more commonly so, provoke arguments to try and recreate that first excitement after it has worn off."

"Trite, Bartlett, but not entirely untrue. Our marriage was based on that first excitement, which I've no doubt you'll lecture me on the foolishness of."

"No, no lectures. Besides, you are your mother's daughter."

She looked at me darkly. "Did we know each other in a former life? I'm beginning to half-believe some of your crap."

I wasn't to be diverted. "You get into bed with me, I wake with your head on my chest, then you leap out of bed as if scalded because, well, you tell me, if you thought I was gay how could you be like that with me?"

"Now you're talking rubbish, you of all people know about women and gay men?"

"Yes, but it felt much more than that, it felt so, oh, what the hell — so loving."

"That's rather the point," she said quietly. "It was."

"And then later, at the mission, when they untied us and you didn't move away…"

She stood up, her eyes blazed. I'd never felt the full force of her anger before. "Don't you dare! That was the most humiliating moment of my life. Wasn't it obvious enough for you? You just stood there like a lemon with a vacant look on your face. How the fuck do you think that made me feel? I thought you were taking the piss out of me, you do that and only the next day try to ask me out! What were you playing at? I still don't know." I opened my mouth but no words came out. "You don't know yourself. I cut you dead because I was bloody furious, so much so that I actually enjoyed watching your face drop like a stone, although it hurt at the same time. You understand that?"

"Mortification of the soul."

"Not a term I would use, but I suppose." She paused. "It upset me, that look on your face, until I imagined you shrugging it off as nothing. Then you found me." She smiled shyly, not an expression I'd seen before. "I shouldn't tell you this, it might go to your head, but when I found you hanging around our place I felt this great surge of happiness, didn't last long though, just until you fucked up again."

"Because I couldn't speak, I tried but nothing came out, acute stress response if you're interested."

She considered me thoughtfully. "What you don't know, something that preyed on my mind a great deal, is that Robinson and Major repeated what you'd said, that 'I wasn't your type.' If what you've just told me is true, why did you say that?"

"Revenge."

Her eyes flashed dangerously. "Explain."

"I thought you were using me."

"Did you?" she said scathingly.

I felt suddenly ashamed. Somehow it was clear to me even through my drunkenness that I'd got this wrong but felt compelled to do as commanded and explain.

"I didn't know what I'd got myself caught up in. I don't know anything about the world you inhabit. I don't live in it. I don't know its rules, in particular whether I could trust anything or anybody, including you."

Penny looked thoughtful. "Well, there's you thinking that, and me wondering if I was some kind of a case study to you."

"We had that meeting in Hampstead, and something about it disturbed me. I had a dream that night…"

Penny's expression returned to cynical. "Oh fuck! And what did God have to say to you this time?"

"I woke up and mulled it all over."

"Well, you would, wouldn't you?"

"And then it came to me."

"Hallelujah."

"It was how you had used Mrs T as an agent, and her so in love with you. It struck me like a cold chill. Was that your modus operandi, to enslave your agents to do your bidding? And then the next day when Robinson and Major came to see me, they knew I'd had the fish."

"Excuse me?"

"Our meeting was supposed to be a secret, and yet they knew what I'd had for dinner."

"Only because I told Lavinia and she leaks like a sieve." She looked at me thoughtfully with an expression I didn't care for. "You're right though, you don't understand me, you know nothing about me at all, and you've actually revealed a rather disturbing distrust, not just in me, but women in general." She looked at me disdainfully. "So what's it all about then? You used that word just now, past tense I notice."

"No, no, present tense."

"Marvellous, I've got a secret admirer, but so secret that he never gets around to telling me. And how does it work, this impressive courtship of yours, that starts as indifference, works itself up to diffidence and builds up to a crescendo of half-heartedness?"

"It's not like that," I protested lamely.

"Well how is it then? Do tell, I'm interested."

"When I first met you, what was not true later was true then, that I thought you weren't my type. It's the first thing a man does when he sees a woman, asks himself — you know."

She smiled unexpectedly. "Women do that too, well, some do. So that was your first thought, that you'd kick me out of bed. This gets better and better, you really know how to make a girl feel special, Bartlett."

"But the more I saw of you, the more you fascinated me, the speed of your thought, the..."

"No, don't do it! Don't tell me you fell in love with my mind, I might be a feminist but you can stick that where the sun doesn't shine."

"It crept up on me."

"The snake in the jungle?"

"There you go, only a second ago you looked murderous, now you're smiling."

"And your point is? I'm not smiling by the way."

"Quixotic, that's what you are."

"And you find that attractive?" She looked and sounded curious.

"At the risk of your fury, this was what first fascinated me, the physical attraction came later."

"Oh, marvellous," she said with heavy sarcasm.

"Things happened that made me think of you, things I wanted to tell you and couldn't because I didn't know if I'd ever see you again. You could snap your fingers and summon me like a genie. I couldn't."

I saw this had hit home and she conceded thoughtfully. "I get that."

"Must take an effort, I doubt if you've been disempowered since you were in your pram."

"You'd be surprised. But I wanted to hear all this before telling you a few home truths," she said grimly. "When I first met you, I saw what I expected to see, what I thought you were — wet, liberal, in touch with your feminine side, a caricature of your profession and just the sort of man I despise, possibly slightly prejudiced by the fact that I'd had you hoist on me against my will."

"And not your type," I said, getting my own back.

"And that. I remember thinking to myself in answer to that unspoken question, 'Oh, God, no.' Nowadays, women are supposed to want men who feed the baby and do the housework and are halfway to being women themselves, but I'm not one of them. I like men to be dangerous, and you, Bartlett, are about as dangerous as a fluffy toy."

I must have looked crestfallen because she hurried to speak. "First impressions, remember, just like yours.

But it's all crap, isn't it? I married a man I couldn't bear to be in the same room with after six months of marriage, what you think you want isn't necessarily it. I mean, yes, it's excitement."

"You really don't need to keep repeating that."

"I was going to say that it's meaningless to try and categorise."

"Yes, but being non-gender-specific, people do have types that attract them, partly conditioning but often…"

"I know what you're going to say, men are attracted to women like their mothers and girls like their fathers, all that creepy Freudian shit."

"Actually, I was going to agree with you about the meaninglessness of generalisation. The one thing you can rely on is the primeval relentlessness of our genes to achieve diversity."

"So fat birds get lucky."

"Exactly, and how delicately put. People are attractive in all shapes and sizes, all levels of intelligence and personality types…"

"Bartlett! You've just brought me back to where I was before we got off on this fascinating digression: my early impressions of you. One of the many dreadful things about you is your tendency to waffle, not just waffle but lecture patronisingly as if no one outside your field knows fuck all about anything. After that first meeting with you, I remember feeling this rush of sisterly sympathy for your poor ex-wife, who I knew all about of course. But your bloody snake had a sister. First of all, because I thought you such a wimp, I was puzzled that you didn't seem intimidated by me. I seem to have that effect on people," she said with an expression that mixed pride with dejection. She continued.

"You annoyed me, I can't tell you how much you annoyed me, but I found myself, just like you from what you've just said, thinking about you. In amongst the garbage there was some stuff that intrigued me, and I will admit I was irritated that you didn't seem to look at me as a woman. So when Robinson said you were gay…"

"Did he really think that?"

"Mrs T did, and those two set out to find out in their usual Machiavellian way, they're as full of mischief as a barrel of monkeys. I guess the idea was to get us together and see what happened, an experiment at my expense, what you might call a win, win situation. I took his word for it at first. It was a relief, I didn't want any entanglement with you, quantum or otherwise, not with anyone but particularly not with you. But it preyed on my mind for a reason I didn't understand at the time and wouldn't have admitted to even if I had. Suffice to say, it mattered more than it should have. When we did that horseplay in the clinic, when I was up against you, that was really peculiar. You know I…?" I nodded and she looked away awkwardly. "I've never… you know… not like that, it was what your friend Morris would call eerie." She returned to being matter of fact. "My point is that I would have sworn it wasn't just me. Why had I misread the encryption? It bugged me, which is why I agreed to the husband-and-wife act, that way I would find out, or so I thought. When we were asleep, I too had a dream, one of those ones you have every now and again that's so vivid that you remember it for years."

My interest in dreams must have revealed itself because she looked at me disparagingly.

"I'll keep the details to myself if you don't mind, but it was about you and me and we were, well, intimate, as if we'd known each other since childhood. When I awoke, I admit to hamming it up a bit, I wanted to see how you reacted. It would have been a hell of a lot simpler if you were that way, but as it was, well, I had a certain feeling that I won't go into."

"Fooled me, I thought you were genuinely distressed, although there was something wrong with your expression, I do remember thinking that."

"I *was* distressed, waking and finding you…"

"A stranger?"

"No, not that, it was the fact that it was you, but not how you were, not how *we* were, in my dream. I suppose after that I started questioning myself. You irritated me intensely as I kept telling myself."

"You didn't keep it to yourself."

"You should understand, being angry with myself, I took it out on you. When I had to explain the blinking finance director to you, you looked so… I saw your face fall and — this is a truly awful confession — I wanted to cuddle you. I mean the last time I felt like that was when I saw my friend's three-year-old petting her guinea-pig which incidentally was nearly as big as her. How pathetic is that?" She looked at me moodily. "And when she kissed him, it was me and her quantumly fucking entangled, two women unbearably attracted to men they couldn't stand."

"Thanks very much."

"I was scared that I'd blushed, I caught you looking at me, I thought you'd found me out." I shook my head and she continued. "Then we were tied up together." She frowned. "You can't say you didn't notice, you complained about me breathing in, I mean, there's no innocent explanation."

"Honestly, I didn't, I mean, you did feel good against me and of course, being a woman, there are certain physiological…"

"Surely, Bartlett, not even you are going to give me a lecture on that of all subjects." She sighed. "In spite of everything, not least of which was thinking we had all been for the chop, I didn't want that to end. I just stood against you after we were untied, in a bit of a trance if I'm honest, and you talk about getting mixed messages and feeling rejected." She looked at me disdainfully. "I don't take kindly to being humiliated." She sounded angry but pressed at her jaw in a reprise of the peculiar mannerism I had seen in the park, and I guessed that her hauteur concealed hurt and I felt ashamed.

She continued. "I'll tell you how it felt to me, like I only just registered, like I was a ripple on the smooth flow of your life, you thought about it, wondering whether you could or couldn't be bothered, decided you could, just about, and tried to ask me out."

"Like Jane Austen, isn't it? The perpetuation of misunderstanding."

"But I knew when you kept turning up with your bloody sandwiches that you were beating yourself up, and I gave you another chance… And you just gawped at me like a fish. Then I really gave up on you, but it upset me as I'm sure my treacherous father has leaked to you."

"He did leak a little."

"What gets me is what does it all mean? Is it just a chemical thing that would fizzle out like my marriage?" She stared at me thoughtfully and smiled suddenly. "Did the leaky father tell you about the boyfriend?"

"He did."

"It was an experiment. I thought maybe now I was getting older, some biology had switched me off alpha males onto something more beta."

"Thank you for not making it omega."

"No, you're not a wimp, Bartlett. You ticked me off for being disrespectful to Trevor and Morris. I was provoking you on purpose, not so much strategic deception as just being a girl, I was curious to know if you were soft right through. I liked it that you weren't. But to return to my experiment, I wanted to find out what was going on with me. One of my friends had ditched her husband last year. I've always liked him and knew it was mutual." She looked at me with exasperation. "Women know these things, present company excepted. I rang him up and we went out. I took him to bed but couldn't stand him near me. To be honest he revolted me. Physically there was nothing wrong with him, nice legs, narrow waist, broad shoulders, strong arms and firm…"

I winced. "Sorry, but I feel about physical descriptions of men the way a lot of women feel about girly calendars."

"How odd. Anyway, I had to tell him nicely that I was sorry."

"Did you really — nicely?"

"I explained," she said coldly. She looked at me moodily then dropped down in front of me with her elbows on my knees. Her physical presence was overwhelming. She blinked, first slowly, then with increasing rapidity. She smiled. I got the message this time. I kissed her. Her arms stretched around my neck. I felt her sigh.

"Thank fuck for that." Her mouth, pressed against mine, closed in a smile but her eyes were open and dark, even in the act of lovemaking she looked dangerous. She got up suddenly.

"Assuming you don't hang from the rafters at night I guess you have a bed, Doctor Bartlett."

Which is how it all happened. Like everything associated with Penny, our affair proceeded at what I considered to be an unnatural pace. We slept together on that first night, something more graphic in Penny's vocabulary. The reality of being with her, kissing, holding hands, sleeping naked tightly entangled and making love, was intoxicating for me.

But that was the easy part. Incorporating each other into our lives is more fraught. We argue frequently, mainly due to the polar difference in our natures. She doesn't understand what she calls my inertia, which I would describe as normal. Whereas if she presented to me with the behaviour that comes naturally to her, I would prescribe a medication for hyperactivity, Ritalin would be my first choice.

More serious arguments are usually punctuated by the appearance of Mr Robinson and Major at my workplace, much to the delight of Sister Harris, looking glum and pleading with me to mend my ways.

After a few weeks, I was invited to Penny's family home. My first curiosity was the interior of the house. I had visualised it so vividly during our piece of theatre at Doctor Hamilton's clinic, that I had become convinced of the authenticity of my vision and was disappointed by the reality. I consoled myself with the sight of the dado rail and the extreme tastelessness of the decor. Every colour clashed hideously, every ornament was tacky and grotesque, the wallpaper and soft furnishings incited a dissonance so extreme that I wondered at the possibility of their use for some exquisite form of psychological torture.

My second curiosity was Penny's mother. I found it difficult to hide my professional interest. She was a short voluptuous woman, with steely grey hair, dark brown unfathomable eyes, and fast jumpy movements, but with some indefinable quality of sexuality. She also had a magnificent haughty black cat that followed her everywhere, perhaps the 'Rutterkin' of Trevor's 'Highfalutin'.

In time I came to know her better. Her spite towards Penny was painful to watch but also fascinating. The very presence of her daughter agitated her so severely that she could hardly function, so aware of her presence and so needful of attacking her in any way possible. Toxic mother daughter relationships are not uncommon but I don't think I have ever encountered such an extreme example, and without knowing the background it is impossible to guess the cause, although that didn't stop me mulling over the possibilities: lack of bonding at birth due to postnatal depression or medical trauma; envy; narcissism; and finally, childhood abuse or trauma suffered by the mother disabling her own ability to form a maternal bond.

The remarkable feature about her was guilt, it saturated her every interaction and was painful to witness. This was interesting to me because all too often in these relationships, the responsibility becomes deflected towards the daughter as a mechanism to relieve the mother of the burden of it. The persistence of this guilt suggested a strongly developed conscience that refused to be subsumed, but not without cost.

It was startling to an outsider, how this extreme behaviour was tolerated, had even become normalised, within the family, requiring an unspoken conspiracy of consent from all participants to perpetuate. An example of this was the Admiral's shed.

One afternoon, I was in the garden with the Admiral, admiring his rhododendrons. As we walked, we came to a structure that if it had been a quarter of the size, I would have called a shed. I remarked on it and the Admiral's expression changed to unmistakeable wistfulness. He rummaged furtively in his coat pocket and pulled out a pocket-book full of photographs with an expression that made me wonder if I was going to see some scantily clad ladies, but the photos were of another kind of model: magnificently carved wooden ships. I expressed my admiration to the Admiral's evident pleasure.

"'Victory', 'Royal Sovereign', 'Neptune', 'Bellerophon', twenty-seven ships of the line at Trafalgar when we trounced Villeneuve. I only had three to go." He sighed deeply. "The little woman commandeered my shed for potting plants: scuppered."

I looked through the window, there was nothing but rubbish. I gave the Admiral a look of sympathetic understanding, but felt the hair on the back of my neck stand up at the memory of that strange accusatory tirade against Penny's mother from Trevor, alluding to the emasculation of her husband.

I wished I could help, but on the rare occasions when I was alone with her, she was wary of me. I think this was because of my profession rather than any personal animosity, we got on well enough. She had a surprisingly off-beat sense of humour, even if caustic. She was extremely sharp, more so than the Admiral. The only dissonance was when my conversation strayed anywhere near the personal. By nature and habit, my interest in people inevitably reveals itself, and on occasion when unthinkingly I strayed too close, she closed the conversation down rapidly, in the Admiral's parlance, fired a shot across my bows. I soon realised that any suggestion of seeking professional help would be fiercely rejected. And even if I'd succeeded, I had a strong suspicion that her case would defeat the most skilled therapist. Changing dysfunctional thought and behaviour involves rerouting neural pathways, but these are like rabbit runs worn into ruts by constant scampering, and hers were as deep as canyons. I tried to discuss it with Penny, a knowledge of the family history might at least give a pointer, only to find that she too shied away from the subject. Her only concession was an apparent curiosity to know whether I liked her mother. I admitted that I did, though with the caveat that I was appalled by her behaviour towards her daughter.

She nodded thoughtfully and said, "Good." The only word she spoke on the subject.

Over weeks and months Penny and I got to know each other better. Our rather frenetic courtship had not gifted either of us with any real knowledge of each other. For my part, she turned out to be very different from my first perception of her, much more complex, and understanding her is still work in progress. Her feelings for me are hard to fathom because she is so much more reserved than me, almost comically so. The advantage for me in falling for her slowly is that I had that earlier pattern of behaviour to fall back on, allowing me to maintain some poise. Even so, I was more demonstrative than her, showing affection in public and buying things, nothing expensive, just small things that made me think of her. In that way, and that way alone, I was actually more spontaneous than her. But her reaction made me uneasy, I wondered if I embarrassed her, and rather than persist, asked if I should stop. Her answer was revealing. She looked at me with a cold hard stare that I imagined she would give a terrorist being denied clemency, and said decisively, "No." Then as she turned away, almost inaudibly, whispered, "I like it."

One morning, I arrived at work, to find The Colonel in my office. He looked dreadful; haunted, delusional and with a strange light in his eyes. He turned on me with apparent recognition.

"Oh God in Heaven, Doctor, not you as well, the one person I thought I could trust."

I was mortified, this was how he was at night, not during the day, and not only was I incorporated into whatever hallucination tormented him, but upsettingly, he knew me as my real self, and I had betrayed him.

He died later in the day, and I was more affected by his death than by any patient since Anne, the girl with anorexia. Penny was loving that night, I was used to her being passionate but this was different. We slept in each other's arms. I felt closer to her than ever before.

In the morning, she left early as usual, but did not come home. I received no word from her, which was unheard of. I was distraught, what if something had happened? I rang the Admiral, who evidently knew something and was remarkably kind and reassuring.

"Just stick at it, Doctor, you're doing fine."

"But where is she?"

"Gone walkabout. It's what the Abo's do, Down Under."

I winced. The Admiral is beyond redemption. "But why?"

"Ah," the Admiral chuckled knowingly. "Feelings, all that malarkey, she erm, you know…"

"Loves me?"

"That's the thingy, no doubt about that. That's why she's panicked, you see, losing her independence, big thing for her, bound to be a reaction. I'm sure I don't need to explain that to you."

"You do, actually."

The Admiral chuckled. "Don't you know anything about women, Doctor?"

Sure enough, three days later she was back. The Admiral had been on the case, it turned out that her feelings had been developing in a way that she had not confided in me — typically — and had unsettled her. She even accused me with a touch of hostility of having power over her, which I thought a little far-fetched. But to my surprise, her 'walkabout' seemed to have effected a change, and not just a temporary one; it seemed that she had found some new inner peace.

Although determinedly avoiding the subject of her absence, she did confide in me some days later the content of her dream in the hotel room that she had been so reticent about. I had assumed that her shyness was due to it being rather fruity, maybe along the lines of Sam's dreams that had threatened a national crisis. But, in fact, it was just that, in her dream, I had been very tall and strong and held her tightly and she had felt safe! I only stopped laughing when she punched me but started all over again when I observed that this revelation had made her blush pink with embarrassment.

Whether connected or not, I don't know, but shortly after this, the subject of marriage came up in discussion.

Penny's attitude came as a surprise to me. I asked for her views in an academic sort of way. She smiled sweetly.

"Yes. I realise you weren't asking but yes anyway."

So it was agreed, probably the wettest, nerdiest most unromantic marriage proposal that ever wasn't, in the history of human relations. But I was happy, the huge test for me had been for us to get together, to take this further step was, just as Penny had misinterpreted my feelings for her, a ripple on the flow of my life. And I was surprised how important it was to her, the dreadfulness of my non-proposal didn't seem to trouble her at all. It was a strange contradiction that probably the most unconventional person I have ever met outside the consulting room, should wish to be married, and in a church.

I had thought myself more cynical on the subject and yet when the day came and we were up before the vicar, I was unexpectedly moved. The vows were far from orthodox, conceived by Penny and fiercely contested by the vicar.

I invited Trevor and Morris, but Trevor just shook his head. It would be an ordeal for him and I didn't press him. I am aware that it would be a mistake to romanticise the depth of our relationship. Emotionally Trevor is in his own way more limited than Morris. The fondness that I feel for him is reciprocated by a kind of bonhomie on his behalf which is his maximum capacity.

Morris enjoyed himself immensely, not just the food but collaring various unsuspecting guests and impressing them with his latest feat of truck driving. A two-hundred-tonne transformer, which he had seen on television being transported from Vladivostok to Magnitogorsk, had somehow gotten itself stranded on the Godalming Bypass.

And later, at the reception, Mr Robinson and Major openly wept on each other's shoulders because, as I have come to learn, they are two very sentimental gentlemen. Even the Admiral was clearly moved, clutching my hand and forgetting to let go.

"Look after her, old boy, look after my best girl."

I was saved from making a fool of myself by the absurdity of the idea of me looking after Penny; I understand father and daughter well enough now to know they would not appreciate any wanton displays of emotion. Penny's mother, however, was inspired to attempt to hug her daughter, which conducted at arm's length, was one of the most embarrassing sights I have ever witnessed.

Printed in Great Britain
by Amazon